# BABIES, BULLETS, and BEE STINGS

## MEMORIES OF A MISSIONARY MIDWIFE

# Dedication

To Rex,
my husband of thirty-four wonderful years
and my very best friend;
and to my parents, Delmar and Shirley Kaufman,
whose words and example taught me
the joy of living for Jesus.
I love you.

# BABIES, BULLETS, and BEE STINGS

# MEMORIES OF A MISSIONARY MIDWIFE

## HANNAH MCDOWELL

PUBLISHING & MANUFACTURING

Copyright © 2014 by Hannah R. McDowell, RN, CNM
rhmcdowell1980@gmail.com | 570-837-6064

Second Printing—December, 2014

ISBN 978-1-63452-087-4

Editors: Priscilla Oldaker and Rex McDowell
Printed by M & K Publishing, Hobe Sound, Florida

The stories in this book are all true. However, a few names have been changed to protect the privacy of the individuals.

All profits from the sale of this book go to support Christian missions.

Printed in the United States of America

 Cover design and page layout:
Jon Plank, Media-Spring

# Contents

# Acknowledgments

———

No author can write a book without the assistance of many who come alongside and make it possible. I would like to give special thanks to:

First and foremost, my heavenly Father, "who is able to do exceedingly abundantly above all that we ask or think. To Him be glory forever and ever" (Ephesians 3:20).

My husband, whose love, support, and patience have been unwavering. Thank you, Rex, for believing in me and nudging me to follow God's leading to tell my story. Without you, this book would never have been written. I am more grateful than I can ever say for the gift of your excellent editing skills and for all those hours that you spent meticulously combing through the final manuscript.

My children, Rex II and Missy, Benjamin and Jaylena, and Jeffrey. You have encouraged me to think that I could do this and supported me through the L-O-N-G process. Thank you. You fill my life with joy and meaning. I love you!

My mother, who inspired me with her own skill at story writing. Thank you, Mama, for your always-cheerful response the many times that I called to ask your opinion about this sentence or that idea and for your gift to help fund the printing. Your labor of love as you temporarily moved in with us to cook, clean, and do laundry after my surgeries gave me the chance to write a major portion of Part One.

My sister, Priscilla Oldaker, who had the courage to critique the first draft with sometimes painful, but always loving, honesty. Following your valuable suggestions has made the final product much better than it would have been. Thank you for your practical advice and editing ability. You are a blessing!

My niece, Marilyn McDowell, whose enthusiasm for this project has been constant and abundant. Thank you for all your inspiring letters across the years, urging me to put my e-mails into book form and assuring me that I really could be an author. You gave me the courage to tackle the job and see it to completion.

My long-time friend and college roommate, Sandy Hanson, for donating a computer and a camera so I could write and illustrate my book.

My brother-in-law and sister-in-law, Jeff and Pam Fleming, who purchased a program for my computer so I could dictate a number of chapters of the book after an accident and surgery on my hands made it impossible to type.

My friends, Alice Freer, Michelle Wrightsman, Frances Stetler, Debbie Bubb, and Crystal Gingrich, who, along with my sister, mother, and niece, read and commented on my manuscript.

Jon Plank, whose creativity is amazing. Thank you for your patience in working with me. You have done a fantastic job on the cover and page layout.

Mike McCoy, who walked me through the steps to publishing a quality product and was unendingly friendly and courteous during our many phone conversations to figure out all the details.

Anita Brechbill, whose godly example has inspired us since we first met her during our orientation with Evangelical Wesleyan Mission in Key West, Florida. Thank you for the many good missionary biographies you sent to our boys and for faithfully "holding the ropes" in prayer for our family.

Fellow missionary biographers Ron and Anna Smith, Irene Maurer, Faith Hemmeter, Becky Keep, Glenn and Helen Reiff, and Leroy and Myrtle Adams, for your helpful advice.

My cousin, Paul Kaufman, and my friends, Steve Hight and Steve Mowery, for honoring me with your kind endorsements.

J. Stevan Manley, former president of Evangelistic Faith Missions, who first invited me to work in the clinic in Honduras. Without that opportunity, the book would never have been born.

My family, friends, hospital coworkers, and the Penn View Bible Institute missions students who gave your opinions about the book cover.

The many readers of my "Honduran Happenings" e-mails who said, "You ought to write a book."

Well, here it is.

# Foreword

In the summer of 1995, I traveled to Costa Rica to hold revival services in a little place called *Los Llanos de Santa Lucía,* a suburb of the town of *El Paraíso,* in the Central American nation of Costa Rica. Rex and Hannah McDowell were missionaries there, accompanied by their three sons, Rex II, Benjamin, and Jeffrey. That was the beginning of an abiding friendship that has been marked by several interesting experiences.

There was the time, on a subsequent visit, that I was awakened at 2:00 a.m. by an alarm clock that buzzed incessantly somewhere in my room. I opened every drawer, looked under every piece of furniture, and investigated every nook and cranny, before I finally found the clock and turned it off. One of the boys (I won't say who, but he later "confessed"), had played an exquisitely planned practical joke.

Another time, we had finished the day's activities, including special services in the church, and were relaxing with some classical music and popcorn. We were all tired, and I, at least, a little silly. As the music played and we began to mark the tempo, one of the boys brought out some plastic animals and trees from a toy farm set. Soon we were making the trees wave and the cows dance in time with the music, laughing together and relaxing from the day's tensions.

Hannah, the author of this book, is a special person. Her parents strongly influenced her in the direction of Christian service in her youth, especially awakening interest in missions by providing her with numerous missionary biographies. Their own lives were freely given in ministry, so they were a constant, consistent example of what they were teaching her.

Married to Rex I, she has supported him in his missionary ministry, his teaching at Penn View Bible Institute in Penns Creek, PA, and now, his new appointment as director of the missions division at PVBI. Rex and Hannah served together in Nicaragua and Costa Rica as full-time missionaries. They later ministered in Honduras over several summers, Hannah working in the maternity clinic, Rex teaching in the Bible institute, and both joining forces to give marriage seminars together.

But Hannah McDowell has also actively developed her own unique missionary career. She received her nursing degree in the summer of 1983, immediately beginning to work as a registered nurse in labor and delivery and in the newborn nursery. Her interest in expectant moms, the delivery of their babies, and the well-being of newborns led her to the Medical University of South Carolina, where she became a Certified Nurse-Midwife in November of 1987. She and Rex left for Costa Rica six months later.

Hannah has used her medical skills to serve God in six countries: Costa Rica, Nicaragua, Honduras, Haiti, Mexico, and now in the U.S.A., where she works in a Pennsylvania hospital and has served as school nurse for Penn View Bible Institute. To date, she has delivered 120 babies (including three of the MKs at Evangelistic Faith Missions); has worked with some fifteen young people in the Honduran maternity clinic, helping them with missionary and medical internships; and has accumulated nine years and four months of mission-field service.

The official periodical of Evangelistic Faith Missions, the *Missionary Herald*, has been blessed with several of Hannah's articles in which she has narrated some of her missionary-nursing experiences. We have often said that the maternity clinic in Honduras might be in the doldrums, with few people seeking medical help, but when Hannah arrives, new babies are suddenly due and the people of San Luis unexpectedly have urgent needs. When Hannah comes, things get interesting!

The title of this book, *Babies, Bullets, and Bee Stings*, is only a suggestion of what you will encounter on its pages! Who can forget Hannah's article about stitching up the wounds on an injured horse, the hide so tough that she straightened several heavy-duty curved needles trying to do the suturing? (By the way, the horse recovered and, as far as I know, is still alive, though now retired from ministry.)

Who would not hurt along with the poor man who was stung a thousand times or more by bees? Hannah was faced with the painstaking task of pulling the stingers out of his face and arms.

Whose heart would not be touched by descriptions such as the one of a fourteen-month-old girl whose parents brought her to the clinic, dirty, listless, weak, and malnourished—and whose heart would not be warmed by Hannah's report that just a few hours of good food and care began to revitalize her?

These stories, and more, await you. If you have read Hannah's articles in the *Missionary Herald*, you will rejoice at the prospect of reading more of them. If you have never read Hannah's stories, you have a treat in store. I'm glad that she has put these narrations into book form, and I am sure that you will agree.

Enjoy!

Steven E. Hight, President
Evangelistic Faith Missions
Bedford, Indiana
August 2014

# Preface

———

Psalm 139 tells me that before I was ever formed in the womb, God knew me. What an awesome thought! The Creator of the universe, the One Who spoke the world into existence, Who hung the stars in space and keeps all of the planets in their perfect orbits, is such a personal God that even before the single cell contributed by each of my parents united to become the dark-haired baby girl who would be born to them nine months later, He knew *me*, as an individual, Hannah Ruth Kaufman-to-be-McDowell.

Not only does He know me, but the prophet Jeremiah assures me of another breathtaking idea: He has a design for my life—something that He wants me to do, that no one else can accomplish. I am not just a random individual, one of a few billion others drifting haphazardly through life, here for a few years and then gone, with no purpose or meaning. "I know the plans I have for you," God says.

As I look back over my life, I am absolutely certain of the truth of those verses and tremendously comforted by the thought that God works in unique ways with each of us to make His will clear. Sometimes, it seems as though it would be nice to hear a clarion voice from heaven saying, "This is the way, walk in it." But that has never been my experience. Instead, at each critical turn of the road, God has been there to gently guide me in the way He wanted me to go.

Part of that guidance has been through the loving encouragement of my husband, Rex, my mother, Shirley Kaufman, and my niece, Marilyn McDowell, who for years have insisted that I should compile everything that I have written about my missionary-nursing experiences and publish it. "Someday …" I would respond. But more of God's guidance became increasingly evident through the voices of many of you who have read the e-mails that I sent to keep you updated on my "Honduran Happenings" during the summers that I worked in the Evangelistic Faith Missions maternity clinic in Central America. As the comments like, "You really need to put those stories together into a book," kept coming in, Rex finally said, "Honey, I believe the Lord is trying to tell you something. You had better listen."

So God has spoken, I have listened, and the end result is the book you are holding in your hands. It is my story, yes; but much more than that, it is a testimony to the enabling grace and sustaining power that is ours in abundance when we are doing our best to find and follow His will. It is also a joyous confirmation of the fact that in doing God's will, we will find peace and contentment. Sometimes, we will also find more excitement and fun than we could ever imagine! My purpose in writing and my prayer as you read is that God will use my story to help you realize that there is no greater blessing than that of serving Him with your whole heart—no matter where that may lead you. Go with God, and you will find joy in the journey!

Hannah R. McDowell, RN, CNM
Penns Creek, PA
October 17, 2014

# BABIES, BULLETS, and BEE STINGS

## MEMORIES OF A MISSIONARY MIDWIFE

Part I

---

*Accept my talents, great or small,*

*Choose thou the path for me,*

*Where I shall labor joyously*

*In service, Lord, for thee.*

– STANZA 2 OF "TEACH ME THY TRUTH"

# 1

## Diary of a Nightmare

*June 28, 2009 ~ San Luis, Honduras*

1:37 a.m. – "¡Hermana Ana! ¡Hermana Ana!" The night guard's voice on the walkie-talkie startles me from a sound sleep. I leap out of bed, stumble over to the dresser, and fumble in the dark to find the button on the radio to answer him. He does not give any details, just that I am needed at the *Clínica de Maternidad Luz y Vida,* the twenty-one bed Light and Life Maternity Clinic tucked in a beautiful valley high in the western mountains of Honduras, Central America, where I am helping out for a few weeks this summer.

1:42 a.m. – "Pray for me, please," I beg Rex as I run out the door. "I know they wouldn't call at this time of night unless it's an emergency."

1:44 a.m. – No question about the emergency part! I am greeted by the sight of a woman lying on her back in one of our labor beds, a five-inch loop of pale-blue umbilical cord trailing out between her legs onto the mattress. "It's a breech presentation," Maribel, the night nurse, informs me as she hurries to call the ambulance.

1:46 a.m. – Quickly gloving up, I gently check the position of the baby who is doing his best to enter the world knee first—definitely the wrong way. I help the mother turn over and kneel, chest on the bed, to take the weight of the baby off the cord, while I listen anxiously for a heartbeat. The little one is still alive, but his heart is beating too slowly. I explain to the mother what we have to do, and I have prayer with her, asking God in His mercy to spare the life of her baby so she can raise it to serve Him.

2:38 a.m. – "Where is that ambulance?!" Oxygen mask fitted to her face, IV fluids rapidly running into her vein, the mother has been ready to go for a while. The Red Cross Toyota Land Cruiser finally pulls up to the porch, its attendant apologetically explaining why they could not get here sooner. "The ambulance wouldn't start. We had to push it to get it going."

3:06 a.m. – We bump across the rocks and out of the yard on our way to the large maternity hospital in San Pedro Sula, normally a two-hour-and-fifteen minute trip. I brace my feet and fight to keep my seat on the narrow bench next to the stretcher, my hand still in place on the baby's leg, firmly keeping him inside and off his umbilical cord until we can get to the operating room for the cesarean delivery that will save his life. The woman's husband sits beside me, holding aloft the bag of IV fluid in one hand and gripping his wife's hand with the other. With the portable tank of oxygen and large garbage bag with emergency supplies that Maribel packed and sent "just in case," there is no room for anyone else in the back. The ambulance itself carries only a toolbox with a few supplies and a vinyl-covered stretcher, without even a sheet to cover the threadbare spots that have worn through with long use.

3:17 a.m. – I glance again at the tube feeding into the mother's arm. This time, instead of a clear stream of fluid, there is dark-red blood backing up the line. Briefly letting go of the baby, who has been staying up inside where he is not pressing on the cord, I grab the IV bag and work to get the fluid running properly again.

3:18 a.m. – Glove on once more, I check the baby and discover with horror two inches of leg and knee that have insisted on being born. I ease things back inside with one hand, stretching with the other to slide open the tiny window opening into the driver's compartment. "The baby is trying to come. Please hurry all you can!" Instantly, I feel a change as the driver accelerates. "Dear Lord, please keep us from having a wreck," I silently plead. At least it is not raining, so we do not have the hazard of slick mud added to the danger as we barrel along through the darkness.

3:34 a.m. – I am still praying, but the words are different now. "Oh, God, don't let me throw up, PLEASE don't let me throw up, please, God, help me ... BLAAH!!!" I lose everything in my stomach, thanks to the rocking motion of our speeding vehicle over curvy dirt mountain roads. I am thankful that at least I have not eaten since 6:00 the evening before, so it is mostly liquid.

3:39 a.m. – The woman's husband follows suit, and I grab for the IV bag he can no longer hold as he miserably empties his stomach as well.

4:03 a.m. – We have been jouncing and bouncing for nearly an hour and have finally gotten to the paved road. The smells of sweat, diesel fuel, vomit, and amniotic fluid swirl around me as the driver accelerates even more. I discover that I can drape the bag of IV fluid over my shoulder and hold it there with my cheek, giving one arm a rest. The other hand has started to cramp, but I grimly bend over and keep the baby pressed up inside as his mother coughs repeatedly. I gently rub her leg and smile at her. I cannot imagine the agony she must be feeling. All this time, she has been lying helpless, thrown from side to side and a few times banging her head against the back door as the ambulance careens down the mountain. Off and on she feels the urge to bear down, but valiantly grits her teeth and obeys my commands to "breathe, don't push." She is doing incredibly well. I greatly admire her courage; the only evidence of her trauma is an occasional groan.

4:23 a.m. – I *thought* my stomach was empty. With both hands again occupied, all I can do is bend over and let the rest of what is in there splat on the floor. At least that is only two times for me, compared to the husband's four. The siren wails as we fly along, swerving back and forth to miss the cars that do not readily yield the right of way.

4:30 a.m. – We whip around a corner and pull up to the hospital's emergency entrance, making the trip in slightly less than one-and-a-half hours. I count five people lying asleep on the ground, with many others standing around outside as they wait for word from the staff on a loved one's outcome. There is no such thing here as a husband or mother giving support to a laboring woman. No one is allowed to accompany her inside the hospital. But I trot determinedly beside my patient as she is wheeled through the doors, keeping the baby's leg inside and off the cord until we get into an exam room and a troop of doctors and nurses converges, one of them taking my place. Another glides an ultrasound wand briefly over the mother's abdomen. With relief, I notice that the baby's tiny heart is still beating. Thank God, we have made it in time! I follow the stretcher around a corner and down a short hall, stopping outside the operating room to wait for our equipment to be returned.

On the ride back to San Luis, I sit up front between the driver and the attendant, who politely attempt to include me in their conversation. I am so tired that I cannot keep an intelligent dialog going, and they finally give up, allowing me to doze fitfully while they talk back and forth over the top of my nodding head.

6:57 a.m. – The ambulance pulls up once again to the front porch of our clinic. I stiffly step down to the ground, clutching my aching back, thankful to have the nightmare over and to have arrived back home in one piece. I am so grateful to God for His help and for the part He allowed me to have in the drama, but I want nothing more in life at the moment than a hug from my husband and a hot shower.

\* \* \* \* \* \* \* \* \* \*

Although we did make it to the hospital in time for the baby to be delivered successfully by cesarean section, the mom showed up in our clinic a week later with a raging infection and an extremely tender abdomen. We had to transfer her once again to the city hospital. Ironically, when they opened her back up, they discovered that the source of her problem was a gauze sponge that the surgeon had mistakenly left inside her abdomen when he stitched her closed following the delivery of her baby boy. So goes the saga of missionary nursing.

There have been fewer times than I can count on one hand when I have had to remind myself why I do what I do, although this incident came close. But I have not a shred of doubt in my mind as to God's call on my life, a call that has thrust me into more interesting adventures and landed me in more exotic locations than most people can even imagine. To get a better picture of how God led a shy Ohio farm girl into being knocked about in the back of a primitive Honduran ambulance, you must understand about the influences in my life that made hearing and accepting His leading the most natural thing in the world. I know with absolute certainty that God has guided me every step of this journey, starting at the very beginning with the godly influence and encouragement of my parents, Rev. Delmar and Shirley Kaufman.

# 2

## The Value of a Ruined Bottom, and Other Lessons in the Making of a Missionary
### *1962 to 1976 ~ Salem, Ohio*

A three-year-old girl stood in her crib, clutching the chest-high rail and sobbing. For a recently committed "crime," her father had spanked her and then deposited her in the crib with strict instructions to stay put. When she glimpsed her mother peering around the door to check on her, the little girl tearfully questioned, "Mommie," (sniffle sniffle) "if I get out of bed, and Daddy has to spank me again," (whimper, gulp) "will it … *ruin my bottom?*"

I was the little girl in the crib, and that is my first memory. My misdeed on that fateful occasion was telling a lie in an attempt to convince my parents that a piece of gum I was chewing had been a treat from our neighbor. Mama found out that Mrs. Horner had *not* given me the gum. It was, instead, an already-well-chewed wad that I had discovered on the ground on my way home. The subsequent discipline session assured that I have never forgotten the lesson learned that day on the importance of being truthful.

Not only were my siblings and I taught to always tell the truth, gossip was *not* tolerated, either by us or by others in our presence. On one occasion, a visitor to our home started to recount a juicy tidbit of information about someone in the Lord's work whom we all knew. Before the report was little more than launched, my father saw which direction it was headed and kindly but firmly brought the story to a standstill. "I don't want my children to go to hell because of disillusionment with God's work," he told the shamefaced talebearer. As a child and young person, I never once heard Papa say an unkind or critical thing of anyone. I am certain there were people with whom he disagreed, but his philosophy was, "If you can't say something good about someone, don't say anything at all."

In addition to giving us a sterling example of guarding our speech, my parents lived before us the value of a close personal relationship with a loving heavenly Father. God was an everyday part of our lives, and family worship after supper was more than just a ritual. Papa would read a chapter from *Egermeier's Bible Story Book,* followed by all of us who were old enough to talk reciting a passage of Scripture along with him, stumblingly at first, but with more confidence each day, until it was permanently etched in our memories. Well before

I ever learned my ABCs, I remember being lifted to stand on a chair so I could see over the top of the pulpit in the church we attended while I quoted Psalm 23. In fact, when I got to college, the Bible memorization parts of my classes were often made easy by the fact that many of the verses required by my teachers were ones that I had stored in my brain as a child in family worship.

After the "hiding God's Word in our hearts" portion of worship, we would sing from a hymnal, with Mama's beautiful, clear soprano leading us in the melody while Papa's somewhere-between-baritone-and-bass notes blended with the piping tones of us five children. As we grew older and learned to sing recognizable parts, we would contribute to Papa's evangelistic meetings by standing in a row up front and quoting a Psalm or two, followed by singing "Surely Goodness and Mercy" or another such hymn. One of those occasions is still the source of a rueful chuckle at family reunions. It happened in a Wednesday night prayer meeting in the fall of 1967 at God's Bible School in Cincinnati, shortly after my father started teaching there. On the high platform overlooking a vast, scary sea of ever-so-much-older-than-we students, Papa lined us up: eight-year-old Hannah at the far left, followed by Robb, Paul, and Lois, ages seven, five, and three. Baby Priscilla, a few months from her second birthday, sat quietly next to my mother.

All went well as we began our oft-practiced recitation of Psalm 24. Mama and Papa leaned forward slightly from their seats just behind us, ready to whisper a prompt if needed. We started to relax a bit as the familiar phrases rolled glibly off our tongues. Then I noticed a student down near the front of the chapel suddenly bend over, covering her mouth as she tried to smother a giggle. My eyes darted anxiously back and forth as others of our audience dissolved into mirth. "What did we say wrong?" I wondered, glancing at Robb, who surely was aware of the waves of merriment rocking the student body, but was plowing on with our assignment anyhow. Acutely embarrassed, I followed suit, thankful not to be alone in my humiliation. As we finished and bolted back to tumble into seats near our parents, I tried to figure out what we had done to merit such a response. Priscilla, sedately seated next to Mama, was blissfully sucking her two favorite fingers, totally oblivious of the untoward response that her mortified brothers and sisters had received for their efforts.

Not until the end of the service did we discover that it was not *our* efforts that had produced the generalized amusement. Immediately after the closing "Amen," Naomi Downing, a long-time family friend, made a beeline for my mother and, trying hard not to laugh, informed her of what had happened. While both parents focused on their older children's reverent recitation, baby Priscilla, naïvely unaware of her surroundings, lay down in her seat and enthusiastically pedaled her long-stocking-clad legs in the air, bloomers fluttering,

uselessly modest long skirt flung over her face, in full view of a quickly convulsed audience. Fortunately, that occasion did not sour us for life on reciting
Scripture, and we continue to benefit today from those verses memorized so
many years ago.

To close every family devotion time, Papa or Mama would lead in prayer,
followed in turn by each child praying aloud. Even the youngest of us could
lisp a petition for God to "Bless Daddy and Mommy and my brothers and sisters and aunts and uncles and cousins, and help the missionaries, Amen." My
father had his own private prayer "closet" in a corner of the basement where he
had placed a wooden chair on a small rug. Time after time, I remember hearing his voice come floating up through the heat register into the living room,
pleading with God for the souls of his children, as well as for specific missionaries and for the lost around the world. For us children to omit "the missionaries"
in our requests would have been like leaving out a member of the family. It was
no secret that nothing would please my parents more than if all five of us ended
up on a foreign field, helping to reap the ripened harvest of souls.

My father taught at Bible colleges most of my childhood. Of course, my
mother worked as well, her before-sunup to after-sundown job being that of a
full-time wife and ministry partner, mother of five, cook, laundress, gardener,
seamstress, farm helper, and for several years, elementary teacher. In the 1960s,
Papa's wage was $40.00 a month. A decade later, he had advanced to a whop-
ping $200.00 a month. Still, no matter how large or small the income, they
found money to support missionaries. One of my vivid memories is of the
small piece of paper under the large pane of glass that covered Papa's desktop
in his study. It was a reminder of the $5,000.00 my parents had pledged to
missions that particular year. Remember, that was on a $2,400-per-year salary!

I asked my mother recently, "How did you do it?"

"We prayed it in, preached it in, and worked it in," was her reply.

We children definitely knew the power of prayer. An incident that occurred
the winter that I was four years old still reminds me that it gladdens God's
heart to answer the petitions of His children. The morning that we awoke to
the enchantment of the season's first heavy snowfall, my brother Robb and I
could not wait to gulp down breakfast and dash outside to play. Visions of a
colossal snowman and beautiful snow angels danced in the whirling flakes and
beckoned us to romp in the fluffy, white blanket covering our front yard. The
problem was that our feet had grown, but our winter footwear had not. Much
as we pulled and strained and shoved, this year's shoes simply would not fit into
last year's boots.

Mama would have been extra glad for us to play in the snow that morning
to distract us from the fact that we had no bread, nor much of anything else,

for breakfast. Perhaps the paycheck had been late that month. Maybe there had been unexpected expenses. At any rate, we were overdue for our periodic trip to the discount bakery outlet where we normally bought a gigantic (to our eyes) fifty-pound-sized, heavy-duty paper bag full of outdated bread and rolls, for one dollar. Some of the bread in the bag might be smashed, but no matter; there would be plenty to make toast, sandwiches, or bread pudding. With rumbly tummies, we sadly watched the eddying drifts pile higher, enviously imagining neighbor children frolicking in the winter wonderland, feet snugly warm and dry in their bright rubber boots.

What could be done? At family worship that evening, we each prayed as was our custom. We were ready to conclude with "The Lord's Prayer," quoted in unison, when Robb, age three, chimed in with one last appeal. "Please, dear Jesus, send us some boots and bread," he asked simply. We children went to bed, confident that his request would be granted.

Early the next morning, Papa, as usual, drove the two miles to Salem Bible College where he taught. A few hours later, the school president summoned Papa to his office and handed him an envelope that had just arrived. The return address named a Hannah Stuyvesant, someone Papa did not recall ever meeting, and the postmark was from a Pennsylvania town that he had never visited. His idle curiosity as he slit open the envelope turned to amazement as he pulled out a short note—and a check made out to Rev. Delmar Kaufman. You can imagine the tingles that raced up and down his spine as he read Miss Stuyvesant's words:

> *You don't know me, but I have heard you preach at Stoneboro Wesleyan Methodist Camp Meeting, and I appreciate the way God uses you to reach the lost. I am on my way to California by train as you read this, to take a position as a helper for an elderly invalid. I have been saving money for my personal expenses once I arrive in California. Yesterday, God spoke to me very clearly and told me to send all of the money to you. I was going to wait until I arrived in California, but God urgently impressed me to mail it to you immediately, so that is what I am doing. May God bless you and your family in His work.*
> *Sincerely,*
> *Hannah Stuyvesant, your sister in Christ*

Overwhelmed with gratitude, Papa rushed home to share the letter—and that wonderful check—with Mama. Bundling their children into the 1950 Ford that Papa had been driving since his bachelor days, my parents went first to the bank to cash the check, then to Strauss's Department store. There, Robb and I were fitted with sturdy, roomy boots that slid on easily over our shoes.

The next stop was at the bakery outlet, where they bought enough bread to fill the nearly empty freezer with plenty to last for weeks to come. God not only answered my brother's prayer, He started the response on its way before Robb ever uttered his simple nine-word request, thereby proving His love and faithfulness in a way that none of us would ever forget.

Yes, we certainly knew about the prayer part of our needs being supplied. At a young age, we each learned about the work part as well. Being raised on a farm gave us ample opportunities to do our share toward bringing in the bacon, quite literally. Hours of toil in the orchard and garden during the spring and summer yielded between six and seven hundred jars of home-canned fruits and vegetables that we enjoyed in the fall and winter. All of those thousands of weeds we pulled and crops we harvested, plus the chickens, goats, cows, and pigs we tended morning and night, 365 days a year, not only provided our daily bread (or rather our veggies, milk, and meat), but also instilled a strong work ethic and sense of responsibility that is still a blessing decades later.

Along with learning how to work, we grew up believing that, if we did *our* part, God would do *His* part to provide for us. Trusting God for everything, big or small, was as natural as breathing. We children did not even know we were poor. Mama spent hours on her sewing machine, stitching love into the dozens and dozens of shirts, pants, dresses, and skirts that her nimble fingers crafted for us. Credit cards? Our parents did not own one until a few years ago. They saved for months to pay up-front for the gifts we eagerly tore open each Christmas. So the **BIG** package I received on December 25, 1969, when I was ten years old, was thrilling in its own right. It was even more exhilarating when I saw what was inside. TEN BOOKS! WOW!!! I *loved* to read! Oh, my! Let me see, *Trail Maker*, the story of David Livingston. *God's Madcap*, the story of Amy Carmichael. *Young Man in a Hurry*, the story of William Carey. *Mary Slessor, the White Queen of Calabar....* Ten *missionary* biographies. What a treasure! Avidly, I dove into the first chapter of *On the Clouds to China*, about the life of Hudson Taylor, and was soon lost to the world, caught away to a land of pig-tailed, almond-eyed, yellow-skinned people who needed to hear about a God who loved them and died to save them.

Those ten books on my tenth Christmas had a profound impact on the rest of my life. As I read and re-read the stories of those long-ago missionary heroes and heroines, I gradually became aware of the gentle yet undeniable call that God was placing on my own heart. From that year forward, God's will for me was unquestioned. I was to be a missionary.

Did my father know the effect those books would have when he chose each one from the shelves of the God's Bible School bookstore? I am sure that was his hope when he placed them under the tree that unforgettable Christmas.

But the "book" that I read in my father's life—his heartthrob for missions that compelled him to raise hundreds of thousands of dollars for missionary support and to personally influence and assist thirty-six missionaries, including his own children and grandchildren, to go to "the ends of the earth," telling lost people of a Savior—that book left me no choice.

In the spring of 2003, at the ages of eighty-four and seventy-two, my father and mother packed their suitcases and boarded a plane for Ukraine, to take the place of a missionary family that was returning to the States earlier than planned. There they preached, prayed, and loved the people of the area, winning their way into hearts. Then, the mitral valve in Papa's heart ruptured, and they were forced to return home. Until he went to heaven five years later, almost without exception, my phone conversations with him would end with his query, "Do you know of anyone who can go to _____ (any of several mission fields needing workers)?"

What a heritage. What a responsibility! What a privilege to follow in my parents' footsteps and answer God's call to missionary service. And what delight to see Him lead me to just the perfect companion to help me fulfill that call. Although, on that sunny September Sunday morning of 1976 when I first met my beloved-to-be, you could never have convinced *him* that I was the one God had especially chosen to be his wife. Far from it ....

# 3

## An Angel Plugged His Ears
### *1976 to 1980 ~ Cincinnati, Ohio*

It was a bright, cheerful Sunday morning on the campus of God's Bible School in Cincinnati, Ohio. Stepping out of the front door of Rev. and Mrs. R.W. Dunn's home directly across the street from the school and glancing down, I saw a tall young man standing beside their car, the sun reflecting off his wavy, red hair. As I walked closer, I realized that it was more than just his hair that was attractive! We arranged ourselves in the car, the pastor and his wife in the front, Good Looking Guy (who had introduced himself as Rex McDowell) and I in the back with a wide expanse of seat between us.

Rex said almost nothing during the twenty-minute ride to church. I stole occasional discrete glances at his profile out of the corner of my eye. Mercifully, I could not read the thoughts that chased their way through his mind, something like, "My, she is really cross-eyed, isn't she? Rather plain faced ... I'm surely not interested." After the service, we stood on the sidewalk in uncomfortable silence while the Dunns cordially shook hands with each member of their congregation. As we walked together into the school dining hall for lunch, Rex told himself, "Oh no, now everyone will start thinking of us as a 'couple,' just because we are the only students to attend this church."

I was asked to provide the special song the next Sunday, and Rex sat up in startled amazement as I began to sing. Back in the solitude of his room after lunch, his mind drifted, unbidden, to the girl who had sung so beautifully that morning. "Hmmm," he mused. "Maybe she wouldn't be so bad after all, especially with a voice like that. You know, I think I was mistaken about the cross-eyed part. She really isn't bad looking when you get beyond the Coke-bottle-thick eye glasses." Then he sternly jerked his thoughts back into line, reminding himself that he was *not* attracted.

A few weeks later, Rex stopped the reminders. He wondered how he had ever thought she was plain. He was quite content to talk on the sidewalk with her while the pastor and his wife greeted each member after service. He was still puzzled, though, as to how he had ended up at this particular church.

The first chapel service of the school year, Rev. Dunn, the GBS business manager, had informed the new students that they were to choose a local place of worship, encouraging them to attend a church of their own denomination. "Now, I pastor a Wesleyan Methodist church. If that is your background, we would welcome you to join us." Rex attended a Wesleyan congregation back home. He knew none of the local pastors, but since Rev. Dunn pastored a *Wesleyan* church, Rex decided to ask if he could ride with the Dunns to their Sunday services.

Rex is still convinced that the word *Methodist* was omitted, but I was in the chapel service as well and can assure you that no word was left out. You see, God knew what a perfect match we would be. Knowing also that it would take divine intervention to bring us together, He urgently dispatched one of His swiftest angels that morning to attend chapel. At the precise moment that the word *Methodist* left Rev. Dunn's lips, the hovering angel clapped his hands over Rex's ears, assuring that he only heard the word *Wesleyan*, thus choosing the church where he would meet his future wife.

Lest you question the theological soundness of my explanation, you should know that Rex and I have laughingly debated the matter of the unheard-vs.-unspoken word for over thirty years, and we still do not know what happened. The important thing is that God brought us together, and if there had been a need to angelically plug Rex's ears for that to happen, it would have been no challenge for the One Who made blind eyes to see and deaf ears to hear.

However, I was only seventeen years old when I went to college and not allowed to date until I turned eighteen. Even if Rex *had* wanted to date me that year, I would not have been permitted to do so until my birthday on May 5. But the official eligible-to-be-someone's-girlfriend day came and went with no indication of Rex's intention to change his status with me.

Although I enjoyed the summer with my family, I could hardly wait for the next school year to begin. Once again, I traveled on Sundays to church with the Dunns. Rex, however, started working at the Pendleton Street inner city mission, one of ten such outreaches run by GBS students. I missed our weekly curbside chats, but soon found a substitute for them.

Someone had informed me that Rex was a good Ping-Pong player who served wicked spins. I had been tutored in Ping-Pong by a master at the game, Jerry Glick, who had lived with our family during his freshman year of high school. My brothers and I spent hours under his patient coaching, learning to return his signature spins. Later, Robb and Paul continued to hone my ability to successfully slap a spin ball back across the net in intense, late-night contests.

Rex accepted my invitation to a match one Friday night, and over the next month, those weekly competitions fueled our growing interest. This state of affairs was not lost to others, but neither was the fact that we were not officially a couple. With a friendly desire to be helpful, the dean of men pulled Rex aside for some advice. "Son, you know pumpkin pie tastes mighty good. Just remember, though, if you leave the pie sitting on the shelf too long, it will spoil."

Still Rex held back, until one mid-October night in the library when he nonchalantly walked behind the desk where I was studying and dropped an envelope onto my open book. It contained a letter explaining why we could be nothing more than friends. I was bewildered to learn that it was my missionary call that stood in the way. Rex knew that God had led him to Bible school to prepare for Christian service, but since he did not have a call *specifically* to missionary work, he was afraid that his interest in me could "call" him in that direction when God might have other plans. He suggested that we stop playing Ping-Pong on Friday nights and spend that time praying for God's leading. I did pray, quite earnestly, over the next several weeks. It was tempting to ask God to change Rex's mind, but I knew that I wanted His will above all else.

Rex prayed as well, but he took things one step farther by seeking counsel from one of his godly professors. Explaining why we could not date and anticipating a figurative pat on the back for his willingness to sacrifice his own desires, Rex was surprised when Rev. Edsel Trouten told him that since both of us wanted to please the Lord, had felt no decrease in our interest for each other, and were not called to incompatible ministries, perhaps God was in favor of our relationship.

Three weeks later, on November 11, 1977, Rex walked through the double glass doors of the girls' dorm and signed me out in the date book beside the dean's desk. He wrote these words on the back of the picture of himself that he gave me that evening, which I still carry in my purse:

*Dear Hannah,*
*This is a beginning of which we don't know the ending;*
*but I pray that as we acknowledge Him in all our ways,*
*He shall direct our paths.*

We have tried to acknowledge Him, and God has kept His promise to direct. Two years and seven months later, we joyfully followed as He led us down the aisle of Faith Community Chapel in Thomasville, North Carolina, to exchange our wedding vows.

But what about the missionary call that God gave me when I was ten years old? How did that fit with marrying a man without a similar summons? God has many ways to make His will clear when our hearts are open to Him. Knowing without question that God had brought us together led to the next logical step. Since I had a rock-solid certainty that I was to be a foreign missionary and Rex had no opposing call from God, then he, too, was to be a missionary. That conclusion has held him steady from then until now; today, he cannot imagine *not* being involved in missions.

On the sweltering evening of July 4, 1980, when we said "I do," we had no idea that our first term of missionary service was eight long years away. During those years, God guided us faithfully, just as He had promised, never allowing us to see around the bend in the road until we were actually rounding the curve, but always giving enough light to take the next step. And that time of maturing and preparing proved to be invaluable, as you will see. I am so glad that the angel flew speedily and arrived in time that long-ago morning when God sent him to stop Rex's ears!

# 4

## Cow Pies and Kisses

*July 15, 2006 ~ San Luis, Honduras*

Fast-forward twenty-six years and a few days from our wedding date. The temperature was still sweltering, but the setting was nothing like the orange-carpeted church in North Carolina where we promised to love and cherish each other for always. The unfolding of those vows in our own marriage prepared us for a new, unexpected chapter in our love story, written much farther south, in a rustic country setting in Honduras.

They had announced it for weeks on the radio: "International conference speakers, Rex and Hannah McDowell, will be giving a marriage seminar in San Luis, Santa Bárbara, on Saturday. Be sure not to miss it." We certainly did not recognize ourselves from the description, but I guess "international conference speakers" may not be totally inaccurate if you count that we have worked in Mexico, Costa Rica, Nicaragua, and Honduras. Oh yes, Rex has taught short term in Ukraine, Bolivia, and Guatemala, as well.

At any rate, the date was set and the romantic setting prepared. Everyone dressed up in nice clothes for the big event. We stopped on our way out of town to get forty copies made of each of the fifteen pages of notes we had prepared to pass out. The three scheduled sessions were to be fifty minutes each, but that was not nearly enough time to cover all the material we wanted to give, so the handouts were to supplement the information in our talks.

"Look for a bunch of people in a cow pasture off to the right," Rex told me as we bumped along the rutted road, raising a cloud of dust.

"In a *what?*"

"In a cow pasture. I guess it must have fit the definition of 'romantic' better than merely meeting in the auditorium at the Bible institute. Just wait till you see it." (He had already been out there earlier that day for a morning teaching session with only the pastors, not the couples.)

Sure enough, several dozen potholes, sharp bends, and mud-and-stick houses later, we saw them, gathered under a large white awning emblazoned every few feet with the distinctive Red Cross emblem and name, out in the middle of a field liberally sprinkled with cow pies in various stages of maturity. The well-dried, crusty ones were easy to walk around, and Rex told me they had thoughtfully raked dirt over some of the fresher ones when they erected the awning.

We set up our material on the small folding table at the front while the young pastor in charge, himself married less than a year, pulled letters out of the gift-wrapped shoe box labeled *Correo de Amor* (Love Mailbox) and read them aloud into the microphone. Anyone who was daring enough had written a love note to his or her spouse. One at a time, the letters were shared with the whole group, to many giggles of appreciation when each writer's and recipient's name was revealed.

We passed out our pages to the thirty-one couples in attendance, a few less than the number at our first marriage seminar several weeks ago in a city about four hours from here. I could not help comparing the settings: that private, reserved room with a catered meal in an air-conditioned hotel restaurant, and this fresh-breeze-cooled awning in a country field. Quite a contrast, wouldn't you agree? This might not have been what many would have considered the more *romantic*, but it was definitely the more *interesting* of the two. After all, what more elegant and expensive perfume could Rex have enjoyed during the course of the evening as we sat close together than my "Essence of Bug Spray" that he had warned me to generously apply?

At the end of our first session, there was to be a meal ready for everyone, so we tried to be careful to keep within the time limit. We did not need to worry about being too long-winded. Around forty minutes after we finished talking, a pickup truck finally jounced and bounced into the field, carrying big pots full of delicious smelling something. Each husband was instructed to go to the serving area on the tailgate of the truck and get two plates of food, one for himself and the other to serve to his wife. The various couples carefully scouted around for a cow-pie-free spot to sit on the ground and enjoy the piece of chicken, scoop of rice, one or two tortillas, and spoonful of cabbage salad on each plate. The food really was quite good, but Rex and I declined the glasses of fruit drink offered with the meal, unwilling to risk the possible consequences of the unbottled water that had likely been used to make it. You can understand our reluctance when you see the water that fills the toilet bowl in our house after flushing and notice that it is slightly darker in color than the yellow that you just flushed down. Not quite so bad after a few days without rain, it still does not inspire much confidence in its purity.

When everyone gathered back under the awning for Round Two, the names of three couples were drawn from another box that had each couple's registration card in it. The three wives were seated in chairs at the front with their respective husbands standing behind them. A container of hair brushes, barrettes, combs, clasps, and so forth was set on another chair. Each husband was ordered to remove from his wife's hair anything she had used to arrange it, muss up the hair really well, and then redo it as quickly and attractively as he could, using whatever he wanted from the treasury of things provided.

Plenty of chuckles erupted from the watching crowd as the guys fumbled around, doing their inexperienced and inept best to finish an acceptable hairstyle first. After the second set of three wives had suffered through the "beauty salon" session, the rest of the group voted on the results, and the winning husband was instructed to get down on one knee in front of his wife. The coordinator handed him an artificial rose and a card with a flowery declaration of love printed on it, which he had to read aloud to her. As one of the seminar teachers, I was exempt from having to get my hair redone—a blessing worth all of the hours that we had spent in preparation for the evening!

With the lateness of supper, the games, and the letter reading, night had fallen by the time we were ready for session number three, and we were wishing we had brought a flashlight so we could see our notes. Not to worry—they were well prepared. A wire with four widely spaced lightbulbs was draped around the edges of the awning, and the bulb directly over our table provided plenty of illumination. It did a fine job of making it possible to read our notes ... and it attracted every flying insect within a quarter-mile radius. We talked our way through that session while swatting at, spitting out, brushing off, and waving away too many bugs to keep track of. I succeeded at fishing out the one that flew down the front of my blouse, but I had to stand up and get Rex to pull out my blouse tail and reach up my back to get the one that managed to migrate down there and remain fluttering against my skin in its vain efforts to escape. Talk about romantic! It is a bit disconcerting to be dealing with the more delicate physical aspects of marriage, especially in a mixed group, in such a setting. Kisses and cow pies and bugs are definitely not your usual marriage seminar mix.

About twenty minutes before we concluded, the bus that had been rented to transport everyone to and from this special event chugged up, parked, and sat there with its engine idling, adding diesel exhaust to the other country-air scents. The driver finally turned off the motor, and we were told not to worry, to just go ahead and finish what we had prepared. Following our final words of advice, the young pastor handed us a pile of beautifully printed and decorated certificates which we signed as rapidly as we could, handing one out to each couple as their names were called.

The participants trudged through the pasture in the dark (not much good to say, "Watch your step!") to climb on the bus for the ride home. Rex and I stood off to the side for a short, private counseling session with a young couple while the event coordinators stacked and loaded chairs and took down the awning. Rain started before we left, and although we had brought umbrellas, we had left them in our Chevy Blazer, parked a good distance away from the center of activity. By the time we got into the vehicle, we were wet, tired, and ready for the romance to end. But there was a final highlight to the day: getting stuck in the mud as we tried to leave—or maybe it was just a fresh, giant cow pie.

# 5

## Gearing Up and Counting Down
### *1980 to 1987 ~ Thomasville, North Carolina*

As newlyweds, Rex and I were blessed with a made-to-order job and living quarters. Three years before, my family had moved to North Carolina so my father could help Rev. Dan Parker, one of his former students, start Carolina Christian College. After two years at God's Bible School and a year at the University of Cincinnati for premedical studies, I moved back home with my parents to continue my education at CCC. Rex joined the faculty there two months after our marriage, so in my final year of Bible college, my new husband was the instructor for my Pauline Epistles class.

I worked harder in Rex's class than I did in any other, determined that no one should legitimately accuse me of earning a good grade just because I was the teacher's pet. All went well until the final oral exam. I studied until I was confident that I could answer anything he might ask, but when my turn came for the battery of questions, I was struck with a petrifying case of terror-of-the-teacher syndrome. Eyes glazed, tongue wooden, I sat across the table from this suddenly intimidating man who scared the wits out of me, and my rattled brain could not remember a single fact. Mercifully, Rex allowed me to write out my answers, and when I did not have those captivating blue eyes focused on mine, my heart quit racing and I calmly answered the questions. I did get an "A" for the course, but I am sure I expended more effort for it than I did for any other such grade my entire school career.

The summer after my graduation with a Bachelor of Religious Education degree, Rex and I traveled with the college ladies' trio to churches and camp meetings across the United States, recruiting new students. Those thousands of miles that we drove and multiple homes that we visited helped to prepare us for hitting the pavement as missionary candidates a few years later, before our first term in Costa Rica. Prior to that, though, there was still some important medical preparation that I needed in order to fulfill my missions call.

I was accepted into nursing school in the fall of 1981 and quickly fell in love with the study of God's crowning creation, the amazing human body. The more I learned, the more I agreed with Psalm 139:14: "I will praise you, for I am fearfully and wonderfully made; marvelous are your works." Hours of poring over textbooks, days of practicing in the skills lab, weeks of scribbling notes, months of rotating through the area hospitals, and two years of commuting to and from classes finally culminated in the solemn moment when our director fastened the school pin on the crisp collar of my new white uniform, conferring on me the long-anticipated title of "Graduate Nurse."

Throughout the ceremony, Rex stood near the back doors, bouncing our infant firstborn in his arms and vainly trying to shush his unhappy wails. I squirmed in my seat, desperate to slip back and comfort my baby, but not wanting to cause more distraction. Just before I walked across the platform to receive my pin, a fellow graduate's sister coaxed our little one into her arms and took him outside. Quickly drying my eyes, I tried to relax and enjoy celebrating this hard-earned goal, but my red-eyed, blotchy-cheeked graduation picture testifies to an occasion made memorable by our little boy's discordant, unsolicited solo that had not been on the program.

Knowing that I needed some practice before putting my fledgling degree to the test on a mission field, I worked for a year as a labor and delivery nurse at our local hospital. It was a great place to start, since I had enjoyed the maternity section of our nursing school program more than any other. Petite, bouncy, no-nonsense Bobbi Hunt, my instructor for the course, taught with a contagious enthusiasm that instilled in me a love for the subject. She had shared the excitement of observing births in a traditional hospital setting with her nursing students, but had never attended a midwife-assisted birth. She happily accepted the invitation to join Rex, me, and our certified nurse-midwife, Leah Albers, at the Siler City Birthing Center for the birth of Rex Allen McDowell II, four months before I graduated. Bobbi also faithfully supported me through the challenges of exclusively breastfeeding my baby while going to school full time. All these years later, as I think of the hundreds of babies and their mothers that God has allowed me to help, I thank Him again for the motivation of a Christian nursing instructor at a secular university, who played such an important role in what I am today.

A year out of nursing school, having had the chance to become relatively experienced as a labor and delivery nurse, I was looking forward to finally getting to the mission field; but God had still more training in store for me. His gentle nudge in that direction came when my brother Robb and his wife Veda chose to go to a birthing center for their first baby's birth and invited me to join them as a support person. When Veda's labor progressed MUCH faster than any of us anticipated, however, I had the exhilarating privilege of welcoming their daughter, Jamie Loray Kaufman, into the world in her mommy and daddy's bedroom. As a labor and delivery nurse at the hospital, I had witnessed dozens of births, but this was my first hands-on delivery experience, all the more special because it was family. I absolutely loved it! The more I thought about it, the more I felt that God wanted me to go to the mission field not only as a nurse, but also as a certified nurse-midwife, which would greatly increase my ability to become His hands extended.

After Rex and I prayed until we felt clear to pursue this idea, I contacted the Medical University of South Carolina just one state away. The several-page application which they sent required me to submit an essay telling why I felt that I would make a good nurse-midwife. I poured my soul into that composition, likening my educational journey to the labor process and eloquently painting a word picture of my desire to use the skills I would receive by being birthed from their program to better the lives of underprivileged women in third-world countries.

In the days between mailing the application and receiving a reply, whenever nervous jitters threatened to overwhelm me, God sweetly reminded me that He was in control of my future. If He wanted me in the Medical University of South Carolina's nurse-midwifery program, He was well able to orchestrate events to accomplish my acceptance. Little did I realize how much orchestration He had to do. Many of the other candidates had much more obstetrics experience than I did. Most of them had graduated from bachelor's degree nursing programs, rather than an associate's degree program such as mine. In fact, that year was the last one in which an associate's degree RN was granted a coveted spot on the class roster. Talk about God's clocks keeping perfect time! And clocks are not the only things subject to His will. He works through many sources, as I found out well into my training when I learned why my application had not been added to the tall pile of rejections. "Look at what she wants to do with her training," one of the instructors, a Catholic sister had urged. "Think of the good she can do in a third-world country. Let's give her a chance!"

On the red-letter day that the envelope with the news of my acceptance arrived in our mailbox, the magnitude of what we were planning to do suddenly hit us. Rex II (or "Rexie," as we called him) was three years old and still very much required the attention of his mama, who was planning on going back to school full time. Many days during my last four months of nursing school, Rexie had gone to class with Rex, tucked cozily inside a baby carrier worn on his daddy's chest. At first, Rex's students were a bit distracted with *both* their professor and his baby up front for the lecture, but the baby slept through most classes (probably to the envy of some of the students) and caused no problems. My mother and sisters took over his care during the year that I worked to gain experience, but Charleston, SC, would be too far away for grandma and aunties to help with babysitting.

What about a job for Rex? Teaching at Carolina Christian College provided a paycheck as well as our housing. Since I would be in school full time, he would need something with flexible hours so he could care for Rexie. As the "what if's" swirled through our minds, we reminded ourselves that just as God had made His will for us clear, He would certainly supply everything we needed to fulfill that will. We made our plans accordingly, excited to see how He was going to provide.

Rex decided that, since he was going to be the chief cook and bottle washer, he had better start honing his culinary skills. One evening before our move to South Carolina, he pulled out a cookbook and started to concoct our supper. A few minutes into the job, he jerked open the back door, ran outside, dashed completely around our house, and came panting back into the kitchen, carrying in his hand the pepper shaker. He met my bewildered look with his mischievous grin and a very logical explanation. "The recipe called for a dash of pepper, so I was just doing what it said." Can you blame me for being skeptical of the end results of his meal preparation? Actually, over the course of the next year, he produced some pretty tasty dishes and became quite adept at navigating his way through the maze of such terms as "sauté," "caramelize," "julienne," and "braise." Cooking was not the only thing at which Rex excelled during his stint as "Mr. Mom." Along with handling the laundry, cleaning, and child care, he also volunteered to decipher my late-evening or wee-hours-of-the-morning handwriting and type up my papers.

In an unprecedented move to retain midwifery candidates, the university administration that year gave each of us in my class a grant to help finance our education. It not only covered my tuition and books, but also went a sizable way toward paying our monthly rent as well. Little did the officials of this secular university realize that they were equipping a medical missionary with tools that would help her touch lives for Christ, as well as helping to provide for her family's needs.

Fifteen of the original twenty-two students who began the year-long program graduated that summer of 1987, but the coveted status of "Certified Nurse-Midwife" was not yet ours. First, we had to pass the national qualifying exam, a formidable marathon of essay questions that necessitated filling pages and pages with writing that would prove our mastery of women and baby care. To gain experience and confidence, we also had to complete an integration with a nurse-midwife mentor. Once more God stepped in, landing me a thirteen-week integration, the longest the university would allow, with Leigh Wood and Sharon Bond, two exceptional certified nurse-midwives practicing at a birthing center in Bamberg, SC. Rex and Rexie moved back to North Carolina with my parents, while I settled down to three months of delivering babies.

All practicing certified nurse-midwives in the United States are required to have a back-up physician with whom they can consult. Leigh and Sharon's doctor was Michael Watson, MD, another of those special people whom God directed my way to help round out my preparation. Active in his Methodist church's mission work, he had been to Africa on various medical trips. When he learned of my plans to use my training on a mission field, he took a personal interest in helping to equip me with practical training in areas other than just midwifery. I learned from him some of the finer points of suturing and wound care that would prove invaluable down the road.

I finished my integration in mid-September and took the National Certifying Exam two months later on November 14, 1987. The day the mailman brought a certificate announcing that "Hannah K. McDowell is entitled to be known as a Certified Nurse-Midwife" was another red-letter one, and my gleeful squeal of exuberance and jubilant dance of excitement were appropriately celebratory. We now had the last piece of preparation in place, and the countdown for our takeoff to the mission field was nearing zero!

# 6

## How Do *You* Define "Maternity" Clinic?

*July 13, 2009 ~ San Luis, Honduras*

All those years of study earned me the title of certified nurse-midwife, correct? So how does it figure that when I started my shift last night in the Evangelistic Faith Missions maternity clinic in San Luis, Honduras, my three patients were an eleven-year-old girl admitted that morning with a temperature of 104° and severe dehydration from several days of nausea and vomiting, a twenty-two-year-old man with similar tummy troubles, and a thirty-seven-year-old woman with unstable diabetes?

When I reported off and left for home at 8:00 this morning, I turned over the care of those same three people, plus an eighteen-year-old mother and her second baby, a six-pound, four-ounce beautiful little girl, who was born at 6:29 a.m. Of the eight brand-new lives welcomed into the world in the past ten days, it has been my privilege to deliver four of them, all girls, ranging in size from four pounds, fourteen ounces, to nearly seven pounds.

In a maternity clinic, you would expect babies to be born, right? Just what is going on here with the dehydration and diabetes, anyhow? It is like this. The clinic, built on seventeen acres of land donated by the town of San Luis, opened its doors for business on May 2, 1979. The first patient arrived that morning, and by evening, she had delivered a healthy baby girl. Not only in name, but in practice as well, it was a "maternity" clinic. But over the years, as the demand for expanded services grew, so did the clinic.

The nearest major hospitals are in Santa Bárbara and in San Pedro Sula, both over two hours away. San Luis itself boasts close to 39,000 residents, counting the outlying *aldeas* (sort of like suburbs, but very much what we would consider the boonies). There is a public social security clinic on the edge of town, where during weekdays one can get prenatal care as well as diagnosis and treatment of minor illnesses. But a wound needing to be cleaned and sutured, or a child with dehydration in need of IV meds and fluids, or especially a woman in labor, is never attended there; and not even minor problems are treated at night or on the weekends.

That is where we step in. Though the lighted sign above our door proclaims "maternity" clinic, we do not turn *anyone* away. The national nurses here are experts in triage, treatment, and referral (if necessary) of a vast variety of illnesses and injuries, 24/7. Since its beginning, over 8,000 inpatients have received compassionate, skillful care by the four nurses on staff. Add to those the tens of thousands of outpatients who have stopped in to purchase medicine or sit through a nebulizer treatment, have their blood sugar checked or a Foley catheter changed, get a wound repaired or receive a series of antibiotic injections over several days, and you can see the vital role the clinic has played in the life of the community. I absolutely love being able to help out here in the summers, and it definitely makes for some interesting experiences.

Take my typical shift a few days back. When I walked in, I could not only smell the sickening-sweet stench of a LOT of blood, but also see a splattered path of large dried blotches of it leading me down the hall and into the emergency room, where a sixty-six-year-old man lay on the table, an IV of Ringers Lactate running rapidly into his right antecubital vein. The left side of his shirt and pants, from neck to toes, was *totally* blood saturated, as were several towels and the sheet under him. His left forearm was wrapped in a bulky pressure dressing through which the blood continued to seep. Rosmery told me he had arrived two-and-a-half hours ago, and she was still waiting for the Red Cross's only ambulance to return from its transport of an earlier patient to San Pedro.

The poor fellow kept lamenting the fact that he had taken food and water to the cow tied up on the hill near his house, since that is when the accident occurred. His foot slipped, and the heel of his shoe caught on a protruding rock, ripping off. He fell, landing on top of his machete, which sliced through muscle and tendons down to the bone and two-thirds of the way around his arm. Forty minutes after I got there, the ambulance arrived, and we loaded him onto the stretcher inside. In a spurt of flying gravel from the Land Rover's tires, he was finally on his way to get the surgery he needed.

While waiting for him to be transferred, I dashed back and forth from our one-bed-and-a-standby-stretcher emergency room, to the front desk, to our tiny pharmacy, monitoring his condition and reinforcing the bandage with even more layers, grabbing an emesis basin for his nausea, and reassuring his family, in between selling "two pills for a headache" to one man, "two ounces of the green liquid for stomachache" to another, checking blood pressure on someone else, and counting out ten pills "for breathing trouble" for the ancient, barefooted little woman who crept up to the door but would not venture inside, asking her questions through the screen and waiting on the porch for the medicine I took her. Of course, I did run out of one- and two-*lempira* bills in the cash drawer in the middle of all that, but the three people who could not be given their correct change were very gracious about losing a *lempira* (equal to about five cents) and thanked me anyhow for the medicine I sold them.

After the ambulance left, it took me twenty-five minutes of vigorous scrubbing with bleach to clean up all the splattered blood on the porch, in the hall, and on the floor and treatment table. Thankfully, I finished shortly before the next casualties arrived: three women who had been in a car wreck, two of whom were thrown from the car. Amazingly, only one of them was seriously injured, a twenty-year-old with multiple scrapes and bruises and a nasty laceration on the back of her head. No possibilities here of a CAT scan to check the extent of damage from the blow to her skull. Her pupils were equal, round, and reacted normally to the beam of my pocket flashlight, and she denied any bleeding from her nose, mouth, or ears. All I could do was thoroughly clean and stitch the jagged gash, pausing while tying off my last stitch to hold her head while she leaned over the edge of the table and vomited into the trash can.

I had not even finished cleaning her various scrapes when I heard loud moaning out in the hall, and someone poked a head in the emergency room door to inform me that a woman in labor needed my attention. I peeked out and saw a very uncomfortable about-to-be-mother, doubled over with a strong contraction, leaning on the front desk, surrounded by the friends and family of the accident victims. Her helpless-looking husband stood uncertainly off to the side.

Quickly escorting her to our three-bed labor ward, I found out that her baby's birth was not as eminent as it appeared, in spite of its being her sixth, and the little one's heartbeat was just fine. I could settle her into a bed and hurry back to finish getting my accident lady ready for discharge and cleaning up the instruments I had used in her care. Before I even had the treatment table washed and a clean sheet on, another patient was waiting, thankfully someone who just needed an injection for his migraine headache. A blood-pressure and fetal-heart-tones check on the mother-to-be, yet another pain injection and more pharmacy sales later, and a second woman in labor walked through the door.

I hurried back to the labor room to set up the large folding screen that we use between the beds to give privacy. This one was having her first baby, and though her contractions were neither regular nor very strong, she "just wanted to be sure." Since she was only dilated one centimeter, I sent her home with lots of reassurance and instructions on when to return. The problem was, she had walked past the bed of the first woman on her way into the room, glancing over and greeting her. According to their beliefs, if a first-time pregnant woman looks at another woman in labor, the second woman's labor will last a lot longer. So before she left, the not-in-active-labor, first-time-mother-to-be complied with the for-sure-in-good-strong-labor, sixth-time-mother's request to uncurse her. I watched, fascinated and incredulous, as the younger woman spit on her finger, then touched it to the other woman's bare skin, drawing a cross across her belly button several times with the saliva. The two women smiled at each other, satisfied, and I managed to keep a straight face and any thoughts on the matter to myself.

Interestingly, for a sixth-time mother, the labor *was* unusually long. I had figured the baby would deliver before my shift was over, but since that did not happen, I stayed on to give some continuity of care and to have the chance for the excitement of another delivery. I also felt an inexplicable niggling sense of needing to have an extra person on hand, though there was nothing really to put my finger on to explain why. All I can say is that God was in control and gave me the urge to hang around. Although her heart rate had been in a healthy range the whole time her mommy was in labor, when the tiny, five-pound, two-ounce little girl slipped out into my hands, she was limp, blue, and not breathing or responding, with the largest amount of very liquid meconium (the sticky, tar-like stool passed by an infant during the first two days after birth) I have ever seen at a delivery pouring from her bottom, testifying to the struggle she was having to live. Her one-minute Apgar score (a predictive value of a newborn's well-being) was a mere two out of a possible ten, and at five minutes had only increased to a nonreassuring six out of ten. *Thankfully* there were two nurses there instead of just one, as there would have been had I not paid attention to that sixth sense and stayed over. Head nurse Miriam and I hovered urgently over the tiny form, working with her and willing her to breathe, while the mother lay sobbing on the delivery table, at one point screaming, "After all that I went through, is my baby going to die?"

Finally, five hours after my shift was to have ended and more than three hours since her birth, Little Miss was able to maintain her color without supplemental oxygen, though her lungs still sounded wet, doubtless from the meconium she aspirated. With Miriam on hand to monitor the baby closely until she could consult with our good town doctor later that morning, I could go home and get some sleep. It was an interesting day in the "maternity" clinic, wouldn't you agree?

## 7

# "I Need a Kilo of Squished Up Cow, Please"

*Spring and Summer 1988 ~ Caballo Blanco, Costa Rica*

While I was still in midwifery school, we were approved as missionary candidates with Evangelical Wesleyan Mission, directed by Rev. Raymond Shreve. In March of 1988, four months after my graduation, we drove to the mission headquarters in Key West, Florida, for a month of orientation. On the way, we stopped see Leigh and Sharon, my integration preceptors. I wanted to update them on our plans, but I also hoped they could give us some good news. They were happy to do a pregnancy test on me, especially since they knew about the baby that I had miscarried four years earlier and our fears that we would never be able to add to our family. When their broad smiles confirmed that Rexie was going to be a big brother, I am sure there were no happier people in the world than we.

Both sets of prospective grandparents received our ecstatic calls announcing the joyful tidings with mixed emotions as they realized they would have to wait four years to meet this new grandchild. We had accepted the fact that being missionaries would mean missing out on sharing the joys of Rexie's growing-up years firsthand with our family. Now there would be *two* children who could not pick up the phone to tell Grandpa about a first lost tooth, or sit in Grandma's lap for story time. This was, of course, long before the days of technology which makes it possible to send pictures of the new baby to family and friends minutes after his birth and sit in front of a computer to catch up face-to-face on all the news from home.

The short interval between leaving Key West and departing for Costa Rica raced by in a blur of traveling to churches to help raise our support, packing, and exchanging the last emotional farewells with family and friends. Wildly waving arms from three rolled-down windows of our car the morning that we pulled out of my parents' driveway were responded to in kind from the front porch. We craned our necks for a final glimpse of their beloved faces, thankful beyond measure for the blessing of going with the approval and encouragement of both sides of our family.

Our plane left Miami International airport at 2:00 the afternoon of May 11. Because we had packed enough clothes, household, and baby paraphernalia for our entire first term, we had a total of thirty-one boxes and suitcases, each one weighing as close to the seventy pound limit as we could get it. The

customs officials in Costa Rica took one look at our mammoth pile and directed us to the end of the line. When it was finally our turn for inspection, the
examiner gave only a cursory glance in three boxes and waved us on through,
not charging a single penny, or *colon*, as their currency is called. It was a wonderful answer to the prayers of many people.

Donovan DeLong met us at the airport. His small pickup truck was nowhere nearly big enough for us plus all of our luggage, so we hired a van
to help get everything to the little village of Caballo Blanco (White Horse),
where we would be living. Considering what an hour-long taxi ride with all
of those boxes would have been in the States, we were happy to pay the 2,500
colons ($33.50 at the exchange rate of 74.40 colons per dollar) that the driver
charged. On the way, Don pointed out *Clínica Bíblica,* the hospital where
the baby we were expecting in five-and-a-half months would be born. "If you
have any major injury or other emergency, that's the place to go," he informed
me gravely. "Don't even *think* of going to the local social security hospital in
Cartago, close to where you will be living. It's better to die trying to get to
*Clínica Bíblica.*"

When we arrived in Caballo Blanco, Marilyn Olson, teacher to Don and
Maydean DeLong's three children, gave us the key to her little house, where
we would be staying for four weeks until the DeLongs left for their furlough.
Adjusting to our location on the edge of the village was not a problem for this
farm girl. I enjoyed watching the black cow that came grazing along at eye level
on the hill bordering our back yard, six feet away from my kitchen window.
The brown hen that brooded over a nest full of eggs in a hole in that same hill,
the three goat kids that our neighbor lady staked out in the thick grass across
the dirt road every morning, and the oxen that plodded past on their way to
plow a nearby field made me feel right at home. We were in a valley overlooked
by volcano Irazu's impressive peak on one side and other lovely mountain tops
all the way around us. The scenery was magnificent—when you could see it.
We arrived in the middle of the rainy season, typically with sunny mornings
followed every afternoon and evening by a steady downpour that blotted out
the beauty of our surroundings. The drumming raindrops also churned the
dirt roads into sticky mud that clung tenaciously to our shoes, making me very
thankful that our house had no carpeting.

I quickly discovered that Costa Rican housewives are quite proud of their
glossy, richly dyed cement floors, which they sweep, scrub, wax, and polish every morning before the afternoon rain creates more mud to be tracked in. The
most popular floor color is deep rhubarb red, with asparagus green running a
not-very-close second. Polishing is done with a coconut hull cut in half, which
gives a round sort of hard bristle brush that is placed on the floor and vigorously

slid back and forth with one's foot. Following the brush, a fine steel wool pad gets skated all around the room, and finally a piece of wool cloth. The whole process wore me out. When I learned that the going rate for a maid was thirty cents an hour, I was more than happy to find a teenage girl from the church who wanted to do it for me.

Getting accustomed to water rationing was more difficult than some of our other adjustments. Americans are used to turning on the faucet at any time and having plenty of fresh, safe liquid for drinking, bathing, or laundry. In Caballo Blanco, the water came on at 4:00 a.m. and went off at 1:00 p.m. During those hours, I made sure to use a short length of hose to fill the fifty-five gallon drum that took up a large amount of floor space in my tiny kitchen. After one o'clock, any water that we used had to be dipped from the drum.

We took our morning showers under the one source of hot water in the house, a four-inch-diameter heating showerhead screwed onto a skinny metal pipe protruding from the wall in the bathroom. The water warmed up as it flowed through the showerhead, but since the heating element was so small, it could only get a small volume of water really hot. If we wanted a nice abundant spray of water, we had to settle for its being a tepid temperature. The tricky part about the heater was the need for great caution in turning it on. Its popular name was "Widow Maker," due to the danger of getting a significant electrical jolt if one forgot to plug the heating element's cord into the electrical outlet *before* getting into the shower. Woe to the unfortunate soul who touched the plug while standing under the stream of water!

We had one sink in our house, a concrete monster called a *pila* cemented to the floor and wall in the corner of the kitchen. It had three sections. In the deep middle part, I washed our dishes in cold water, using a paste soap that did a great job of cutting grease. One of the two shallower sections had a corrugated bottom that was ideal for scrubbing the dirt and dyed floor wax out of Rexie's pants. The other side gave me some work space and a spot to drain the dishes after rinsing them with bleach water. I soaked our fruits and vegetables in an iodine or bleach bath to kill the microscopic creepy-crawlies that liked to hitch a ride from the parasite-infested soil to one's stomach. Of course, I either boiled all of our drinking and teeth brushing water or treated it with sixteen drops of bleach per gallon. I did sometimes wonder which was worse for us, the bugs or the bleach.

The days before the DeLongs' departure, after which Rex would be responsible for preaching in five church services a week, sped along rapidly. Since I could not give much support to my pastor-husband until I did not have to call on him to translate for me any time someone knocked on our door, I figured that I could at least do our weekly shopping.

My first foray for fresh meat gave the two young men who ran the local hole-in-the-wall butcher shop a day's worth of laughter in the process. I discovered that one did not simply walk in and pick out a nicely wrapped package of hamburger or chicken. Large hunks of beef and pork hung from hooks above the counter, and a small glass-topped cooler held chicken. A shopper had to choose the meat that she wanted. The shop attendant would then slice or grind it, weigh it, and slip it into a plastic bag. The problem was that I did not think to ask either Rex or Maydean how to say what I needed until *after* I got there. "Do you speak English?" I inquired hopefully of the young man behind the counter. He shook his head. Thinking fast, I looked around for some clue to help me. I recalled the painted pictures of a pig, a cow, and a chicken on the outside wall beside the front door, all of them with their respective names printed underneath: *pollo* (chicken), *rez* (beef) and *cerdo* (pork). I stuck my head out the door and thoroughly studied the words, repeating the one I needed to myself. Smiling confidently, I asked for (I thought) some *"rez,"* making kneading motions in the air with both hands to signify that I wanted it ground up. The man regretfully indicated that my desired item was not available. I was fairly certain that it *was*, if only I could get him to understand my request. Next I tried asking for *"hamburguesa,"* but he said he did not have any of that, either. There was nothing to do but to trudge home and get my request written down in Spanish. When I returned to the little store and read the paper's contents aloud, one of the men pulled down a hunk of beef, sliced off a goodly portion, and took it to the back to grind it, but I heard him howling with laughter as he did so. He managed to put on a straight face before bringing my kilo of "squished up beef" to the scales, but as soon as I had paid for my purchase and walked out, both men burst into renewed gales of mirth.

I went back to that store only one other time, a few months later. This time I was armed beforehand with my cheat sheet. The young men obligingly weighed, ground, and bagged my requested portion without the excessive hilarity with which they had fulfilled my first request. But something was vastly different with *this* meat. Normally, ground beef gets brown when it is cooked, right? This stuff not only refused to turn brown, it seemed to get *pinker* the longer it simmered in the pot on the stove. Besides, it had a horrid smell. Although we smothered it under a thick tomato sauce in stuffed peppers, the taste was revolting. We ended up feeding the whole mess to Marilyn's dog, but the ungrateful animal took one sniff and curled his lip, turning away without even an exploratory lick. Not until months later did we find out why even the dog would not touch the stuff.

"Did it get pinker and pinker the longer you cooked it?" queried Don DeLong, down on a visit.

"Oh yes, it certainly did," I replied.

Don began grinning. "And did it have a nasty odor while it was cooking?"

I wrinkled my nose in disgust, remembering. "It was so bad I almost threw up from the smell."

He started to chuckle, a hearty, full-throated enjoyment of the joke. "You didn't have ground beef," he managed to get out between guffaws. "They sold you ground horse meat!" My only consolation was that they had evidently tried the same trick on others who were more knowledgeable than I. Shortly after they pulled a fast one over on the stupid American, they forever closed their shop, forced out of business, no doubt, by those who were discerning enough to distinguish a quantity of squished up cow from a similar-looking quantity of squished up horse.

# The Virgin of the Angels

*August 2, 1988 ~ Cartago, Costa Rica*

Exactly four weeks after we arrived in Costa Rica, the DeLongs returned to the United States for their furlough, and our family settled into their larger house. Now, instead of a grassy field with leisurely grazing cows and goats just outside our windows, we had a busy thoroughfare with rushing cars and lumbering buses. At that time, Costa Rica bore the dubious distinction of having the most dangerous highways in all of Central America, a statistic which made us thankful for the wall that enclosed our property. It gave Rexie a safe place to play and assured that he would not impulsively run into the road after a wayward ball. The wall provided no guarantee against uninvited visitors, though, as we discovered the first time that he forgot to bring his bright, distinctive Mickey Mouse ball inside for the night. A couple of days later it reappeared, not in the front yard where he had left it, but being boldly kicked back and forth by the children who lived next door, who had no intention of returning it to its owner.

Our home in Caballo Blanco was conveniently located between Cartago, with its renowned market, and Paraíso, where the DeLongs had recently started a church. A three-mile bus ride in one direction would take us to do our weekly shopping. Three miles of travel the opposite way would land us at the dirt road leading to the newly erected, tin-walled church building in Paraíso. The church property was located on the edge of a community of shanties that had sprung up seemingly overnight after the government promised free land to anyone who would build a home and live there for seven years. In the rush to claim such an unprecedented windfall before the offer ran out, families had slapped together "houses" from anything they could get to stand upright and provide a meager shelter. One of the men who attended the new church got some big cardboard boxes from which he fashioned walls to form rooms in the corrugated tin shell where he, his wife, and five children lived. We hardly thought that "Paraíso," which translates "Paradise," was an apt name for the sprawling, ugly neighborhood of muddy lanes and ramshackle dwellings.

In contrast to such dilapidation, Cartago was a picturesque mix of centuries-old colonial churches, up-to-the-minute glass-fronted department stores, and quaint, tile-roofed villas. As the oldest Spanish settlement in the country, it was the national capital from its founding in 1563, until 1823, when the president moved his seat of government twenty-two kilometers west. It is still one of the nation's largest cities. On Mondays, we often took a picnic lunch and a good book to read aloud to Rexie and went to a Cartago park with lovely flower-bordered walks and sculptured bushes, located in the ruins of a mammoth cathedral that had been destroyed by an earthquake, leaving only the outer stone walls standing. It was the perfect way to unwind after the demands of a Sunday schedule that included services in three different locations.

Our church in Caballo Blanco was perched on a hillside reached by a ten-minute walk from our home. It was a nine- by fifteen-feet wooden structure with a tin roof but no ceiling, illuminated by two lightbulbs on wires dangling down between the rafters. A Sunday school building equipped with a long, low table just the right height for children to use for handcrafts or coloring was located a couple of hundred feet from the church on the edge of the hill overlooking a creek. Neither building had bathroom facilities, but this was no problem for youngsters who were accustomed to the common practice of finding a convenient bush or tree for such purposes. In fact, the accepted means of raw sewage disposal for the residents of some of the poorer homes that hugged the banks of the stream was a length of PVC tubing running from their toilet out the side of the house and into the tumbling water below. I vividly remember how my stomach churned the day I saw two little tykes playing on some large boulders in the middle of the creek, gleefully splashing each other with the murky liquid that I was certain swarmed with millions of wicked microbes.

Our newer church in "Paradise" at least boasted an outhouse, but neither place of worship had running water. The pocket-sized squeeze bottles of hand sanitizer that are so common today were years into the future, so we tried to be vigilant with five-year-old Rexie and create in him the good habit of "washing off the fellowship" as soon as we got home after every service.

The third site for ministry was El Guarco, a small village far up the mountain where Rex held services on Sunday afternoons. It was a rough trip at best, and in my pregnant state I did not accompany him often. I was especially glad I had not been along the Sunday after a stray cat had wandered into church unnoticed. Since no one realized he was there, he got locked in the building when everyone left. Apparently the cat was accompanied by an entire battalion of fleas. The fleas evidently found the dirt-floored church to be a friendly environment, and a good number of them decided to camp out there instead of continuing their journey among the crowded ranks of fellow traveling companions on Sir Cat's mangy hide. When he was discovered and released the following service, no one immediately realized the legacy he had left behind. It did not take long, however, for that bequest to become overwhelmingly evident as dozens of hungry fleas jumped at the chance to take advantage of the smorgasbord of fresh, warm blood available from the ankles and legs of the congregants. First one and then another of those present bent over to scratch the spots where the tiny dark-brown creatures were contentedly guzzling breakfast. The service had to be cut short because of the distraction caused by the miniature carnivores.

Knowing that the problem would only multiply with time, Rex took a hand sprayer with pesticide back up to the church early in the week and meticulously fumigated the entire building. His lower legs were thoroughly flea bitten when he returned home. Being a good wife, I was properly sympathetic with his plight, but my feelings of compassion were overridden by the thought of all the fleas that were likely hiding in his clothes, eagerly awaiting the opportunity to exit his person and become cozy with me.

Now, you must understand that my paranoia about fleas was based on recent painful experience, not just a casual aversion to the possibility of a bite. Upon our arrival in Costa Rica, we were welcomed by fleas. Although Don had fumigated the little house on the edge of Caballo Blanco just before we moved in, I was the unhappy recipient of more than 100 bites in our first two-and-a-half weeks. They swelled, blistered, and turned hot and painful. Their intense itching was the worst thing, and it nearly drove me crazy. Although Rex and Rexie were both bitten a few times, they are among the fortunate people who, when bitten, know that something has gotten them because there is a small red mark that mildly irritates for an hour or two and then ceases to be noticeable. The effects of my bites lasted for several weeks; they were so miserable I was seriously tempted to turn around and head back to the United States. We sprayed the house twice more, the final time using a powerful commercial-grade concoction that we obtained from the agricultural department, before our unwelcome visitors were evicted for good.

When Rex told me that he had been liberally chewed upon while he was trying to rid the church in El Guarco of its problem, I panicked. Desperate to avoid another flea-infested house, I made him go into the shed in the back yard, where he patiently waited for me to fill our small washing machine with water from the hose. When that was done, he disrobed completely, put all of his clothes into a large plastic garbage bag, and then carefully passed out the tightly closed bag while I in turn gingerly handed in his bathrobe. Cautiously carrying the bag into the enclosed back porch that housed the cement wash sink and our washing machine, I completely submerged it in the wash water before opening it. I knew my concern had been valid when the fleas in his clothes popped to the surface of the water one by one. I did not feel a smidgen of guilt about my inability to summon even an ounce of pity for them as I coldheartedly watched them being sucked down the drain hose at the end of the wash cycle. Although we had run-ins with fleas off and on throughout all of our years in Central America, things were never as bad as those first few weeks had been.

In a country where the official religion is Catholicism, our congregations were the only conservative holiness voices in a chorus of conflicting religious beliefs. Some insisted that once a person was saved, he was eternally assured of a place in heaven, no matter how righteously or sinfully he lived the rest of his life here on earth. Many believed that the only way for someone to prove that he was filled with the Holy Spirit was by speaking in an unknown tongue. Catechism instructors in the public schools taught the children that prayers to the Virgin Mary would lead them to Christ. Others trusted in their good deeds or church attendance to earn them a spot in heaven. The need for the message that salvation is only through faith in Jesus, whose blood cleanses us from sin and enables us to live holy lives, became acutely real to us less than three months after we arrived in Costa Rica, when we witnessed an event that moved us as much as anything we had seen to that time.

Cartago is the site of the Basílica, an enormous stone cathedral erected over the spot where, according to legend, the seven-inch sculpted image of a brown-skinned mother with a male child in her arms appeared to an indigenous Indian girl, Juana Pereira, on August 2, 1635. Juana took the statue to her home on several occasions, but each time it disappeared, only to turn back up on the same large boulder where she had found it. Finally, the local priest decided that the mysterious happenings meant that the statue should be left where it had been discovered and a cathedral must be erected over the boulder. This was done, and "La Negrita," or "Little Black One," as the dark Madonna is affectionately called, was officially declared the patron saint of Costa Rica in 1824.

Since then, the second of August has been a national holiday to commemorate Mary, the Virgin of the Angels. On this day, hundreds of thousands of people gather in Cartago to participate in a celebration that starts before sunup and lasts until late in the evening. Starting weeks before this date, people walk for hundreds of kilometers to reach the cathedral. From the farthest reaches of Costa Rica, from other Central American countries, and even from realms as distant as the United States and Canada they come, a vast sea of pilgrims. Many spend the night sleeping in the cathedral or on the ground outside so they can be assured of a spot for the next day's activities.

The center of activity is the Basílica, where the black statue rests on its magnificent gold and jewel-encrusted pedestal. We quietly slipped into the back of the massive edifice late in the afternoon of August the first and soberly watched as multitudes of people crawled on their knees down the long central aisle. Some of them kept their heads down and their hands folded, others gazed raptly ahead to the statue. Still others reached out a hand to help along someone else, perhaps a grandmother whose rheumatic knees found the long trek to be more difficult than she had anticipated, or a small child whose wandering attention had slowed his progress.

At 9:15 that evening, I sat by the window in our darkened bedroom and in five minutes counted 153 people who streamed by on foot and by bicycle. One was even being pushed along in a wheelchair. A drizzly rain was falling, but the procession continued. Even as late as 2:00 o'clock the next morning, when I looked out for the last time, the stream was still passing, though considerably diminished in volume. I could not help but think of the great rivers of people all over the world who slip into eternity, never having asked Jesus to forgive their sins, pursuing the false hope that penance, or good works, or faithfully going to church will get them into heaven.

The newspaper estimated the crowd at 200,000 the next day. We inched and wormed our way through a considerable number of those, trying to get up close for pictures. Rex's six-foot height put him at an advantage as he snapped photos of the priests and archbishops in their embroidered robes and mitres, and the nuns and seminary students in their wimples and capes. Thousands of brightly colored umbrellas gave shade from the scorching sun to the fortunate ones who had prepared enough to bring them, and provided a vibrant backdrop for the ceremony. The country's most important dignitaries were present, including President Oscar Arias. Despite the solemnity of the occasion, ice cream vendors pushed their carts along the edges of the crowd, ringing bells to advertise their tempting cold treats. Lottery ticket salesmen wove in and out of the horde of people, hawking their wares. During the formal mass, though, all other noises were obliterated in the swelling sing-song chant of thousands of united voices. Following the mass, President Arias consecrated his country to the Virgin, praying, "As President, responsible in these moments for the destiny of the country, I consecrate myself to you, Lady, and I trust in your help that the peace that the angels declared at Bethlehem may always reign in Costa Rica, and come to reign in Central America and in all the peoples of the world." We returned home that day praying that God would help us to know how to share the true message of that peace, which only comes when Jesus forgives our sins and lives in our hearts. He is the answer to the emptiness and longing of every human heart anywhere in the world.

# We Wish You a Merry Christmas

## *December 25, 1988 ~ Caballo Blanco, Costa Rica*

As we approached our first Christmas in Costa Rica, seven months after arriving in the land that was to be our home for the next four years, we were both sad and excited. The sadness was in part related to the fact that Grandma Kaufman left to go back to the States just a few days before December the twenty-fifth. She had been with us for nine weeks to share in the joy occasioned by the gift of seven-and-a-half-pound Benjamin Daniel's safe arrival exactly two months before Christmas and to help with the extra work that such an event produces. As we thought about the family gatherings that would be taking place without us, part of me wanted to just pack us all into one of her suitcases and fly back home for a week. We were finding out what missionaries the world over have discovered across the centuries: Being far from family and friends during the holidays is one of the most painful aspects of answering God's call to service in a distant country. Our pangs of homesickness gave a whole new depth of meaning to the thought that Jesus left His homeland to come to earth as a foreign missionary. Did He ever miss the angelic hosts gathered around His heavenly Father's throne and wish that He could have slipped away to join them for a short visit?

Since the stowaway-in-Grandma's-luggage option would not work, we figured a good way to beat the blues would be to share some of our holiday traditions with our new friends, as well as joining them in their unique ways of celebrating the season. It was not too hard to decide which American Christmas custom we would choose to do. What could be more enjoyable, both for giver and receiver, than baking and eating decorated cut-out cookies? Of course, we did not want to give something that might not be top quality, so extensive taste-testing of each batch by the male members of the McDowell household was required to be sure that the cookies were just right before they could be safely packaged for distribution. In spite of the zeal with which Rex and Rexie tackled the sampling part of the job, there were enough stars, bells, and trees left to wrap two cookies for every child and adult who attended our services, as well as a few of each shape to have for ourselves. Of course, those were the ones that actually made it into the oven, as both of my testers preferred the taste of a scooped-out spoonful of raw cookie dough over having it rolled out, placed on a cookie sheet, and baked to a golden brown.

*You do need to know that the taste-testing would change drastically just three years later when we moved to Nicaragua and discovered that the flour there was universally worm ridden. I had not been accustomed to sifting my flour before using it during the years that we lived in the United States or in Costa Rica, but an experienced Nicaraguan missionary wife warned me that I would want to be sure to do so in our new country. The first time I scooped a cup of flour into the sifter and shook it into the mixing bowl below, I promptly understood her word of caution. Left at the bottom of the sifter was a wriggling mass of disgusting, pasty-white creatures that made me nauseated to watch. Out of morbid curiosity, I counted the gleaning of worms and was amazed to discover fifty-two of them, ranging in size from tiny babies to fat grandmas and grandpas. After that object lesson, the guys in our house never again begged a snitch of raw cookie or bread dough the remainder of our term there.*

Another stateside treat that we had always enjoyed was the flavorful, juicy orange received from the church the Sunday before Christmas. The idea of duplicating this custom in our local Costa Rican congregation seemed like a good one, especially since the church budget was not large, but neither was the price of oranges in a country where they are one of the crops raised for exportation. Someone had informed us that nearly all of the parents, even those in the poorest families, saved to be able to buy a bunch of grapes to divide among the family members, and to get each of their children an apple. As December ushered in the start of the holiday season, sidewalks along the main streets of Cartago and San José became crowded with dozens of carts piled high with these fruits, their vendors doing a brisk business. Mouths watering with remembered pleasure, we could barely keep from drooling at the enticing rows of Red Delicious apples and clusters of Concord grapes, all imported from nontropical countries and all so expensive that we only looked longingly as we walked by.

It was also customary for the church to give out those same treats on Christmas Sunday. The problem was, at almost $1.00 apiece for the apples and a proportionately high price for the grapes, both of the traditional fruits were entirely out of the question because there was just not enough money in the church treasury without having to borrow from somewhere. Since we were trying to help our *Tico* (affectionate term for Costa Ricans) brethren avoid the trap of dependency on the supposed deep pockets of generous *gringos* (North Americans), we figured that purchasing oranges at three cents apiece for the Sunday school treat was a sensible solution and would be a good lesson in stewardship.

Being the novice missionary and very conscious of his need to work with the church leadership and not mandate his own ideas, Rex submitted the oranges-instead-of-apples recommendation to the church board. All of the members agreed that it was a fine idea. Pleased that there would still be a special treat for the children and determined to help make it as nice as possible, Rex went by bus the week before our Christmas program to a valley some miles away where we had recently discovered especially succulent oranges that could be purchased for a better price than those in our local market. He bought a large grain sack half full of the tasty fruit, slung it over his shoulder, and boarded a different bus for the trip back home. Unfortunately, he was not too familiar with that bus route and got off one stop before he should have. By the time he had lugged the heavy sack of oranges the extra distance on foot to our house, he was sweaty, tired, and not nearly as enthused about the savings that the trip had been.

After a good, tall glass of water and some rest had restored his energy, he carried the oranges up the hill to the church, sorting through them to pick out the very biggest and most juicy looking to dispense first, and readying the box of cheap, colorful plastic whistles that would also be distributed as part of the church's gift. Meanwhile, I was busy preparing to give out the cookies that we had baked. At one of the stores downtown, Rex had purchased some pretty Christmas paper, which he cut into rectangular strips, then folded and glued to make cute, non-expensive little gift bags. After sliding two cookies into each of these, I carefully stacked them in one of our large market bags. Around 4 o'clock in the afternoon on Christmas Eve, Rex, five-year-old Rexie, two-month-old Benjie, and I picked our way up the broken sidewalk to begin our delivery of Christmas cheer.

In Costa Rica, December 24 is a bigger day of celebration than Christmas itself. Each housewife prepares a small mountain of *tamales* to share with friends and family. The basic tamale is made with a corn-flour-and-water mixture that is patted into a three by five by one-half inch rectangle. The toppings that are pressed into this dough are as varied as the women who concoct them. Those who can afford it use succulently seasoned strips of chicken, pork or beef. Poorer families resort to a chunk of rubbery white fat that adds interesting texture if not flavor. Thinly sliced green beans and carrots are often used, along with tough green peas (invariably picked after they have dried in the pod), bits of red or green peppers, a sprinkle of cooked rice, and a tablespoon of garbanzos. This is securely wrapped in a banana leaf, tied with a bit of twine, and boiled in a big pot of water over an open fire. The resulting product is a delicious treat that, to a Tico, bespeaks Christmas as much as candy canes and gingerbread men do to a *gringo*. Just as American families share their Christmas cookies with one another, so Costa Ricans do with their tamales, visiting with relatives on Christmas Eve to celebrate and snack.

Accordingly, laden with our sweet treats, we set off shortly after an early supper with the goal of stopping by the home of every parishioner. At *doña*

Beda and *don* Juan's, we were greeted heartily, welcomed in, and offered a spicy steaming tamale, as well as the requisite cup of sweet black coffee and a crumbly pastry stick. This was our first experience with authentic south-of-the-border tamales, and we thought they were delicious. Rex was especially profuse in singing their praises, to the great delight of our hostess who generously offered him another and topped off his cup of coffee as well. A good hour later we waved good-bye, only to repeat the same performance at each of our next stops. After five tamales and as many cups of coffee, I simply could not force another bite down. Remember, one of these tamales makes an adequate meal, and two are more than enough. Five is definitely overkill! At our third from the last stop, I explained to yet another generous hostess that, although I truly would love to try her cooking, my stomach had reached its limit. When she heard how many I had already eaten, her eyes widened in amazement, and she laughingly offered to send her tamale home with me. Rex managed to stuff his in, although I noticed that his eyes were slightly bulging as he washed it on its way with his sixth cup of coffee. Only two more houses to go! By this point, we were seriously wondering if we would make it home with the contents of our stomachs intact, but there was nothing to do except forge on. We knew that visiting some but not all of our church families could cause hurt feelings, and we were determined to not let that happen.

One tamale later, Rex had absolutely arrived at his maximum capacity. This time, he had trouble mustering up sufficient enthusiasm to properly praise the cook. Still, he made a valiant effort, and we started toward our final home. Now it was a few minutes before 12 a.m. Everyone was still awake, however, children vibrating with excitement at the anticipated midnight visit of *el Niño* (the Christ Child), who, somewhat like an American Santa Claus, brings gifts to good boys and girls. There are no chimneys in Costa Rica and no snow for Santa's sleigh, but none of this is necessary since the Christ Child leaves His gifts tucked under one's pillow instead of stuffed into a stocking.

No little ones lived at the last home we visited, so our knock on the door did not interrupt a major celebration. *Doña* Socorro and *don* Efraín accepted our cookies and chuckled sympathetically when we explained why we could not possibly sample their tamales. We waddled our way homeward, Rex carrying an exhausted Rexie while I toted a long-since peacefully slumbering Benjie. I did not normally drink coffee, so the five cups I had imbibed on this cultural adventure should have kept me up the rest of the night. At that time, Rex was not yet a regular coffee drinker, either; he certainly had never before downed seven shots of caffeine in seven hours of time. Nevertheless, when we stumbled to our beds, we slept soundly and dreamlessly, unfazed by the "high" of our blood caffeine levels. I was somewhat puzzled the next day at how jittery our normally easy-going baby was ... until it occurred to me that he was almost certainly downing second-hand coffee when he nursed.

In spite of our until-the-wee-hours-bingeing, when the sun peeped cheerfully in our bedroom windows not very much later that morning, urging us out of bed and promising a beautiful Christmas day, we were excited at the thought of the activities in store. The smaller children of our congregation had been diligently memorizing Bible verses, and the youth had enthusiastically practiced their choir songs. Although the verses, songs, and sermon would all be in Spanish, I knew that the sweet presence of the One who came to earth as a baby nearly 2,000 years ago would communicate to my heart as well as to the hearts of those who could understand the language, with a message that transcended any linguistic barriers. What a privilege to be able to have a part in sharing the story of the gift above all gifts, God's Son, Jesus!

Faces beaming, we watched from our seats on the simple plank pews as seven little children lined up across the front of the church, each one holding a carefully cut out and painstakingly decorated cardboard letter nearly as tall as himself. Vibrantly outlined in red, green, silver, or gold glitter, the letters spelled *N-A-V-I-D-A-D*, and each child quoted a Bible verse to go along with the particular letter he or she held. Five year old Rexie's blond hair and rosy cheeks were a striking contrast to the jet-black tresses and swarthy countenances of all the others in the row of small faces. Even so, his pronunciation of the words sounded native enough to have convinced a casual hearer that he had been raised speaking Spanish from birth.

God greatly helped Rex with his sermon following the youth choir singing, and the congregation packing the sanctuary listened attentively to the old-but-ever-new story of love incarnate. Then came the moment that, to the children at least, was the highlight of the occasion: the distribution of the Christmas treat. Rex smilingly handed each one an orange and a bright whistle as they exited the building, receiving a polite "Gracias" in turn. Immediately upon stepping into the yard, the youngsters tried out their new toys, filling the air with piercing toots and gleeful giggles as each one attempted to outdo the other in producing more noise.

Several of the children were our next door neighbors, and as the day wore on, we quickly regretted the moment of temporary insanity that had inspired the purchase of those whistles as part of the church treat. We *were* pleased to think of the pleasure each person would have in eating the juicy orange he had received, and we were happy that the church budget was not wiped out completely due to the wise choice that the board had made to forego buying apples and grapes.

Not until a number of years later did Rex discover the true sentiment of the men who had agreeably given approval to his idea of the fruit substitution. He was talking with Henry, one of the original board members, who had also become a close personal friend over the intervening years. By that time, we had spent one full four-year term and part of another in mission work, and although we will always have more to learn about interpersonal relationships and communication between missionaries and nationals, we had made helpful progress down that road since our first months in Costa Rica. Apparently, our development was enough that Henry felt comfortable in freely expressing his thoughts to Rex on the matter of differences in thinking and customs between missionaries and nationals and the problems that can arise between them as a result.

"Yes," chuckled Henry, "new missionaries can do some pretty strange things. I remember one year at Christmas when a missionary decided to give out oranges for the Christmas treat. Oranges!!! Think of how it made those children feel, when they can have an orange any day of the week, and they look forward all year to the apple from the church at Christmas. Why, it was almost an insult!"

Chagrined, Rex realized that, mercifully, Henry had completely forgotten who that "strange missionary" was. As he thought back on the incident, Rex knew that his motive had been correct; he had not intentionally done something to offend. After all, he had not insisted on his own idea. He had given the board an opportunity to vote on the cost-saving option, although not a single member had expressed any reservation with the plan. But it was another good reminder that we were the foreigners in this land. Even though we had been made to feel welcome, we would always need a great deal of tact and flexibility in our relationships with people whose customs and ideas of what was best might vary widely from ours.

## 10

## "Please Pass the Mosquitoes," or,
## They Didn't Teach Me *That* in Language School
### *August 1989 – August 1990 ~ San José, Costa Rica*

What could be frustrating, fulfilling, fascinating, and fun all at one time? Acquiring a new language, that's what! Before moving to Costa Rica, I knew that one of my major tasks would be learning to talk all over again. I had studied Spanish to some extent, but it did not take me long to find out that there is a big difference between having a list of words in your head, and getting them to come out of your mouth at the proper time, in the right order, and with the correct inflection so as to be understood.

Along with having had the benefit of an excellent foundation in high school Spanish, Rex had spent a summer of intensive language study in Costa Rica in 1984, to equip him for teaching Spanish at Carolina Christian College. Little did we know at the time that the Lord was preparing him to begin preaching in Spanish five services a week the month after we arrived in Costa Rica as a family. Capable as he was at general communication, though, it was frustrating not to be able to get across some message that God had laid on his heart for lack of the precise word or expression. So that August, Rex went back to language school and completed the five-days-a-week, four-hours-a-day final trimester of the course. Believing that a call to service is a call to preparation, and wanting that preparation to be as thorough as possible, Rex continued private tutoring sessions twice weekly with one of the best Spanish grammar teachers in the country for another two-and-a-half years.

Far from being a needless expense of time and money, language school was one of the best investments we ever made. We knew missionaries who viewed it as a bothersome period of wasted months, a necessary evil to be endured while they chafed to finish it and get on with "real" missionary work. Thankfully, our mission board recognized how absolutely essential an ability to communicate well is for anyone who wants to minister effectively. We were grateful for the opportunity to better equip ourselves as God's laborers in the ripened harvest fields of Central America and rejoiced to be able to share the gospel of salvation and holiness with increasing ease.

Of course, even the best language training does not guarantee that the words which roll off your tongue are what you are thinking in your brain. In a children's meeting shortly after our arrival, Maydean DeLong was telling the story of Moses and the burning bush. As she described the solemn occasion when Moses saw the flaming branches that were not consumed by the fire, the room erupted in a chorus of giggles. Puzzled, Maydean stopped short, wondering what had provoked the unexpected gaiety. Replaying in her own mind the words she had just spoken, she too chuckled as she realized she had experienced another of those "Oops, what I really meant to say" moments that any speaker of a foreign language is familiar with. Over the next several years, Rex and I would become all too acquainted with the sometimes mortifying, sometimes hilariously funny results of switching one vowel for another in a word, thereby totally changing its meaning. In this case, the Spanish word for "flame" that Maydean intended to use became "egg yolk" by the simple substitution of the vowel "e" for "a." Throughout the rest of our first term and even into our second and beyond, whenever either of us had a similar mind lapse and said something equally absurd, Rex and I would look at each other and grin, remembering how encouraging it was that first month on the field to realize that even a veteran missionary with many years of speaking the Spanish language was never immune to such hazards.

Once the DeLong family left, Marilyn Olson's focus of ministry changed. Instead of primarily working as an elementary school teacher to English-speaking children, she became a Sunday school teacher and mentor to Spanish-speaking children and youth. Of course, that meant a drastic change in how she needed to communicate, so after Rex graduated, Marilyn entered the *Escuela de Idiomas Costa Rica* (Costa Rica Language School), making the hour-long drive over the mountain morning and afternoon just as he had done.

The subject of holiness came up for discussion in class one day. This was an entirely new concept for one student, and the period ended before she had time to hear a full explanation of the doctrine. When class convened the next morning, she was eager to resume the conversation. "*Entonces, ¿es possible vivir sin pecas?*" she asked. ("So, is it really possible to live without sins?") Marilyn was dismayed when someone in the class emphatically responded, "No, not for *you*." Then she realized that the girl had said *pecas* (freckles) instead of *pecados* (sins). Since the student had a generous dusting of those little brown spots all over her face and arms, it was indeed impossible for her to be freckle-free, and she was a good enough sport to join in the amusement at her own expense.

Maydean told us about another incident when the word *pecados* was a problem, this time by what would seem to be the minor error of adding an extra letter to the word. She still chuckles when she recalls the preacher who earnestly exhorted his listeners to forsake their "fish" (*pescados*) instead of their "sins."

Some of our Costa Rican friends were very good at helping us learn from our mistakes by giving the appropriate correction when we stumbled over a word. Others thought that to point out an error would be rude or disrespectful, so they were reluctant to tell us when we said something wrong. However, on the Sunday evening that Rex requested prayer for one of our parishioners who was suffering from health problems, even the most polite among the congregation could not refrain from joining in the titter of amusement that swept the crowd. What Rex thought he had said was *sanguínea,* with the emphasis on the accented syllable. What slipped off his tongue was *san guineo,* with the emphasis on the next to the last syllable, and the letter "o" instead of "a" at the end of the word. "No big deal," you might think. But those two tiny changes in the word altered the meaning in an anything but tiny way, and the poor man, instead of having problems with high blood pressure, was reported to be suffering from his "holy banana"!

After Rex and Marilyn both finished their stint in language school, it was my turn. By that time I had lived in the country for fifteen months, and learning the language was not nearly as difficult as "unlearning" the incorrect speaking habits that I had acquired. I experienced the yo-yo trip of emotions ranging from "I never want to hear another Spanish word the rest of my life!" to "This is fun. I just orally conjugated a reflexive verb in the indicative mood—sixty different forms—and got them all right!" Reaching the point where I could fluently carry on an intelligent conversation was a long journey along the often-uphill road from my first few months in the country when the only two phrases I had well learned were, "*Hable más despacio, por favor*" (Speak more slowly, please), and, "*Lo siento, no entiendo*" (I am sorry, I don't understand).

Did I say "intelligent" conversation? Ah yes, that WAS debatable at times. For instance, there was the occasion several years after finishing my year of language study when our home was broken into one Saturday afternoon while we were out for a few hours, doing our weekly shopping at the huge central market. We arrived home to find the front door, which we had left securely locked, open a crack. Adrenaline pumping, Rex went in alone to check things out while the boys and I waited safely in our closed truck. When he came back and reported that no one was in the house, I rushed in to see what damage had been done. Apparently, the thief had been scared off when he heard our vehicle pull in earlier than he had anticipated, and he did not have time to gather many things and make off with them in his hasty flight over the back wall of our yard.

"Yes," I told an interested and sympathetic neighbor across the street, "God was certainly watching out for us. The only things that he stole were a small luggage bag and some of my husband's skirts ...." My voice trailed off as

I noticed the strange look she gave me, and then I started laughing as I realized that I had done it again. Lest you should wonder why Rex had taken to wearing skirts, let me assure you that his Scottish bloodline had not manifested itself in the occasional donning of an ancestor's traditional kilt. The actual items missing from our closet were Rex's belts (*fajas*), not his skirts (*faldas*).

One source of confusion for English speakers trying to learn Spanish is the existence of occasional "false friends" between the two languages. There are various words which are spelled exactly alike and have the same definition in both English and Spanish, such as "doctor," "pastor," and "hospital." Although in Spanish the accented syllable in these words is a different one than it is in the same English word, the meaning is easily understood. Yet other words, although not spelled precisely the same, are very similar, with the only differences being an extra letter or two on the end. Examples of these are "computer" and *computadora*, "laboratory" and *laboratorio*, or "entrance" and *entrada*. The problem comes when one tries to apply the principle of adding a few letters to the end of *every* word which sounds as though it should mean the same in both languages. Just because *ocupado* means "occupied," it does NOT indicate that *embarazado* means "embarrassed." Fortunately, not everyone has the opportunity to learn the correct significance of that particular word in the same way that I did, but it is quite certain that I am not alone in having had the humbling experience of innocently informing a group of friends that my husband was pregnant. See what I mean? False friend indeed. It is a physical impossibility for my husband to be *embarazado*. Once I got over my chagrin, it was a lesson well learned, and I never again told anyone that Rex was *embarazado* when I really meant *avergonzado*.

As I said, no matter how well one learns another language, the thousands of new words that must be crammed into her brain will, on occasion, twist themselves around each other and haphazardly tumble out her mouth. This seemed to happen to me more often when I was tired, but I do not recall having had a particularly short ration of sleep the night before our friends Gilberto and Milady came over for supper not long before the end of our second term. By that time, I had been conversing in Spanish for eight years and was quite comfortable doing so. That was no advantage to me when I opened my mouth and inserted my foot yet again. I doubt that they still remember everything that I fixed for the meal, but they will never forget the gales of laughter that we shared when I asked Milady to please pass me the bowl of mosquitoes. No, I had not concocted a strange new dish for the occasion. What I really wanted was to eat another helping of carrots (*zanahorias*), not to be served a generous spoonful of the pesky, whining insects (*zancudos*) that delighted in eating me.

# 11

## Though I Walk Through the Valley ... You Are With Me

*June 27, 1990 ~ San José, Costa Rica*

At 2:45 a.m., I woke abruptly out of a restless sleep, somewhat disoriented as I looked around on my unfamiliar surroundings. By the dim light from the hallway, I glanced over and saw Rex dozing beside my bed, legs curled up awkwardly as he tried to adjust his lanky frame to the too-small chair that he had been given for the night. In a rush, memory returned and hot tears slid down my cheeks, making my already puffy eyelids sting. Slipping softly out of the narrow bed I padded silently out of the room and down the hall to the nurses' station, wanting to talk to someone. A white-uniformed woman sat there, blanket wrapped around her shoulders, eyes closed, chin resting on her chest. This was not the same nurse who had so comfortingly caressed my arm in the operating room last evening. I had been crying then, too, and the anesthesiologist, a kind-faced older man, kept stroking and patting my forehead after he skillfully administered the epidural that prevented me from feeling any pain during the procedure.

I wandered back down the hall to my room and stood beside Rex's chair, finally touching his shoulder, hating to disturb his rest, but greatly in need of a reassuring hug. He held me for a long while as together we mourned our loss. Climbing back into bed I opened my Bible, not really choosing any particular place, and started reading:

The Lord is good to all, and His tender mercies are over all His works.
The Lord upholds all who fall, and raises up all who are bowed down.
The Lord is righteous in all His ways, gracious in all His works.
The Lord is near to all who call upon Him, to all who call upon Him in truth.
He will fulfill the desire of those who fear Him; He also will hear their cry and save them.
Psalm 145:9, 14, 17-19

How perfectly the timeless words spoke to my grieving heart, reassuring me that God's love and care for me were sufficient for every circumstance and that He would watch over and uphold us during this difficult time.

The spotting had started Saturday afternoon, four days earlier, but there was not much of it. I told myself not to worry, since that had happened a few times while I was expecting Benjie, and everything turned out just fine with him. When it continued off and on throughout the weekend, I phoned my doctor Monday morning to schedule an appointment. His report after the exam that he did was reassuring. The uterus was the correct size for a ten-week pregnancy, and everything looked like the baby was going to be all right. He gave me medication and sent me home to rest in bed. Tuesday morning, the bleeding returned, and that afternoon at the hospital, an ultrasound showed that somewhere along the way our baby had stopped developing, even though I had all the signs of a normal, healthy pregnancy.

Rexie, who had been so excited at the prospect of another little brother or sister, told me at lunch Tuesday, "Mommy, I'd give all my money if we could save the baby." When I called the house and talked to him after the D&C that evening he asked, "Is the baby in heaven with Jesus now?" I replied that it was, and he responded, "Well, maybe Jesus knew it would grow up to be a bad man, so it's better now that Jesus has it with Him." With a wisdom belying his years, our firstborn son spoke words bringing a comforting reminder that this second precious child that we had "lost" was not really lost it all, but had safely arrived home in heaven with its sibling, the baby I had miscarried six years earlier. They were together for eternity with our heavenly Father.

Assurances of God's sovereign care notwithstanding, the physical and emotional strain brought on by my miscarriage was the beginning of a frightening slide into depression. To be very frank, I was not sure whether to include it in my story, since doing so opens the door to painful memories of a time of great spiritual distress that was a far cry from the "super Christian" image often attributed to missionaries. Actually, though, those of us who have been there realize quite keenly that missionaries face the same struggles, temptations, and possibility of failure as any other child of God. Satan does not care who you are or where you live; he will use whatever tactics he can to defeat God's plan for your life. Being Christ's ambassador in a foreign country does not confer sainthood; rather, it points out very quickly the missionary's utter dependency on the One whose strength is made perfect in his weakness.

At this point, I was in my last trimester of language school. Although I had recognized from our first days in the country how vital it was for me to get a good grasp of the language, I could not realize until I was in the midst of it how stressful trying to juggle the roles of student, mother, pastor's wife, and homeschool teacher would be. Rex and Marilyn had both driven back and forth every day during the week to language school, but the trips added as much as an additional two hours, depending on traffic, to the time spent in class. Rexie was seven and Benjie was ten months old when I began my year of study, and we realized that different arrangements would have to be made so that I would not have to be gone from the home six hours each day.

We rented a house on a quiet side street a ten-minute walk from the language school in San José. Rex could not be at home with the boys all the time while I was away. The going wage for a live-in maid was $80 a month plus room and board, and we hired María, a teenager who stayed with us each week from Sunday evening after church until lunch time on Friday, to babysit and help with some of the meal preparation and housework.

On school mornings, I needed to get up in time to cook breakfast, make sure both boys were dressed and ready for the day, nurse Benjie, and dash out the door at 7:50 a.m. Rex would teach Rexie's first-grade English and math classes to him before leaving for pastoral duties in Cartago. I usually arrived home by 12:30 p.m., ate the light lunch that María had prepared, then started teaching *my* share of Rexie's subjects and supervising his homework. One afternoon while we were reviewing what he had learned while I was away, he excitedly informed me that he and Daddy had studied about Jesus healing the ten *leopards* that morning. I do not remember if I kept a straight face as I imagined the scene playing out in his mind's eye during the lesson!

Rexie enjoyed school—most of the time—but there were those inevitable moments when the lure of spending time outdoors on a balmy afternoon was more enticing than his studies. Such was the case at lunch one day when he prayed, "Dear Jesus, we thank you for this food, and I pray that I won't have any more school today. And dear Lord, we pray that Mommie's sticky buns will be as good as Grandma's, if not better." (If you ever have a chance to taste his Grandma Kaufman's sticky buns, you will know why his first petition was more easily answered!)

Between his classes, I spent the rest of the afternoon washing and hanging out clothes and cooking supper. Being able to buy fresh fruits and vegetables year round was wonderful, but the lack of convenient prepackaged mixes and frozen entrées meant that prep time for meals could consume a couple of hours. Following supper and dishes came family worship, then the fun of storybook night, playing a game, or having a music jamboree with Rex pumping away on his accordion, Rexie jangling the tambourine, and Benjie enthusiastically and LOUDLY beating time with Tinkertoy drumsticks on the bottom of a cooking pot. After two energetic little boys had their baths and were tucked into bed, it was time for me to tackle the nightly sweeping and mopping of the floors. THEN I had the chance for an hour or so of uninterrupted Spanish homework before hitting the sack myself around midnight.

That had been the routine for the first nine months of classes. Life was busy, at times hectic, but manageable. Near the end of the school year, though, the knot at the end of the rope I was swinging on started to come undone. I had been averaging six hours of sleep a night, interrupted in the wee hours of every morning by my little redhead who still woke me for his predawn snuggle. (For the record, Benjie did not sleep through the entire night for the first time until June 7 that year, at nineteen-and-a-half months of age.) Decidedly unhappy with mommy disappearing and leaving him behind every day, he ran after me to the front door when I got ready to go, clutching my skirt and crying. Morning after morning, I pried his fingers loose, exited the gate with tears in my own eyes, and waved good-bye to the little boy who piteously stretched his hand through the bars, calling after me.

Looking back, I wonder how much of his reaction was a developmental stage and how much was a response to being left in the keeping of someone who did not properly care for his needs. We were increasingly frustrated with the amount of time we discovered that María was spending visiting with the maid across the street while she was supposed to be caring for our boys. Many afternoons, I would return from class to find Benjie still in the diaper he had been wearing when I left the house over four hours earlier. This was before the era of disposable diapers with their moisture barrier linings that keep a child's skin dry. The cotton diaper would be totally saturated and usually caked with solid waste as well, all of it held against his chafed skin the whole time by the non-breathable plastic pants worn over it. I tried talking to María about the need to keep his diaper changed regularly, but the message did not seem to register. That is, it did not register until the afternoon that I once again found Benjie in a sodden, smelly state, his whole diaper area inflamed and raw. Rex happened to be home that afternoon. Totally exasperated, I called him into the bedroom to show him the situation. To my shock, my usually mild husband gathered Benjie into his arms and carried him out to María. "Look what you have done to my son!" he indignantly remonstrated, displaying to her the pathetic little fiery-red bottom.

Although the diaper situation did improve, the cumulative effects of a less-than-ideal babysitting situation, chronic shortage of sleep, the miscarriage, followed in two weeks by my hospitalization for dehydration from a stomach bug, and two weeks later, another doctor's visit after several days of hemorrhaging, became overwhelming. We paid María for her last month and dismissed her early from her contract, preferring to lose the money rather than my sanity. Rex rearranged his schedule so he could be with our boys while I was out of the house, and I managed to finish the final weeks of classes, feeling very honored to be the student chosen to give the graduation speech at the end of August.

Once the impetus of getting up and going to school each morning ended, however, so did my ability to cope with the routines of everyday living. I startled easily, nearly jumping out of my skin at the noise of the clapping and tambourine playing that accompanied congregational singing at church. Normally a very sociable person, I found myself shrinking from contact with anyone outside of my own family, even the kind and well-meaning efforts to cheer me up from our colleague and good friend Marilyn. Finally, I stopped attending church altogether, unable to face the thought of having to talk to people.

Concerned for my well-being, Evangelical Wesleyan Mission approved a drastic reduction in Rex's duties as pastor. For the next several months, instead of preaching and visiting various times during the week, he went to Paraíso only on Sundays. I spent *my* Sundays at home alone, listening to sermons that we had on cassettes. I took long solitary walks around our neighborhood, trying to pray but feeling like my words tumbled to the ground at my feet rather than going heavenward. My head told me that God was walking through this valley with me, but my spirit could not sense any comfort in that declaration.

With less to do in the church, Rex completely took over Rexie's schooling and loaned a hand with the meals and house cleaning. He also made one of our rare long-distance phone calls to talk the situation over with my parents. Their advice was for us return to the States for a few months until I had a chance to recuperate from the past year. Although that counsel made sense, I was afraid that if I did leave, I would end up never returning to the mission field and the ministry to which I was certain God had called me.

Thinking that a change of pace might be beneficial, Mama Kaufman offered to come down and lend a hand. All of us traveled to the peaceful rural area of Pital on the northern border of Costa Rica for some time on a farm with our Mennonite friends, Dale and Suzanne Heisey. Mama also stayed with our boys while Rex and I took a weekend trip to the ocean, a totally relaxing break with no schedules, ample opportunity to talk together without interruptions, and extra time with God. These things all helped. Still, I felt like John Bunyan's character Pilgrim in his slough of despond. I was taking baby steps, but making little progress toward a shore that seemed dishearteningly far away.

Meanwhile, Don and Maydean DeLong finished their furlough and returned to Central America in June. They settled in Nicaragua, where they had worked in the late seventies and early eighties until the dangerous political situation forced them to move next door to Costa Rica. The Nicaraguan holiness church had carried on in their absence, but there were new pastors who had never had the opportunity for formal Bible study and were now asking for someone to give them more training. Rex had taught at Carolina Christian College for six years. The mission leadership felt that his experience could be put to good use in Nicaragua. They also thought that a new start in a new location would be a positive helpful change for me.

While praying for definite direction, God assured both Rex and me quite positively that this was His will. The verse Isaiah 30:21 was impressed so strongly upon my mind that I knew it was the Lord speaking in relation to the proposed moved to Nicaragua: "This is the way, walk in it."

From the point of that decision on, the darkness shrouding the path on which I had been walking gradually gave way to sunshine. I was able to begin attending church services and to fellowship with our friends again, although it took a good while longer for me to enjoy, rather than just tolerate, the loudness of the traditional exuberant song services. The move to Nicaragua several months later proved to be a right decision. The chance to have a fresh beginning among people who were not aware of the difficult months after we lost our baby was a major boost to my morale. Finally, I could once again *feel* God's sweet presence and know beyond any doubt that He cared for me.

I still do not totally understand all that happened in those six months, and why God seemed so far away. Perhaps He knew that I needed to better learn to trust Him when I could not trace Him. Perhaps He saw that you would read this someday and would benefit by the reminder that He is always faithful, no matter what life brings your way. Whatever the reason, I can gratefully testify to the truth in the last verse of George Keith's beloved hymn, "How Firm a Foundation":

*The soul that on Jesus hath leaned for repose I will not,*
*    I will not desert to his foes;*
*That soul, tho' all hell should endeavor to shake,*
*    I'll never, no never, no never forsake!*

## 12

## Clinic Clips

*January 24, 2013 ~ San Luis, Honduras*

God does not mind our asking "why" in the midst of disappointment. Although He may not reveal all of His reasons for permitting heartbreaking events such as the loss of a baby, He sometimes allows us to go through difficult situations to prepare us for being a blessing to others who experience similar circumstances. Since my own miscarriages, I can more easily find the words to comfort other women facing such bereavement. Still, much as I may sympathize and even empathize with her, my middle-class, American background will never allow me to totally identify with what a poverty-stricken Central American woman can go through when her pregnancy ends unexpectedly. I remember the swirling mixture of sadness, indignation, and frustration I felt with one such incident. It happened in the midst of another busy shift at *Clínica de Maternidad Luz y Vida.*

\* \* \* \* \* \* \* \* \*

Once again it is after midnight, over midway through a 3:00 p.m. to 7:00 a.m. stint, and I am almost to the bottom of my second mug of coffee with milk. I stirred in a packet of hot chocolate, making this pick-me-up considerably more enjoyable than the drink which was offered to me a few nights ago by the mother of my patient who was having a very long night of labor with her first birth. Grandma-to-be had just gone home and brought back a freshly made thermos of coffee about 2:00 a.m., and I was grateful to accept the steaming hot cup. At my first sip, I knew that something was vastly different with this coffee than with any other I had ever experienced. I took a second cautious taste and still could not identify the strong, overriding flavor. "What's in the coffee?" I queried. "I don't think I've ever had any like this before."

"Oh, do you like it?" she enthused. "It's black pepper." I was touched by her generosity in sharing, but surreptitiously poured the rest of my cup down the sink when she was not looking. Even the few sips I had taken threatened to revolt and exit from my stomach several times before the night was over. You can take my word that it is a combination you do not want to try, although I understand that it is very popular in Honduras. Local housewives add whole black peppercorns to a batch of coffee beans and roast them together, then grind the mixture and brew it just as they would plain coffee. The result gives a whole new jolt to this classic eye-opener morning pick-me-up.

Contrary to many, this shift has been slow. I discharged the last inpatient shortly after 10:00 p.m. Since then, only a few people have stopped in to buy medications or have a nebulization. Throughout the afternoon, I sold various remedies for headache or muscle ache or belly pain. Instead of buying bulk bottles of such pills, we purchase boxes of blister packs, usually with ten to a pack. Most times, few people can afford to purchase an entire pack, so we cut off the one or two pills that are requested. I also dispensed tablets and syrup for de-worming, measured and poured into small plastic bags "some of that green liquid for stomach cramps," and "more of the white stuff you told me to try yesterday; it really worked for my upset stomach." We *do* buy our liquid medication in bulk and sell it for five *lempiras,* or about twenty-five cents, an ounce.

I also handed out vitamins, and I squeezed antibiotic ointment from a tube into plastic bags for the two children whose mothers brought them in with sores that needed treating. I did not have to charge for either of these items, since they were gifted to us in large quantities from an organization that passes along donations of medicines from the U.S. that are only a few months from their expiration dates. Last week, the warehouse in San Pedro that stores the contributions loaded us up with boxes and boxes of pills, ointments, and elixirs, plus numerous pairs of crutches, a pile of bed linens and pillows, and, to our laundry lady's great joy, a mammoth bag of newborn-size disposable diapers. Now she will have a break from hand scrubbing sticky, thick meconium out of the cloth ones.

In contrast to tonight's pace, my day shift not long ago was about as opposite as it could be. I started with seven inpatients, one of whom was a woman in labor whose baby was born at 7:52 a.m., right at the height of the typical morning rush. I was very thankful that our secretary, Marleni, had not yet begun her vacation. She has worked here enough years to be much more familiar than I am with our pharmacy stock and prices, so while I was welcoming into the world a cute baby girl, she handled the sales for people who only came to buy medicine. Anyone who needed lab work, a blood pressure check, an injection, wound repair, or any of the myriad other things that require the services of a nurse had to either wait until the baby was born or return afterwards when I was free. When there is a birth after 4:00 p.m. or on weekends, the lone nurse on duty keeps the keys to the money drawer in her pocket instead of hanging them on their usual nail on the back of the pharmacy door, since the comings and goings of anyone in the rest of the building cannot possibly be monitored.

After the new mother and her little one were settled next to the window in bed number six in the postpartum ward, I turned my attention to the rest of the inpatients. Dr. Maldonado, our collaborating town physician, had already come and gone, leaving discharge instructions for two of them. He charges 200 *lempiras,* equivalent to $10, per patient per stay, to evaluate their progress each morning. Most are not here more than one to three days, since any condition requiring a longer hospitalization is probably more serious than we are prepared to deal with, and such a patient will be transferred to Santa Bárbara or San Pedro Sula. But whether he comes to check you and update his orders only one time before you are discharged or several times over the course of a couple of days, his fee is the same.

I know that compared to what a doctor in your local hospital would charge for a similar service, that sounds like next to nothing. But when you consider that the cost for a whole day's stay as an inpatient here is half that, his five-minute drive and the ten to fifteen minutes he spends examining several patients nets him a proportionately decent return. We keep a notebook in the money drawer in which we record the names of those he has seen and store his earnings, and he periodically collects the money that we tuck between the pages.

One of my patients who did *not* get discharged was a fifteen-year-old girl, twelve-weeks pregnant, with signs of a threatened miscarriage. She had been admitted the evening before and started on IV fluids with medication to stop her contractions. The treatment seemed to be working, but although she was no longer bleeding, Dr. Maldonado wanted her to stay another few hours until the remainder of her IV fluid was infused. However, the last bus out of town that could have dropped her off close to her home left several hours before she was ready for discharge, so she and her mother walked to the Catholic church to spend the night. The church has a room with mattresses on the floor, especially for people in just such situations.

She showed back up at our door at 2:10 the next morning, hemorrhaging and about to pass out. She told me that she had started cramping pretty badly a little after midnight and got up to use the restroom. There was no light to turn on, but she heard a couple of "plops" on the floor, evidently large clots that fell out when she stood up. She could also feel the trickle of blood as it ran down her legs, but neither she nor her mother, nor the other homeless pregnant woman who has been staying at the church, had a flashlight to see how bad things were. At that hour of the morning, the little moto-taxis that zip back and forth between us and the center of town were not running. And of course, they had no phone. She had no choice but to walk the two-kilometer distance back to us, to reach the help she so badly needed.

While Dr. Maldonado did her D & C, she buried her face in my shoulder. I held her hand tightly with one of mine and with the other stroked her hair. My attempt at comforting her was the only sedation or anesthesia that she had for the procedure. This is her second miscarriage. She lost her first pregnancy at the age of thirteen, when she was four months along. Shortly thereafter, she became pregnant again, and her little boy is now sixteen months old. Her boyfriend is twenty-four and "very responsible," she told me. I could believe that a lot better if he had not become involved with a thirteen year old when he was twenty-two and gotten her pregnant three times in less than three years. He showed up once, briefly, during her two days with us. I took the opportunity to talk to both of them about how important it was that she not become pregnant again for a couple of years *at least*. He sat and listened, blank-faced, making no comment. I talked to her afterwards, alone, about how much God loved her and wanted her to be His child.

During a brief space later that morning when no one urgently needed my attention, with Marleni there to keep a vigilant eye on things and call me for any emergency, I took a few minutes to run over to my house next door and fix the girl and her mother some scrambled eggs wrapped in tortillas. It was their first meal since the evening before. I also made enough to give a generous serving to the mother who brought in her baby yesterday with dehydration from severe vomiting and diarrhea. Her little one is doing much better after a day of IV hydration, but no one from the woman's family had arrived to bring her any breakfast, either.

When the girl had stabilized enough to leave, I hugged her good-bye, and she hugged me back hard, clinging longer than would have been necessary out of mere courtesy. I have seen many similarly sad cases of "children having children" on my trips here, and I have frequently wondered why God has allowed my life to be so different than theirs. Often, my mind goes back to my own miscarriage while living in Costa Rica and the vast difference between the love and support of my husband and the exploitation and neglect that this girl has suffered from her "mature" boyfriend. One thing is certain: I cannot experience such things and continue to enjoy the comforts of the status quo unchanged. May God help each of us to be more grateful and to live so that our lives can bless those less fortunate, wherever and whenever the opportunity is given us.

## 13

# Feliz Navidad

*December 25, 1990 ~ San José, Costa Rica*

As we approached our third Christmas in Costa Rica, our ears had become accustomed to hearing "Feliz Navidad," our tongues were prepared for dozens of tamales, and we were resigned to the fact that the only snow available would be in the scenes pictured on the lovely Christmas cards we eagerly looked for in our mailbox. The photo on our calendar of a white-capped evergreen beside an icy stream provoked homesickness for a real northern blizzard, but outside our living room window a red rosebush was blooming, and with the thermometer stuck at somewhere around 70°, it looked as though we would just be "Dreaming of a White Christmas" this year as well. We were still feeling pretty homesick for family and dear friends on special days, so in our December newsletter we decided to invite everyone down to spend the day with us. That was twenty-five years ago, before I ever imagined that I would be writing this book. Thankfully, my parents kept all of the correspondence we sent to them, and when I dug it out of the files to re-read it, I thought you might enjoy a look at that original invitation.

\* \* \* \* \* \* \* \* \*

*As I write to you this evening, the cassette on our tape recorder is playing "Walking in a Winter Wonderland," and miniature colored lights are blinking off and on around our doorway. My cookbook here on the kitchen table is open to the recipe for the candied-fruit-decorated orange yeast breads I was just looking at with plans to make for the families in our churches this Christmas. We would love to have you stop by and sample some as well! Just so you can be certain to find us, our official address (not the post office box number) is "San Francisco of Two Rivers, 200 meters to the south of the Central Hardware, on the right-hand side." In Spanish, that is* San Francisco de Dos Ríos, de la Ferretería Central, doscientos metros al sur, a mano derecha. *Street names and house numbers are virtually nonexistent here, but just give that address to any taxi driver, and he will get you to us with no problem.*

*If you arrive in time, we will go to market together, since I am sure you will want to sample typical Tico foods and will no doubt find it interesting to follow the whole food-fixing process from acquisition to consumption. Feel like walking? Good! Grab a couple of sturdy woven bags with handles, and let's go shopping. I* hope you are not nervous in a crowd. Keep close together as we squeeze through a narrow walkway between streams of people and mounds of produce. We'll respond with a smile and a "No, gracias," to the numerous invitations to buy this or that, for we are heading over there to where "our" vegetable lady has her stand. Of course, you had your cash changed into Costa Rican colons when you arrived, but until you get more used to dealing with different money, we'll figure up the bill in dollars and cents.

First, we need carrots, at 24¢. Not too bad, you say. But wait. That's not 24¢ a pound, but 24¢ a kilogram (the standard measure here). At 2.2 pounds per kilo, that's 11¢ a pound. "Un kilo, por favor," we request. The lady tosses some into a plastic basin which she plops on her scales, then pours the carrots into your bag. Next we'll get that nice big cauliflower for 44¢, and two bell peppers at 11¢ each. There, that ought to be enough for a nice platter of fresh vegetables with sour cream dip. We'll also take a half kilo of green beans for 10¢. They are delicious cooked whole, dipped in beaten egg, and lightly fried. Let's get a kilo after all. Rex really likes them that way, and we want plenty to go around.

Now for a salad. Lettuce is 32¢ a head, and we will need two, since they are smaller than what you are used to. Tomatoes at 59¢ a pound are exorbitant this time of year compared to the usual 16¢ a pound, but since you are here, we'll go ahead and get a couple. Cilantro, an herb with a pleasant tang, adds enjoyable flavor to salads and is used in a lot of other dishes, so let's get two bunches (16¢). Have you ever eaten yucca? No? You must try some, then. It's that brown, root-looking thing over there that costs 12¢ a pound. Peeled, diced, pressure cooked, and then sautéed in margarine with a fresh lemon (2¢) squeezed on top, it is delicious.

Let's see, what else? Oh yes, chayote. It is a pear-shaped green vegetable, a variety of squash with a nice, tender texture. We'll take three for 23¢. That is, unless you would prefer a more American-tasting summer squash. We can get an eight-inch-diameter one for the same price. And finally, pick out two nice-looking beets at 15¢ each. We'll fix them Tico style, in a sauce with chopped hard-boiled eggs. Yummy! Not bad, all of that for about $3.

Now, let's thread our way (watch out for your full bags!) over to the fruit vendors to get a papaya, that red-orange fruit about the size and shape of a small skinny watermelon. It is delicious in a salad with fresh pineapple (70¢ apiece) and bananas (8¢ a pound). At 15¢ a pound, we can afford to get a good-sized one and have some left over for breakfast tomorrow.

Are you tired yet? I hope not, because we still have a bit of walking to do. Let's get eggs next. Oh, wait, there is one of the meat booths. Look at all the interesting things hanging in the open, suspended from the ceiling on hooks. What shall we have for our meat dish? Let's skip the tough, leathery mondongo (beef intestines), even though it is a bargain at 21¢ a pound. After my first sample, I won't take it *free! Chicken feet make a good soup stock, but you must be sure to strain out the toenails after cooking them. Turkey at $2.17 a pound is a bit high, so how about meatloaf? We can get nice lean ground beef for 79¢ a pound.*

*Ahh—here is the egg stand. We'll get a kilo (fifteen or sixteen large ones) for $1.22. Be careful with them. The man is putting them all into that paper sack with only a piece of newspaper on the bottom for a shock absorber. In this crowd, it will be easy for them to get jostled and cracked. I know all too well from past experience.*

*All right, only one thing more at market: black beans* (frijoles). *We'll ask for the cleaner, 70¢-per-kilo ones. It is worth the price difference not to have to spend as much time picking out so many tiny stones, dirt clods, and bugs before cooking them. And of course we will have beans, no matter what else we fix. They, along with rice, are daily staples here, often eaten at every meal.*

*Now for the grocery store. It is not much different than what you are used to, except for the prices. Anything imported from the States in a can, jar, or box is ridiculously high. For example, this little can of Campbell's chicken and stars soup is $1.37, that quart of apple juice is $4.73, the nine-ounce box of Del Monte raisins over there is $3.09, and a 29-ounce can of pears will set us back $3.14. Fortunately, there are alternatives to expensive imports. A one-pound bag of U. S. Hyde Park rice, for example, is $1.76. Let's pass it up and get our usual Costa Rican-grown rice at 24¢ a pound. It is no hardship at all to substitute fresh fruits and vegetables for canned ones, and they are quite good buys, as you have seen. I think you could live with the price of most staples as well. Milk runs $1.38 a gallon; flour and sugar are 79¢ and 92¢ respectively for five pounds.*

*Well, do we have everything? Let's tote it all home and start cooking! We want to serve lunch at a good time so you can join us in our "tropical snowball fight" Christmas afternoon in the living room, with the wadded-scrap-paper snowballs we have been saving up for a couple of weeks. Last year it was Daddy, Mommy, and Rexie against each other, all of us having chosen a strategic spot behind a chair from which to fire the paper balls at each other until the floor was generously littered and our arms were tired. The best thing about our method is not having to worry about melting snow running down our collars, or changing out of icy, wet clothes afterwards. Benjie missed out on the fun his first Christmas 'cause we had it during his nap. This year, he will be big enough to participate. You will want him on your side for sure; although his throwing arm is not very strong, he is terrific at tackling the opposition at about knee level and hanging on until his victim is too distracted to aim well.*

*We sure hope y'all can come, but just in case you have to spend some time in the snow and sleet before your arrival, you might like to know of a good local remedy that is guaranteed to chase off a cold. At the first sign of wheezing, rub a generous amount of vegetable shortening on your chest, followed by a tablespoon or so of* paste floor wax (Irex, Nugget, or Genie are good brands) blended in well with the shortening. Cover the whole mixture with an old cloth diaper and go to bed. In the morning, you ought to feel just fine. Of course, if you have an earache along with your cold, then more drastic measures are needed. You will have to have a friend help you with this. Roll a sheet of newspaper into a cone shape, making the small opening about the size of a pencil. Put that end into your affected ear and have your friend set fire to the large end with a match. When the flame gets close enough to your ear, you should both hear and feel a "whoosh" of air rush out, and your earache will be gone. Do remember to hold a water soaked towel over your cheek so it does not get too hot, and by all means make sure your hair is well pinned back out of the way. I cannot vouch for either of these remedies since I have not tried them yet, but I will be glad to help you find out if they work while you are down here.

Even if you do have a cold, that will not be a factor in keeping you from going caroling door to door. Not that we would not like to take you; it was one of my favorite things of the season up north. However, when we proposed such an event to our church people last year, they told us that caroling was a Catholic tradition in which the evangelical churches do not participate. So no matter if our throats feel perfectly fine, we do not gather at the church, pile into a bus, and join other families in spreading cheer to elderly parishioners or shut-ins, with hearty renditions of "Hark! The Herald Angels Sing," "Joy to the World," and "We Wish You a Merry Christmas."

Instead, we sat in service last year and listened as the clear, high voices of a group of children led by a boy and girl dressed to represent Joseph and Mary wafted to us through the darkness. They traveled from door to door, singing a special song asking for a sheltered place for the birth of the Holy Child. I am sure that the people who answered the knock at each house, only to send them on in their search, had no idea of the significance of their actions. Our hearts are saddened as we think of the many who, not only in "Catholic Costa Rica," but also in "Christian America," will again this year refuse entrance to the Christ.

Oh yes, the majority of homes around us will have a manger scene displayed, some of them with quite costly and elaborate figures. Yet, for too many, the Christ of Christmas is only that—a figure to be brought out and displayed in a miniature stable in December, and then put back into a box in the closet until the next year. Aren't you glad He is more? It is wonderful to know not just the Babe of Bethlehem's manger, but the risen Christ of Calvary as well. May this Christmas be special for you because of His presence in your heart!

Love,

Rex, Hannah, Rexie, and Benjie

CHAPTER

# 14

## When God Answered "No"

*May 24, 1991~ Costa Rica-Nicaragua Border*

The final weeks of our three years in Costa Rica flew by rapidly, filled with packing, last-minute running around on business, and a few unexpected extras that had not been on the schedule. On April 22, an earthquake measuring 7.2 on the Richter scale shook us up both physically and emotionally. The epicenter was quite a bit south of us, down near the Panama border, so other than a gritty sifting of dirt from the ceilings and a few fallen books, nothing in our house was damaged, at least not during the quake itself. After the first shock, which lasted 35 seconds, there were numerous shorter tremors throughout the afternoon, during the night, and into the following day. It was nerve-racking, never knowing when to expect another, or if the next one would be even worse. Rexie was especially edgy, jumping for protection into the nearest doorway at the merest perceptible quiver of the ground and hollering for us to grab Benjie and hurry to join him. The continued shaking gradually loosened our porcelain bathroom sink which inched its way up the metal brackets holding it onto the wall and finally fell loose, landing with a crash on the tile floor by my feet and shattering into a kajillion jagged shards. When we called the landlords to report it, they were sorry for the inconvenience, but said it would be impossible to replace it before we moved. I was just glad that it was not the only sink we had in the house.

A few evenings later, Rex sprayed for fleas, something we had to do every so often, since the fleas and I maintained a love-hate relationship the entire time we lived in Central America. They loved me, gleefully taking every opportunity that presented itself to vault from a passing mangy dog's hide to my hide and chow down. That in itself would not have been so bad if said flea had been content with staying in one spot, eating his meal and then bidding me adios. What I hated was the fact that whenever I got attacked, it was never just a solitary bite. A single flea would often leave a dozen or more tiny red spots in a line where he had moved along the banquet table, each nibble itching and blistering for weeks. Strange as it may seem, the fleas were probably the worst trial I faced as a missionary. I was so fanatically worried about them that I viewed every tiny black speck on my clothes or skin with suspicion, viciously nipping it between my thumb and forefinger and hurrying to the sink to submerge it in a glass of water. If the speck was merely an innocuous piece of lint, all was well. If it did, indeed, turn out to be another of those detested, bloodthirsty, jumping creatures, I had no compunction about drowning it mercilessly.

On one occasion, Rex and I were sitting on a sofa in the home of a couple who had recently started attending services. At some point during the visit, I felt the all too familiar burning itch that indicated a flea in the process of filling his tummy. Glancing down at my leg, I saw the culprit unabashedly slurping his fill. In what I hoped was a casual maneuver, I leaned over and nabbed my tormentor, pinching him firmly between my tightly closed right forefinger and thumb for the remainder of our stay. All was well until it was time to say good-bye, when I needed to politely shake hands with our hosts. How in the world was I going to do that without letting go of my captive? Somehow, I managed to transfer the flea to the opposite thumb and index finger and properly dis-miss myself without anyone taking notice of the awkward way in which I was holding my left hand. It was a ten-minute walk from their home back to ours, during which I kept those fingers clenched in a death grip, not certain if Sir Flea had managed to escape, but unable to find out until I could fill a glass with water from our faucet, dunk my fingers underneath the surface, and open them. Amazingly, probably close to an hour after his apprehension, he was still there, alive and well, but he had eaten the last meal he would ever enjoy.

An unexpected side benefit came of the final attempt at flea extermination in the house we would soon be vacating, for when we got up the next morn-ing, whole families of *roaches*—I mean BIG roaches, some of them a couple of inches in length—had been rousted out of hiding, and many were lying belly up all over the place. All that day we chased others of the nasty critters, some that were barely limping along and easily disposed of, others that skittered at a rapid clip across the tile floors with me in hot pursuit, flyswatter in hand and murderous gleam in eye. It was like a circus, with the various members of the McDowell family going into acrobatic leaps to escape the occasional roach falling from the ceiling almost on top of him as he sat studying at the kitchen table (Rexie), or discovered one crawling on his sock (again Rexie), or heard another racing up the wall directly behind his chair (Daddy), or .... While we were sitting down to dinner, at least eight or nine of them came sneaking out of somewhere and dashed across the kitchen floor. Each one gave Benjie and Rexie great entertainment as they would holler, "Here comes *another* one!" and then burst into hilarious giggles at the sight of Mommy leaping out of her chair to grab the swatter and beat one more of the repulsive creatures senseless.

Within the same week as the earthquake and the flea/roach fumigation, Benjie fell headfirst off a bike, driving a good-sized pebble into his forehead. I was able to dig it out, but we took him to our doctor at *Clínica Bíblica* for a thorough cleaning of the wound, which would have been impossible for me to do without lidocaine to numb it. Benjie was not at all in agreement with the process, but was ever so polite about it, hollering "No, thank you! No, thank you!" the entire time that Dr. Pérez was preparing the injection. This boo-boo was at the exact same spot where he had previously connected with the ground after other major tumbles, thereby creating a permanent, palpable knot on his skull and earning himself the nickname "Benjamin Bump." After the pebble episode, we thought he ought to be called "Goliath," although, thankfully, the stone in his forehead did not have the same effect as the one that David threw at the giant of Bible story fame.

In the midst of the busyness, we were delighted with the opportunity to attend one last performance by the National Symphonic Orchestra of Costa Rica. At 85¢ apiece, the ticket price was a music lover's dream, and we had taken advantage of it on several other occasions. Bypassing the ornate front foyer of the symphony hall with its soaring ceilings, crystal chandeliers, and solid marble floors and columns, we entered an unassuming back door into a dark hallway and climbed a steep set of stairs to the fourth-floor gallery section, where our economy seats on the front row allowed us to lean on the balcony railing, from which the sound and view were excellent. I am sure we enjoyed it every bit as much as the people on the ground floor who paid $6.75 each for their prime seating.

Donovan DeLong and his eleven-year-old son Stephen came down from Nicaragua to help us with the move, bringing with them the national church president, Luis Aguilera. At 10:00 a.m. on Friday, May 24, 1991, our caravan pulled out of Marilyn Olson's front gate in Cartago, Costa Rica, and headed north for Managua, Nicaragua. Rexie rode with Don, Luis, and Stephen in the DeLongs' big blue Ford van, which was loaded to capacity and pulling a trailer packed full with furniture and boxes. Not only were we taking our personal belongings, we also had a set of bunk beds and a single bed box spring and mattress for Don's children, plus a kitchen table and six sturdy chairs for Luis's family.

The men had removed the trailer top so they could fit everything in. Since the rainy season had started and we were expecting to be driving in a downpour during the afternoon, they spread a large, heavy-duty tarp over the jumble of bed headboards, table legs, chair backs, bookshelves and boxes. Still, with the load piled so high, even the "super grande" size tarp was not big enough to cover everything. I was praying fervently as we started out that the Lord would hold off the rains that day so our furniture and boxes would not get soaked.

Behind the van and trailer came Rex, Benjie, and me in our pickup truck. It, too, had this and that stuffed into every available crack and crevice, making me feel as though I had something in common with the early pioneers and their wagon train expeditions westward. We made good time to the border, with nothing more eventful occurring than Rex's getting attacked by fire ants who did not appreciate his tearing the roof off their house. Since there are no such things as rest areas in Costa Rica or Nicaragua, we had stopped along the road to answer Mother Nature's call to Benjie. When Rex pulled up a clump of grass to cover the deposit, he did not realize it was part of a fire ants' nest. If you have ever been bitten by one of those creatures, you realize why they have earned their name.

The border between Costa Rica and Nicaragua is not just an invisible line as it is between states in the U.S. On the Costa Rican side, there is a group of buildings including a restaurant, restrooms, customs offices, and an unloading dock, all spread out over several acres. We arrived there around 4 o'clock that afternoon with the sun still smiling down on us. Getting through Costa Rican customs went well, and we left an hour later, thankful that we had not had to unload anything and that they had "only" charged us $79 to leave, instead of the $20 it should have been. In a situation like that, they can demand what they want, and there is not much one can do about it. They tend to milk foreigners, especially "rich" North Americans, for all they can get.

After leaving the cluster of structures that officially comprised the end-point of Costa Rican territory, we drove for a few hundred yards through a no-man's land buffer zone to the Nicaraguan customs area. That is when the story changed. Although we arrived fifteen minutes before closing time, several of the people who needed to process our papers had already gone home for the day. In spite of eloquent pleadings on the part of Luis, who had come down for the express purpose of helping us to get through customs, and urgent prayers on the part of the rest of us, the head official just kept shaking his head. There was nothing to do but pull over into a parking area and wait out the night. Don and Rex maneuvered the vehicles into a back-to-back position under a spotlight near the unloading dock just a few yards from the guard house, where the road was blocked with a gate of iron bars and chains and patrolled by soldiers with machine guns.

Don sent Luis on to the nearest town (he, being Nicaraguan, was permitted to leave and managed to hitch a ride with one of the last trucks that crossed the border that day) to call Maydean and let her know what was happening so she would not hold supper for us. The scrambled eggs that Marilyn had given us for breakfast and the tuna salad sandwiches she had fixed for our lunch had long since disappeared, but she had sent along extra bananas and cookies, and with some of the crackers and cheese (unavailable in Nicaragua) which Don had purchased to take back with him, we had plenty for our supper. Thankfully, we also had a large container of wet wipes along. Be sure to pack some if *you* ever plan on traveling south of Texas. I was especially grateful for them after I investigated the restroom facilities. There were no doors on the toilet stalls, and the floor in each one was completely covered with nearly a half inch of putrid liquid. I took one dismayed glance, then searched for the nearest scrubby bush large enough to provide shelter for what I needed to do.

During the few remaining hours until dusk, we listlessly waited in the shade of a lone tree for the sun to go down and give us some relief from the miserable heat. Numbers of grayish-white humpbacked cattle wandered languidly down the dirt road, a few of them detouring to casually investigate our parked vehicles. We watched with envy as they pushed their way past the one spot in the iron-barred gate blocking the road that was high enough for them to squeeze through. Actually the big cows did *not* fit—a calf would walk under the bar, then mama would try to follow, and upon getting stuck, she would wait for an obliging guard to lift the bar so she could join her baby on the other side. Never once did someone ask to see their passports!

Needless to say, it was not the most comfortable night any of us had ever spent. Every little noise jerked us out of fitful dozing, nervous over possible thievery. Our motel accommodations for the evening started out with Benjie and me in the front seat of the pickup, and Don, Stephen, Rex, and Rexie in the van, all of us with windows rolled up and doors locked. The heat was just too unbearable for that to last long, so well before morning, we had opened wide all of the doors and windows in the truck and van, and Rex and Stephen had stretched full length on the cement outside, where it was at least somewhat cooler. The Lord fulfilled his promise to encamp around those who fear Him, and we were not bothered, nor was anything stolen. This protection seemed even more wonderful the next day, when we learned why we had not been permitted to cross the border when we arrived. Apparently, there had been such a massive amount of thievery at customs by the officials themselves that many of them had been arrested and thrown in jail just that week, leaving too few available to attend to us.

The seemingly endless hours of that wretched night did finally pass, and in the morning we had the advantage of being first in line to cross the border. We had made a detailed list of what items we were bringing into the country, and Don had been assured by officials in both Costa Rica and Nicaragua that with such a list, we would not have to unpack for inspection. However, someone neglected to tell the customs people that, so when things got going around 7:30 a.m., here came four or five men to start unloading the trailer. As they began untying ropes, setting things off, and ripping open and going through the taped boxes which I had so carefully packed, it started to drizzle. Frankly, I could hardly believe it. "Lord, we prayed so hard about the rain, and You held it off all last night. Why is this happening *now*?" As the sprinkle changed into a steady downpour and I watched the men slipping around on the furniture in the trailer, my stomach churned into progressively tighter knots. When one of the officials roughly picked up a box and carelessly tipped it over, dumping its neatly organized contents into a jumbled heap on the wet, muddy cement at his feet, I turned away in tears. "Dear God, *please!*" I pleaded. "MAKE THE RAIN STOP!!!"

Remember, as a child I was taught that God always answers the prayers of his children. As I grew older, I realized that, while this is certainly true, He may not give the answer that I would prefer every single time. Much as I may feel that I know what is best for some situation, instead of saying "Yes," to my request, He might see that "Wait," or even "No" is a better response. When God does say "No," it is not because He does not love us or chooses to play games with us. It is because He sees the whole picture, and He loves us too much to allow our finite understanding of the state of affairs to dictate an answer that would not be for our good or His glory. This was just such an occasion. I prayed ... and prayed ... and the rain kept coming down.

The trailer was only about one fourth unpacked when the man in charge waved to the others to pull the tarp back over what was left, and he headed for his office with Rex and Don in tow to process our papers. I am not sure how much of his motive was kindness, and how much was his reluctance to get soaked himself. At any rate, almost as soon as he left, the rain slacked off, and by the time the men came back from the office, it had stopped completely. We repacked everything and left the border at 10:30 a.m. in clear, sunny weather that lasted until the very minute that we had the last of the trailer's contents unloaded into our new home in Nicaragua late that afternoon. Praise the Lord! He sent just enough rain at just the right time to stop any further careless handling of our possessions, proving once again that God's timing is never wrong. When He says "No," it is because He does all things well. I delight in serving a God like that!

## 15

## "There's A *Bunny* in My Bath!"

*September 1991 ~ Managua, Nicaragua*

Our new home in Nicaragua was officially in the city of Managua, but our surroundings definitely looked like the country. On one side of us lived Coronado and Armira, a wonderful older couple who had no children of their own, so they unofficially adopted our boys, giving them a generous portion of grandparent-style loving and spoiling. Across the dirt road that wound by the front of our house was a large field. The family who farmed it lived just at the edge of the road in a simple wooden house with a stained tile roof which was blackened by the drifting smoke from years of open cooking fires in the kitchen below. Out back, we had a little orchard of *jacote* trees which produced a walnut-sized green fruit with a rather unappealing flavor, and *pitaya* plants, a type of cactus that bore a much tastier, bright-purple-and-red fruit, good in salads or blenderized into a refreshing drink.

Since we had moved during the rainy season, there was still time to plant a garden. With high hopes, we hired the farmer's son to break up a patch of ground with his yoke of oxen and a single-bottom wooden plow. Our boys were fascinated with the process, especially when the young man obligingly permitted eight-year-old Rexie to take a turn holding onto the plow handle and guiding it in a rather crooked furrow behind the plodding hooves of the patient oxen. We were all very excited as the seeds which we so carefully spaced in rows began to sprout and push through the ground. Regrettably, our visions of succulent corn on the cob, crisp string beans, and tender green peas vanished as quickly as the tiny plants did, since those same neighbor's chickens voraciously gobbled every bit of green that dared poked its head above the surface of the earth.

This place was both the nicest and the worst of the four homes where we had now lived as missionaries. The nice part was having plenty of shelves and storage areas in all the rooms, a wide front porch with a roof over it where the boys could play on rainy afternoons, and a big front yard that had a large tree with a branch just the right size to hold a rope swing. The house was a four-foot high cement-block base topped by rough vertical boards, some with half-inch gaps (yes truly, I measured them) between which we could look and see the outside world. Most of the window frames were up to an inch shorter and narrower than the space in the wall that they were supposed to fill. Many of the jalousie windowpanes were missing, but at least we were not in much danger from thieves, since all of the windows had bars across them and each of the three outside doors was protected with an iron barred gate. The windows were also covered with nylon netting, which kept at least part of the myriad bug population in its proper location.

The floors were a conglomeration of tile, most of it with an attractive green-and-white swirly pattern ... except where some broken tiles had been replaced with red-and-white swirly patterned ones ... except where other tiles were crumbled away to the cement underneath ... except where even that was missing and there was nothing but bare ground. The grouting had worn away between many of the tiles as well, leaving wide cracks where dirt loved to hide. And there was plenty of dirt! During the dry season, when temperatures hovered in the 90° to 100° range all day long and no rain fell for weeks at a time, the pretty green grass on our lawn withered, crumbled, and vanished, leaving in its wake a bleak expanse of up to two-inch-deep brown powder which the wind whipped mercilessly through the numberless cracks and crevices in our house. I would sweep and mop my floors in the morning, and by evening we could see our footprints in the dust that relentlessly collected each day. Every week when I changed Benjie's crib sheet, I cleaned the plastic mattress underneath it with a wet cloth and then rinsed a stream of "chocolate" water down the drain from the cloth. Although I wiped off the table after every meal, I had to do it again before setting the plates for the next meal, and the accumulated grit would leave a hand-shaped black print on my dish cloth. At times, I would get very energetic and go around with a wet rag in my hand, industriously rubbing windowsills and furniture throughout the day. At other times, the futility of trying to keep things clean caught up to me, and I felt like screaming and giving up. At least, one thing we did not have to contend with was mildew—no great loss without some small gain. In Costa Rica, the dark back corners inside my kitchen cabinets could grow inch-long green mildew "hair" in a couple of weeks' time, but I never had a problem like that in Nicaragua.

The door from the living room to the front porch was a fairly good fit, but the one from Rex's study to the side yard stood well off the floor, leaving ample entrance room for tarantulas and frogs. The frogs were not just the little half-dollar-size jumpers either, but bulgy-eyed bullfrogs the size of an orange that came in at night by holding their breath and squeezing under the door. Once inside, they would deposit puddles of urine and peapod-sized wads of excrement here and there. That was bad enough, but the worst thing was never knowing from where one would jump out at you. There was a broken space behind our toilet with a hole to the outside where they could also enter, and I routinely found several of them a day in the bathroom. Our shower was a six-inch-deep, rectangular-shaped cemented area in the corner, and we quickly learned to inspect for lurking frogs before stepping down into it. The toilet tank leaked so badly that the plastic gallon jug which I kept under it to catch the drips would completely fill four to five times a day. After my startled shriek the couple of times that I picked up the jug to empty it and found a frog happily floating inside, Rex tackled those problems by blocking off the space under the study door and putting a board over the hole behind the toilet. But those frogs were so big that they could push the board up. Our final solution was to store a full bottle of bleach on top of the board to weight it down sufficiently, as well as to shut off the water valve to the toilet, only opening it long enough to fill up the tank for a flush each time we used it.

When the DeLong family moved back to Nicaragua after their furlough, they lived in this house for the ten months before our arrival. It had been in even worse shape at that point, since no one had occupied it for some years before. Maydean made me shiver with her tales of lying in bed at night and watching iguanas and an occasional rat creep stealthily along the rafters over their heads. Thankfully, Don had installed a ceiling before we got there, so even though iguanas still happily occupied the attic, they only occasionally came in to visit us.

Rexie was outside chasing one around the house one afternoon when he was on a break from school work, and it ran up onto our porch. Excited at the prospect of finally catching one, he yelled for me to "Come out quick and help me!" Not knowing what was going on, but fearful that he had been hurt, I jerked open our front door at the precise moment that his quarry reached it. In its frantic haste to escape, the iguana dashed inside. In my frantic haste to prevent its entrance, I slammed the door shut. The poor iguana was literally caught in the middle, leaving his tail whipping back-and-forth on the porch floor, while he, eighteen inches shorter than he had been seconds before, skittered across my living room and down the hall. Rexie pulled up short and started screaming, aghast at the sight of the gyrating iguana-less tail at his feet. I sprinted screaming after the gyrating tail-less iguana, aghast at the thought that he might find a hiding spot before I could shoo him out the door. In spite of the fact that his claws gave him little traction on the slick tile floor, he made remarkably good time from the front entrance clear into the back of the house. Unfortunately for me, (fortunately for him) Rex was away for the day teaching classes, but all the commotion alerted our friend Coronado next door who valiantly came to the rescue, escorting our unwelcome visitor back outside where he belonged. Although his tail never grew back, Sir Stub survived his harrowing experience, apparently none the worse for wear. Throughout the remaining months that we lived in that house, we caught occasional glimpses of him cavorting through the branches of the same tree where Rexie had originally startled him from his placid afternoon siesta on what undoubtedly must have been the worst day of the poor lizard's life.

On occasion, we shared our house with not only the stray iguana, but also other interesting critters. We learned to shake out our shoes before putting our feet into them, thereby preventing a nasty surprise in the form of a venom-loaded scorpion's tail jab to our toes. And while I never succeeded in suppressing a gasp of shock at the sight of a LARGE, hairy-legged, black tarantula unabashedly sunning himself on *my* kitchen floor, neither of those unwelcome visitors caused me as much consternation as THE RAT.

Shortly after we moved in, the government carried out a rat extermination campaign, sending young people house to house passing out poison cubes. We had not seen any rats in our place, but I remembered Maydean's stories and tucked the cubes away for possible future use. About three months later, I caught a glimpse of one of the revolting rodents in our bathroom, so I distributed the cubes here and there, hoping he would quickly be dispatched to his ratty reward. That same evening while nearly three-year-old Benjie was sitting in his pink plastic tub in the shower, he gave a frightened cry and I immediately surmised that he must have seen the rat. Fortunately, Mr. Rat apparently decided that he was clean enough and was already gone by the time I ran in. Benjie was sitting there with a slightly puzzled look on his face, pointing to the shower floor and telling me of the "bunny in mine shower."

We did not see anything more of the "bunny" for a few days until Rexie happened to chance upon him in the kitchen, in the act of jumping down from the top of the buffet and running under the stove. Several days later, he startled a scream out of me when I reached for some keys on a shelf behind our bed, and he scrambled off the shelf and up the wall to disappear into a hole where the ceiling did not quite meet the wall. We stuffed some more poison cubes through the place where he disappeared and hoped for the best.

Monday morning, we were having family worship when Rexie had to use the bathroom. He rushed back out immediately, hollering that the rat was down in the shower. We all went running in, and sure enough, there he was, lying on the shower floor (the rat—not Rexie). He had obviously been nibbling too much of certain goodies, because he was almost dead. Or so we thought. Our thoughts were rearranged quickly when Rex went to get him out and finish him off. He apparently did not like that idea too well and took off running. Well, so did we! Fortunately, he was quite sick and relatively slow (relative to a speeding bullet, that is), but there most definitely was a fair amount of life left in him.

Rex decided that the wisest thing was for Mommy and the boys to go out on the porch while brave hero Daddy fearlessly stalked down the wild beast. Armed to the teeth with an .88 caliber broom handle, he started after him. Ratty tried to escape by hiding in a forest of kitchen table and chair legs, but Rex chased him back into the bathroom and closed all three doors (one into the hall and one each into the bedrooms on either side) so he could not get away. So there they were, Rex and the rat, in a fight to the finish.

The problem was, before the fight was finished, Mr. Rat cheated, cowardly climbing up into the innards of our little portable washing machine. The situation obviously called for reinforcements, so Rex summoned up the Feminine Brigade. Arming me with a broom, he got heavy artillery for himself—Rexie's baseball bat. He tipped the washer over. Gripping the bat firmly at the ready in one hand, with the stick in his other he began trying to encourage the enemy to come forth and fight like a man. The enemy, however, preferred to retreat farther up country to where even the stick could not reach him.

So, Rex hit upon a different strategy. He got a screwdriver and proceeded to remove the back cover of the washer to give him better access to the critter's camp. I was nervously standing by with my broom in one hand and shining a flashlight around in the washer with the other. Still unable to reach him, Rex went around to the front and set the washer upright, hoping the rat would fall out. I, as the rearguard, stood ready for action. There was some! Rex started to ask, "Do you see ...," when the rat ran down from inside and ducked under the washer. I yelped, "There he goes, by your feet!" Having been mustered out unexpectedly, Rex had not put on his combat boots, so he made his flip-flop clad toes move as fast as Mr. Rat's toes were moving, only much higher! His feet were definitely experiencing elevated emotions when the long-tailed "bunny" shot past.

With all exits closed to him, the rat could not get out; however, he could still progress rather quickly. After one dismally ineffective swipe at him with my broom, I ignominiously retreated, leaving the rest of the battle to my courageous husband. The next few minutes were filled with the rat-tat-tat (more accurately, the bat-bat-rat) of rapid machine-bat fire. Incredible damage was being done to the enemy's fortress—namely, the doors, walls, and shelves of the bathroom— but he stubbornly kept on his forced march. Finally, a lucky shot hit him, slowing his progress sufficiently that another couple of direct hits could finish him off.

In the meanwhile, the two-boy Reserve Corps shouted encouragement from the edge of the battlefield. "Have you got him yet? What's happening? Where is he? Why don't you hurry and kill him?" And the entire Feminine Brigade kept up the battle cry: "Oh! Careful! There he goes! Get him! Eeeee!" When the smoke finally cleared, the enemy was completely vanquished. We saw no other members of his army after that time, and there were but minor casualties to our side. Actually, the bathroom was not even noticeably hurt. And without a doubt, those were some of the best aerobic exercises we had participated in for a long time!

(Special thanks to Rex for portions of the rat tale that I used from a letter which he wrote to his parents.)

# 16

## Things That Go "Bump" in the Night
### *March 1992 ~ Managua, Nicaragua*

Rats, frogs, iguanas, and tarantulas in our house in the daytime were less of a terror to Rex than the various critters that I occasionally dreamed about in the night. He had more than ten years' experience of calming me down when I would leap up with a yell to escape the green-eyed spider I distinctly saw crawling on my pillow in the black darkness, or the cat sticking his head up over the edge of the bed, or the deer bounding in through the window, or the lizard darting out of the pile of laundry that I was sorting in my sleep, or ....

Prior to going to the mission field, my most vivid nightmare had occurred the night that Rexie was born. Our infant son was peacefully asleep in his crib when I dreamed that he was falling out of our bed on the opposite side from where I was lying. Rex awoke with a jolt to the sight and sound of his wife diving through the air over top of him only to CRASH!!! into the wall on his side of the bed. I had bolted upright from a sound sleep, leaping to grab frantically at my baby who was not in nearly as much danger of injury as my poor husband was.

Since that incident, Rex had gained plenty of practice in soothing me back to sleep, although sometimes he would have to get up and turn on the light to prove that there was really nothing there. On this particular occasion, I had shattered his peaceful slumber three nights in a row by my jumps and shrieks while trying to escape the roaches that inhabited my dreams. After each rude awakening, Rex heroically rescued me from tumbling out of bed onto the floor and finally got settled back down himself, once his heart stopped racing enough to allow him to doze off.

On the fourth night, I had not been asleep long when I felt a strand of hair slipping down across my forehead and over my eyelid. I reached up to brush it off, but jerked awake instead with another yell, at the same instant throwing something crawly right at Rex. I was *positive* it was real this time and reached over to snap on the bedside lamp, even as he was trying to convince me that it was just another dream, and would I *please* not turn on the light! I frantically peered around the bed and up his T-shirt sleeve, trying to see where WHATEVER IT WAS had gone. He resignedly slipped into his "here we go again" mode, trying to settle me down. We were both sitting up, Rex facing the bottom of the bed and I facing him, when all of a sudden I saw IT—a hairy-legged, inch-and-a-half-long roach, crawling across his pillow. I yelped again and pointed to it with a triumphant, "See, I *told* you so!" He jerked around and snatched his pillow over to the side of the bed so he could brush the invader off when, lo and behold, another giant hairy-legged roach dashed out from under the pillow to join his fleeing mate. Even my calm, sensible husband got a bit excited at that! He jumped out of bed and swept them both down onto the floor, but only managed to smash one with a hastily aimed flip-flop. I prudently scrambled out the other side of the bed to get as far away as possible. Talk about an adrenaline rush!

Rex cleaned the squished roach innards off the floor while I trotted out to the kitchen for the bug sprayer and spritzed around the wallboard at the head of the bed so the one that got away would not climb back in with us. We turned out the light and lay choking in the fumes from the spray, with me, vindicated at last, bursting into laughter every couple of minutes at the thought of the whole thing, and Rex lying there muttering, "Well, if you'd just not cried 'Wolf, Wolf' so many times before...."

Traumatic as that experience was, it still did not convince Rex that any time I woke him in the wee hours, he had legitimate need for concern. Then came the week that Marilyn Olson traveled up from Costa Rica to be with us for the Nicaraguan holiness convention. Nicaragua was a much poorer country than Costa Rica, having been devastated by a major earthquake in the 1970s, followed by years of communist rule from which the economy had never recovered. Crumbling empty shells of once-impressive buildings were a common sight on our weekly trips to the post office. Water and electricity were carefully rationed. We had gotten used to having power only in the morning and water only in the evening on even days, then water in the morning and power in the evening on odd days. As in Costa Rica, we had a large tank up on a platform beside the house, so we usually had a steady supply of water. It was the frequent *unscheduled* power outages that could occur any time of the day or night that were more difficult to deal with, especially since we never knew whether this one would last a few minutes, a few hours, or even a few days. The gas lantern that we kept handy was put to good use on many occasions, and I was very thankful for a gas stove that enabled me to cook meals even when the electricity was off.

During the night that neither Marilyn nor we will ever forget, the electricity had flickered off unannounced sometime after we were all in bed and sound asleep. Unbeknown to us, some ruffians took advantage of the darkness to steal one of our neighbors' oxen, then came prowling across the road to our house to see what they could find. The mission's Datsun pickup truck was parked out back, where they stealthily went to work trying to hot wire it so they could add it to their loot. Flashlights in hand, intent upon their evil deed, they were abruptly startled from their efforts by piercing screams coming from the hitherto silent house beside the truck. Thoroughly frightened, they abruptly dropped everything and ran in a panic for the road, certain that they had been discovered.

Inside the house, I had jumped from bed and was frantically tugging on Rex, shrieking at the top of my voice while trying to drag him away from the mammoth snake that had slithered out of a hole in the wall behind us and was coiled over him, hideous mouth wide open and razor-sharp fangs poised to strike. Jolted awake, Marilyn lay frozen in her bed in the boys' room, hearing not only the screams, but also the sound of several pairs of feet pounding past the house and down the drive. She was certain that some poor, unfortunate woman was being murdered right outside her window.

Rexie and Benjie tumbled from their beds and joined Marilyn in a mad dash from their bedroom into the safety of ours, only to pull up short in astonishment at the sight of Rex, half in and half out of his bed, dazedly peering up at his berserk wife with her feet braced firmly on the floor, still screaming and jerking frenziedly on his arm. Rex finally got me awake enough to realize that it was just another dream and he was not truly in mortal danger. Between us, we managed to calm the excited chattering of our boys and convince Marilyn that no one had been killed, and she could safely return to her suddenly interrupted rest.

Early the next morning, Rex and Marilyn left in the Datsun for the last day of the convention. I was fixing breakfast for the boys when we heard a loud pounding on the front door. "Hermana Ana, Hermana Ana!" someone yelled excitedly. "Where is your truck?" I ran to open the door, and there was our next door neighbor, normally prim and proper *doña* Armira, in her *nightgown*. Seemingly unaware of her odd attire, she anxiously repeated her question. When I assured her that Rex had left with the truck before she got up, she visibly relaxed, exclaiming, "Oh, thank the Lord!" Then she told us of the robbery that had taken place during the night across the road. "When we looked out and saw that your truck was gone, we thought the thieves had stolen it too!"

That evening at supper I told Rex and Marilyn about Armira's visit. Marilyn got a peculiar look on her face and exclaimed, "Now I remember! I heard people running past my window last night after your screaming woke me up, but with all the commotion you were making, I completely forgot to mention it." Not until that moment did we put all of the pieces together to realize what God had done. We knew of course, how He had closed the mouths of lions to save the life of his faithful servant Daniel. In our case, He opened the mouth of a snake and sent it slithering into my dreams that night so my screaming would convince the would-be thieves that they had been spotted and scare them off. It was *their* feet that Marilyn had heard racing by and escaping to safety before they could do us the harm that they had intended.

To this day, I continue to have graphic dreams, and after all this time Rex has become an expert in his ability to settle me back to sleep relatively easily when I startle us both awake yet again. As far as we know, we have never been in another situation where we have needed protection such as we did that long-ago night in Nicaragua. However, should the need ever arise, I am sure it would be no problem for God to send another snake, or a lion, or even just an especially large roach to populate my subconscious brain and drive away the danger!

# "I'll Just Cook Him Here at the House," and Other Interesting Adventures

*May 1991 – December 1992 ~ Managua, Nicaragua*

We had not lived in Nicaragua very long before I discovered that my medical training was a blessing not only to the nationals, but also to our own family as well. It had been helpful on several occasions in Costa Rica to know what to do when one of our boys had an upset tummy or an unusual rash. This knowledge was especially beneficial in a country where the living conditions were less sanitary than they had been in Costa Rica. A lack of indoor plumbing was common even in the capital city of Managua. I could not understand why we all had repeated bouts of diarrhea when I was so careful to soak our fruits and vegetables in iodine water, we washed our hands well before eating, and we boiled or bleached our drinking water. Then, one of the technicians at the laboratory where we had taken yet *another* frothy, foul-smelling stool sample to be analyzed explained it. "Lots of people don't even have outhouses," he told me. "They just go to the bathroom on the ground out back. In this heat, all of the solid waste dries and crumbles, and when the wind kicks up, that stuff is part of the dirt that blows in your face." What a reassuring thought!

The public medical system was far less advanced than that of Costa Rica, and the nearest reliable self-pay clinic was a very long bus ride away. Not that we would have wanted to take a bus there. We had caught our breath a few times while buzzing around the rotundas in Costa Rica, large circular areas where four or five lanes of traffic enter and exit the main road at dizzying speeds. Even though the flow of traffic got a bit wild at times, mandatory yearly inspections and hefty fines for infractions kept most rattletrap vehicles off the streets. Although an occasional ox- or horse-drawn cart could be seen on the roads in rural areas in Costa Rica, in Nicaragua, it was perfectly normal for carts pulled by four-legged, hoof-clopping "one-horsepower engines" to vie for space with smoke-belching, tire-squealing, gear-grinding behemoths many times their size, even on the streets of major cities. As long as a contraption that was hung together with chewing gum and wire could be made to go, it was fine to take it out on the road.

In Costa Rica, car, taxi, and bus owners regularly washed and waxed their vehicles and kept them in good repair. Not so in Nicaragua. A number of our church people expressed to us their regrets at what more than ten years of communist rule had done to the self-esteem of their fellow countrymen. The buses all had a liberal coating of dirt. Spray-painted political propaganda on buildings and walls abounded. Smashed or burned-out headlights or taillights were of no concern. More than once, we came too close for comfort to crashing into a bus that was tooling down a dark street at night with absolutely no illumination, inside or out. Add to the typical "make three lanes out of one" practice an utter lack of courtesy or respect for another driver's right-of-way, and you can understand why I did not like to go out on the streets even with Rex driving, let alone trust my life to an unknown chauffeur.

People told us that before the Sandinista regime, public transportation was adequate and dependable. But the Communists filled a majority of the country's buses with sand so they could not be used. The democratic government that had been voted into power the year before we moved was gradually making more and more buses available. There still were not enough, and it was common to see passengers hanging out the doors, front and back, as well as standing several deep on the running board, clutching whatever they could to keep from falling off entirely. (It would not be correct to say "falling out," because they were never "in" to begin with.)

Hundreds of bicycles and motorcycles crowded the roads, but I can only recall seeing two safety helmets on any of the drivers. The number of people and things that could be piled on a cycle was incredible. The most I saw on one was a family of five: child in front of dad, child sandwiched between dad and mom, and baby in mom's arms. Then there was the one that only had four people: dad, mom, older child, baby in mom's arms—oops, in *one* of mom's arms. Her other arm was holding a flat of two-and-a-half dozen eggs!

The in-town streets were made of four-inch thick, puzzle-piece-shaped cobblestones fitted closely together. On the outskirts of town, asphalt or dirt took over. Of course, with all the grime and grit blowing around, people did not want traffic to go zipping by, stirring up even more filth to blow into their houses. So "sleeping policeman"—speed bumps across the roads—abounded. The cement ones on the paved streets were all right; it was the homemade dirt ones that really caused a problem. Zealous homeowners along our route to church had even dug a wide trench across the road, piling up the dirt from the trench to make the speed bump. That kind was especially effective. If one did not angle the wheels just right, he would get stuck down in the trench before he even reached the hump of dirt on the other side.

Without adequate numbers of buses to handle the masses of people needing public transportation, taxis did a brisk business. In Costa Rica, all of the taxis were red, were supposed to be officially registered, charged a standard fare, and were kept clean and in good repair. In Nicaragua, anyone who wanted a little extra income could paint the word TAXI on his ramshackle old car and start hauling passengers, charging whatever he wished. Vehicles of all shapes, sizes, colors, and stages of disrepair sported the tall black or white lettering that advertised their owner's willingness to take people here or there. If someone wanted to get some place in a *hurry*, though, it was better to walk instead, since he might reach his destination more quickly that way. Even if he was fortunate enough to find an empty taxi, he could not just give directions, settle back in his seat, and expect to head directly to wherever he wanted to go. He might *start* in that general direction, but if someone else hailed the driver and needed to go the opposite way, if it was closer, the original passenger might as well resign himself to going there first. After that, he could be driven to two or three other places with the two or three other people his driver picked up, before finally arriving where he asked to be taken in the first place. If, by some stroke of good fortune, no one else got in the taxi, there was still no guarantee that he would make his appointment. He might end up like the poor middle-aged lady we saw one week. The taxi in which she had been riding stalled out at a traffic light. She was straining to push it up the street, while her driver energetically fiddled and cranked, trying to get the thing going again on its own steam. Rex pulled over to the side of the road and jumped out to help her push. Just as they got up to an intersection, the light turned red. When the light changed, they got good momentum, and the taxi finally chugged to life partway down the next block.

Truck buses, basically anything in size from a pickup or larger, any color or model or year, with a canvas canopy over the top and a wooden bench on each side in the back, were also available. They followed the same route as the real buses and did quite a business, being able to pack in and around and on top an unbelievable amount of people and luggage. After our first ride on such a contraption, Rexie was convinced that he never wanted to do it again, although before we took the trip he had begged and begged for the chance to do so.

First, we had to walk seven-tenths of a mile from our house to catch the nearest one. Rex was teaching classes that day, and I needed some food supplies from market, so I figured I would just take the boys and go. We arrived at the stop only moments before a truck slightly bigger than a pickup pulled up. I was fortunate enough to have a seat and hold Benjie on my lap, since our truck never got very full—the most on at any one time was seventeen. We started out fine, wind whipping through our hair, Rexie enjoying himself tremendously. About halfway to market, however, the engine began to heat up and the truck slowed to a crawl, letting off a terrific series of explosions. No problem! Everything was apparently normal and under control. The young man who stood on the steps at the back to help boost passengers up, collect their fare, and give a loud whistle to signal the driver to stop or start, was well prepared. He hopped down, sprinted up to the driver's side of the truck and reached through the window for a gallon jug of water. Then he ran around to the front and raised the hood, jogging alongside the still moving truck and pouring water into the radiator as we went. That job done, he dropped the hood, handed the jug back through the window to the driver, and dashed back to resume his perch on the step. Apparently the owner knew that his truck would not have gotten going again had he paused to add water, because the same routine was repeated two more times before we arrived at our destination. We did not stop completely, even to let off or take on passengers, for a few blocks. Those needing to dismount gauged when to jump, and those wanting to get on hopped up as we crawled by. By that time, Rexie's delighted grin had faded to a worried frown, and he was all for jumping ship (er, truck bus) ourselves. I did not know where we were or how to get to where we were going, so we stayed put, and by the time we reached the market, our lumbering lorry had recovered from its temperamental spell sufficiently to enable the driver to halt it completely before we climbed down.

You can see why, when Benjamin Bump lived up to his nickname once again and fell down our rough concrete-block porch steps the day he turned three years old, I decided not to try to get him to a clinic in town to have the gash on his head sutured. "Are you going to take him for stitches?" queried Grandma Armira when she arrived, breathless, in the doorway of our living room to investigate the cause of Benjie's earsplitting shrieks.

"Oh no, I'll just cook him here at the house," I informed her confidently. Her look of concern deepened to a puzzled grimace of alarm—until she realized that I was not really planning a cannibalistic feast to celebrate his birthday. The Spanish language had once again nearly claimed a victim. I did not really want to *cocinar* (cook) my little boy, but to *coser* (sew) him up. Fortunately, I had everything I needed for the repair job, and today Benjamin's red curls adequately conceal the nicely healed, half-inch white scar that reminds those of us who know, about the fateful afternoon when his mother announced her intention to do him in.

# 18

## One Little, Two Little, Three Little Indians
### *November 1991 – September 1992 ~ Managua, Nicaragua*

I swayed slowly, drowsily, eyes half closed. The chicken that had fluttered up to perch beside my head, claws tightly gripping the top slat in the unvarnished wooden chair back as he rocked to and fro with me earlier in the afternoon, had gone elsewhere to roost for the night. Shifting slightly, I scooted the rocker to a better spot on the slanting dirt floor to avoid an annoying pebble that bumped under one runner. Squinting across the dark room against the glare of the single bare lightbulb that dangled by a wire from the rafter above her bed, I saw that Patricia was resting quietly. It was more than an hour since her husband had left to take their wriggly toddler to spend the night with Grandma across town. Unfortunately, he would probably not be back in time to share in the birth of their baby, since the buses were no longer running at this time of night, and I knew he could not afford a taxi's fee.

The tranquility of the late November night belied the existence of a normally bustling neighborhood right outside the door. The house was actually just a corrugated tin shack, one of a multitude like it in this poorer section of Managua, the once-proud capital city of Nicaragua. An occasional muffled rooster's crow wafted to my ears. I glanced up and caught the far-away glimmer of a star, shining through one of the many holes in the tin roof over my head. "I wonder if this is what it was like the night that Jesus was born," I mused. There were no warm bodies of farm animals in the dark corners, quietly chewing their cuds, but I could not imagine that the Bethlehem stable was any less accommodating than this simple home. Aside from my rocker, a crude wooden table, two chairs, and the double bed made of rough planks with a cloth covering stuffed with lumpy cornhusks for a mattress, the room was bare.

Luis and Patricia Flores, a sweet young couple from Evangelical Wesleyan's Managua Central church, had asked me a few months earlier if I would deliver this baby. It was actually her third pregnancy, but their second child had tragically died after contracting tetanus from the careless mishandling of his umbilical cord at birth by the staff in the main maternity hospital in the city. Patricia was adamant in her refusal to return there. I was pleased at the confidence their request showed, but a bit nervous at the prospect of being solely responsible for the welfare of both mother and baby in such a primitive setting. Of course, millions of women the world over have given birth in similar circumstances;

nevertheless, it would be a far cry from the hospitals in which I had trained, with their emergency backup equipment and personnel. The Floreses did not even have running water inside their house. Yet, I knew that God had prepared me for just such a situation, and I was excited at the prospect of putting my training to good use and helping to meet such an obvious need.

Patricia had been up and about during much of the day since my arrival mid-morning. Her daughter shadowed her footsteps, unaware of the pending change in her small world, but sensing that something was different. Luis walked to a local market and brought back a papaya for lunch, but I assured him that I had eaten plenty of breakfast and declined their offer to share the only food they had in the house. Along toward evening, Patricia's contractions, which had been mild and irregular up until that point, settled into serious business. There was not really room in the cramped quarters for me to stay beside her as she paced back-and-forth, but each time that she paused to silently grip the bed frame at yet another painful tightening of her abdomen, I stepped over to rub her back and offer encouragement. By that point, the little girl's anxiety over mommy's strange behavior and her fretful insistence on being picked up and given attention was creating too much strain. I was relieved at Luis's decision to take their daughter to her grandma's place, feeling that Patricia would likely relax and make good progress once she could focus her attention and energy on the child inside rather than the one outside. Things did indeed settle down, to the point that Patricia was even able to doze between contractions.

While the majority of Costa Ricans are of fair-skinned Spanish descent, a great number of Nicaraguans trace their roots to Indian ancestors, from whom they inherit their swarthy complexions and a stoic tolerance of pain. True to her upbringing, Patricia birthed baby Luis in the wee hours of the morning with a quiet intensity that once again brought to mind my earlier reflections about the advent of another small babe 2000 years ago. The phrase, "How silently, how silently, the wondrous gift is given," from my mother's favorite Christmas carol, "Oh Little Town of Bethlehem," held new meaning for me as the world around slept unknowing through the nativity of this child as well.

I do not know what provisions Joseph and Mary had available the night that Jesus arrived. Perhaps the innkeeper's wife kindly shared some freshly baked, crusty bread and a bowl of rich, warm goat's milk with the weary new mother. I wished that I could have done the same for Patricia, but the papaya from lunchtime was long since gone, and there would be no more food until her husband returned in the morning. I was regretting not having accepted the fruit they had offered me, but at the time I had not anticipated being there so long, and I did not want to deplete the little that they had. Going to bed on an empty stomach gave me a greater appreciation for my refrigerator with its amply stocked shelves. Not one of the people in this neighborhood had need of such an appliance.

Long after Little Luis had filled his belly and dropped off to sleep, snuggled up next to his mother, I lay awake on the narrow cot which I had dragged out from behind the bed and wrestled open. Aptly named *tijeras* (scissors), these cumbersome contraptions consisted of a folding frame with a strip of canvas nailed to the ends. Once the legs were spread apart, the canvas stretched out to form a bed of sorts, although it was definitely advantageous to be young, flexible and lightweight if one wanted to get a decent night's sleep on it. The heavier one's body, the more it pressed down onto the narrow strip of wood that crossed from side to side just underneath the middle of the canvas to prevent the frame from folding up on its inhabitant. No matter how I twisted and turned, I could not get comfortable. Besides, with the light out, mosquitoes had emerged in droves, zinging about my head and forcing me to retreat, turtle-like, into the collar of my blouse to keep from being eaten alive. Suffice it to say that it was not my most restful night.

When morning finally dawned and Daddy and Big Sister arrived back home, any discomfiture was quickly forgotten in the warm rush of satisfaction over their delight and the gratitude that they so exuberantly lavished on me. Never mind my aching back or the itchy red splotches on my face. It had been worth every minute.

Not only did I have the privilege of helping to assure her baby's safe arrival, I was also pleased when Patricia unhesitatingly accepted my advice on the best nourishment she could give him. Unlike many babies in a country where bottle-feeding was the norm, Little Luis was saved the distress of debilitating episodes of vomiting and diarrhea caused by the use of contaminated water in formula preparation. He developed into a healthy, laughing, gurgling advertisement of the benefits of breast-feeding. The midwifery instructor who had advocated for my inclusion in the Medical University of South Carolina's program had certainly been nudged by God when she appealed, "Think of the good she can do in a third world country. Let's give her a chance!"

My second "Little Indian" was born on March 25, 1992. The house into which he arrived was not quite as humble a setting as the first baby's had been. At least, it had a rough cement floor instead of just dirt, and the walls were all of wood, although I could look through the spaces and cracks between the boards and see people passing by on the dirt path out front. When Mariana's husband called shortly after five o'clock that morning from the pay phone down the street, he said to please hurry; his wife had been in labor all night, and she couldn't stand it any longer. My birthing bag had been ready, sitting on a chair by our front door for the past few days. Two nights before, I had cut and ironed some clean strips of cloth, ready to tie off the umbilical cord.

When I arrived, Mariana was just one to two centimeters dilated, and her contractions were short and mild. An hour and a half later, nothing had changed, so she started scrubbing laundry at the cement sink on the patio, hoping to crank things up to a higher gear. I took the opportunity to use the bathroom, an outhouse consisting of three walls, two of wood slabs and one of tin and plastic sacking. I just hoped that no one passing by on the street could see *in* as well as I could see *out,* since it had no roof or door, and my head poked out over the top when I stood up. Most houses in the States are palaces compared to many of the homes in Nicaragua. I was reminded again that we do not realize how little is really necessary until seeing some of the conditions in which other people live. How much wealthy, self-sufficient, complacent, indifferent America will have to answer for! Oh, that people would realize the need and heed the call of the Master Reaper to gather the harvest while there is yet opportunity!

A few minutes after 9 o'clock, Mariana finished mopping her floor, pausing to lean on the mop handle or against the wall with each contraction. Her healthy, seven-pound, twelve-ounce baby was born at 11:42 a.m. Everything went just fine, except for the fact that their catalog order had gotten mixed up, and the stork sent a boy instead of a girl ... or something like that. After an initial twinge of disappointment, the family warmly welcomed the little fellow. His four siblings, who had been to and fro between the house and yard all morning, met baby brother just minutes after he was born, and nine-year-old big sister helped me dress him.

The third mother that I attended was thirty-six years old and having her sixth baby. Once again, I found myself in a humble little house, in the stifling heat of a windowless room. Before I quite passed out and roasted to death, Teresa opened the back door, a single sheet of tin nailed on some boards and propped shut with a big stick. Her youngest child, a very active four-year-old, bounced in and out of the room, blissfully oblivious to the fact that very shortly he would no longer be the adored, spoiled baby of the family.

They offered me a tall, brim-full glass of cold, freshly blenderized, delicious orange-carrot juice or *fresco,* which I enjoyed to the last drop. In cases like that, even though we knew it was made from common, unsanitary tap water, to refuse it would have been an insult, and we always partook, trusting the Lord to protect us from the "bugs." Besides, I was pretty sure I had unwelcome inhabitants in my tummy region already. A few months back, I been sick with diarrhea, gas, diarrhea, bloated belly, diarrhea, nausea, diarrhea, and then some more diarrhea. Rex took a stool specimen to the lab and found out that I had four different kinds of amoebas as well as Giardia. We spent two-and-a-half hours and went to seven different pharmacies, trying to find the right medication. Although I felt better for a time, recently the same symptoms had returned, although not as ferociously. I figured that since I would have to debug soon anyhow, whatever else was merrily paddling around in my glass besides the orange-carrot *fresco* would be eradicated then.

Teresa was three-centimeters dilated and the baby's head was nicely down when I arrived, but her past labors had all been quite long. I was hoping this one would break the pattern, and when her water broke all over the floor a couple of hours later, it looked as though my wish would come true. She did progress fairly steadily up to nine centimeters of dilation—and then stayed there for three hours, in spite of everything I tried to help her move on. Finally awakening her husband from his nap on a piece of cardboard in the yard, I regretfully told him she was not going to be able to have the baby at home, and we would need to take her to the hospital. Although disappointed for her, I *was* interested to see if all of the negative reports I had been given of this place lived up to the reality.

At 9:09 p.m., our taxi pulled up in front of double glass doors guarded by a burly man who curtly informed us that no one was allowed inside with Teresa. I tried to explain that I was a nurse and had been attending her at her house. He snapped, "Did you bring your nursing license?" Of course I hadn't, not expecting any need for it. "No," I answered, "I have it at home."

"Then you can't come in." he retorted. And I didn't! But neither did any of the other friends or family members accompanying the half dozen or more pregnant women who arrived within the next hour. The doors were kept shut with an iron bar that the guard lifted to let people in. Very few came out. At one point, a policeman approached the door and told the guard to inform someone that he could not find the medicine he had been sent to buy for one of the patients. Much later, some sort of official-looking car pulled up to the entrance. The driver laid on the horn until the guard came out—carefully locking the door behind him before crawling into the car, which disappeared around the corner. I do not know what would have happened if someone in dire need had come seeking help while they were gone, but no one did, and it was not long before Mr. Hostile reappeared to resume his vigilant stance.

By the time another hour rolled by, five ambulances had pulled up and discharged their cargo: a little boy with an eye injury, three pregnant women, and a lady with an IV needle in her arm. A taxi brought another pregnant lady. Her husband started to follow her in, but the guard stuck his arm out in front of the man and blocked his way. He, too, joined the ranks of everyone else waiting outside. A young couple and her mother arrived and, just like all the others, the girl had to enter alone, leaving her family behind. Shortly thereafter, to my surprise, the guard did allow her to exit the doors and walk over to them. She was crying and holding onto her husband, while he did his best to comfort her. The guard watched them for a minute or two, then said roughly to the girl, "Come on, get in here now!" She started for the door, husband at her side, but the guard rudely shut the door in his face.

It was now 1:07 a.m. I was tired and hungry and just wanted to get home. Through brilliant deduction, I had figured out that we would not be getting any word on my lady from the porter at the door. Teresa's husband had asked him earlier if I could use the hospital phone to call my husband to come get me, but, of course, he refused permission.

What about a taxi? Problem was, I was not exactly sure how to give directions to where I needed to go, and I had no money to pay for the ride. Besides, when the next taxi drove up, the driver just parked and turned out his lights. I continued to pray, and right after that, another taxi pulled in with a patient. Thankfully, its driver was well enough acquainted with our area to find the right house. He dropped me off at my door at 1:32 a.m., patiently waiting while I woke Rex up to get money for my fare. Whew! That was one night I did not care to *ever* repeat!

"Little Indian" number three made her grand debut into the most pitifully poor of all the homes where "my" babies were born. Haydee and Carlos already had four little girls, and a fifth baby daughter had been stillborn. They desperately wanted this child to be a boy. Their whole house, if it can be called that, was about the size of our living room, pieced together from odd boards and scraps of tin, just like the shanties of hundreds of other poverty-stricken families surrounding them. At the moment, they were even more crowded than usual, because another family with four children had recently moved in with them. I set up my supplies next to a bed made of nailed-together slats of wood covered with cardboard and topped with a piece of plastic.

At 9:00 p.m., Carlos fixed supper: a bowl of beans apiece and a piece of bread. Just getting enough food to eke out an existence from one day to the next was a major undertaking for many of these people. I had eaten before I came, so I could truthfully assure him that I was not hungry and politely decline his offer of food. Even had I been famished, one look at the tiny, filth-encrusted, grease-smeared, wooden table covered with flies where the food was prepared would have killed any appetite I might have had. Everyone ate with fingers (unwashed to be sure), since there were no utensils.

By ten o'clock, the children were all put down to sleep for the night. The four little ones from the guest family shared a single-bed-sized fold-up *tijeras* cot. There was no room to open it in the house, so Carlos had fixed a place in the yard with four stacks of cement blocks topped with a sheet of corrugated tin for a roof. During the day, there were no walls for this structure, but at night they propped sheets of cracked particleboard against the block stacks to make a chest-high barricade on three sides. Carlos's own little girls stretched out on the floor of the church right next door, each with a scanty piece of cloth under her as the only cushioning on the unyielding tiles. The local belief was that baths at night were unhealthy, so all of them went to bed unwashed, in the same grimy clothes they had worn all day. I guess when there are no sheets to sleep on, there is no need to worry about getting them dirty even if one *doesn't* take a bath.

Haydee was in labor all night. By morning, I had been there long enough that it would have been impolite to refuse the breakfast that they offered me. I prayed for protection, drank the glass of water with a spoonful of ground oatmeal and some sugar stirred in, and enjoyed it. Around mid-morning, Carlos became a bit impatient with his wife's slow progress and asked if he could go buy her a *nido de amor*, or "love nest," since he had been told that it was a wonderful tonic to strengthen contractions and bring on the baby. When he detailed the recipe, a glass of beer with a whole raw egg beaten into it, I was quite certain that was NOT what Haydee needed. But he was insistent that it would do the job and headed out the door for the nearest local bar to get the principal ingredient.

Maybe just the thought of such a disgusting concoction was enough to crank up her motor. At any rate, by the time Carlos returned, tickled to have procured the perfect remedy for her dillydallying around, Haydee's contractions had kicked into full-speed-ahead mode all on their own. She tried to convince him that his trip had been unnecessary. He was equally convinced that she should give the love nest a try. She told him she would throw up if she drank it. He doggedly held a spoonful of it to her lips. She gagged, pushed his arm away, squatted on the floor ... and not long after, pushed baby girl number six out into my waiting hands. I am not sure what Carlos did with the rest of the beer-and-egg potion, but I think he was a bit put out at having wasted his money. At least, they did not have to spend anything for the midwife's services, nor wrack their brains trying to figure out what to call another girl. I was quite pleased to accept the honor of becoming "Auntie" to my little namesake, Hannah Ruth, although I still chuckle when I remember her daddy's ill-fated attempts to speed her arrival.

# How Many Bugs Do You Want in *Your* Milkshake?

*September 1994 – October 1998, Second Term ~ Paraíso, Costa Rica*

"We don't have a house; we just live in our car. We eat in our car, we sleep in our car, and we read books in our car," five-year-old Benjie matter-of-factly informed the nice lady who had just asked him where he lived. We were at yet another church raising our financial support, one of the dozens that we visited during the spring and summer of 1994 before returning to Costa Rica for our second term of missionary work.

I am sure that it must have *seemed* like we were permanent nomads to the little boy who spent hours cooped in the back seat of our Toyota Corolla station wagon as we crisscrossed the country from Canada in the North to Texas in the South, and Arizona in the West to Virginia in the East. At one point, we were away from our home base in North Carolina for three months, spending nearly every night with a different family. It was a great chance to meet old friends and make new acquaintances, but we were more than ready to abandon our rubber-tired "house" in favor of a more stationary abode. I was probably happier than any of us at the prospect of settling down, since Rexie and Benjie's baby brother was on the way, and the combination of motion sickness and morning sickness made riding in a car my least favorite thing to do.

Deputation finally over, we were preparing for our trip back to Central America. By this time, I was an expert at the fine art of packing for international travel. Weighing and reweighing our luggage, then trading the four hefty, hardback books in this box for the Tupperware container in that stack of kitchen items over there, in order to drop the box's weight from seventy-two pounds down to seventy, was the easy part. The challenging task was craning my neck sufficiently to see the tiny black numbers on the scale I was standing on while balancing each heavy box in front of my six-and-a-half-months-pregnant stomach. Rex would have gladly hefted the boxes to weigh them for me, but he had left the country a month earlier to get the house into which we would be moving ready for us.

Don DeLong had started the construction of a parsonage beside the corrugated tin church in Paraíso, Costa Rica. The cement block walls were all up, and the top concrete beam had been poured for the kitchen and living room area, which also had a concrete subfloor and temporary roof. The bedroom and bathroom half of the house was nothing but walls. For four weeks, Rex assumed the unfamiliar role of contractor, using "How To" books to guide him in plumbing and wiring the house before his family arrived. We joined him in October, a week before Benjie's sixth birthday. By then, everything was under roof, but the back half still had dirt floors. There were openings in the walls for windows, but no frames or windowpanes in place. Rex had been working long hours each day and sleeping at night on a cot in the church next door where he could keep the tools and supplies locked up so they would not grow legs and walk off.

Rexie, Benjie, and I moved in with our good friends Gilberto and Milady López, who graciously turned over one of the two bedrooms in their Caballo Blanco home to accommodate us and our small mountain of boxes. We got to see husband/daddy Rex for about forty-five minutes once a day, when he took the bus from Paraíso to join us for supper. After five weeks of this, we were ready to be a family again, even though the house was not fully finished. There were no kitchen cabinets or sink, no closets, no toilet (we used the church's outhouse), no refrigerator or living room furniture, and the bedroom area still had dirt floors. Rexie helped his daddy tear off the corrugated tin coverings and install the frames and jalousie panes in the two big windows of the living room the night we moved in. We did not feel super secure with the back door having only a big sheet of tin nailed over its opening, but we figured that if anyone tried to pry it away to get in, we would hear the screech of the nails pulling out of the wood frame.

Carlos, a neighborhood mason, spent the next weeks finishing the subfloor in the back half of the house, laying tile, and plastering the walls. Rex set up the boys' bunk bed in the living room and our double bed in the kitchen, and he laid a couple of planks across some stacked cement blocks to make shelves for my cooking pots and tableware. Our two-burner gas hot plate fit on the corner of a small table, leaving me about two square feet of work space for meal preparation.

We washed our dishes and took sponge baths in the VERY cold water at our only sink, a cement pila in the laundry area, which was enclosed with solid walls on three sides and floor-to-ceiling, parallel, vertical metal bars on the fourth side so the breeze could blow in. Now, a frigid bath in the heat and humidity of mid-July can be refreshing, but this was early December, when the temperatures dropped into the 50's at night. I remember my surprise at seeing the clouds of steam rolling from Rex's wet skin while I stood on a stool at our laundry room entrance, holding a plastic garbage bag over the opening while he shivered through scrubbing up. Since there was still no wall around the property, anyone could walk past and look through the bars into our bath area; hence the need for the garbage bag shield.

Our third son, eight-pound, three-ounce, silvery-blond-headed Jeffrey Ralph, joined the family on December 15. I was thirty-five-years old, and since we knew this would be our last baby, I really wanted to have a home birth. Patty Barnes, a midwife friend of mine, had planned to fly down to do the delivery, but Jeffrey let me know before his due date that he preferred to not wait until her scheduled visit. I tried my best to convince Rex that he should do the honors himself. "It won't be any problem, Honey," I assured him. "I've delivered enough babies that I can tell you exactly what to do." He was not won over by my arguments, so we returned to *Clínica Bíblica* where Benjie had been born six years earlier.

We were greatly blessed just after Christmas by a visit from Earl and Thelma Glick, long-time friends and faithful supporters, who came for two weeks to help on the house. Brother Earl made us much more comfortable by installing a ceiling, and much more safe by erecting a block wall to enclose the property, providing greatly needed protection in an area where thievery was rife. Sister Thelma gave me a hand with meals and laundry, as well as pitching in and helping her husband by handing him this tool or holding that board in place as he worked.

Also, to my great delight, the Faith Chapel congregation back in North Carolina flew my sister Priscilla Oldaker down to help me. Her boss would not give her the month off that she requested, so she quit her job and arrived a few days after Jeffrey's birth, the weekend before our church Christmas program. Jeffrey woke up in the middle of the elementary children's part and decided it was time to eat, while I was up front prompting the little tykes through their lines. Priscilla did her best to comfort and distract him, but he vehemently insisted that his tummy needed to be filled RIGHT NOW! The pews were lined with parents and friends raptly intent on the cute kids doing their thing up front. "Surely he can wait just another minute or two," I thought, doggedly continuing with my task. Jeffrey howled even louder. Just then Laura, a young mother whose baby had been born only weeks before mine, stepped discreetly alongside the platform, tugged on my sleeve and leaned over to whisper in my ear.

"I'll just take him to the back and feed him for you," she offered helpfully, and before I could do more than blink in astonishment, she had gathered my unhappy baby from his Aunt Priscilla's arms into her own and carried him to the last pew, where she promptly proceeded to nurse him. Jeffrey was quite pleased with the state of affairs. Jeffrey's mother recovered from her shock sufficiently to carry on with the program without interruption, but it was a good thing none of the children needed extensive help, because her mind was certainly not focused on the words they were saying.

As a nurse-midwife, I am an ardent advocate of the advantages of mother's milk. Especially in countries lacking a safe water supply, nourishing an infant in this way is not only the ideal diet, but it also helps to prevent a myriad of illnesses. And babies are not the only ones who can benefit from the wonder liquid. I still chuckle when I remember Víctor, the man from our Caballo Blanco congregation, who stopped by our house two days after Benjie's birth, carrying a small plastic container with a lid. "May I please have some new milk for my eye?" he questioned hopefully, thrusting the container toward me. I looked at him in bewilderment. "See how red my eye is?" he insisted. "It's infected, and I need to wash it out with some new milk to cure it." Comprehension dawned as I realized that he wanted some colostrum, or "new milk," to dribble in his eye. I chalked up his request to folkloric superstitious belief until years later, in a seminar back in the United States, when the very well-educated presenter scientifically explained the myriad benefits of colostrum for babies, as well as—surprise!—certain bacterial inflammations of the eye.

In spite of the double dose of protection from illnesses that Jeffrey had gotten from both me and Laura, he was hospitalized with a severe asthma attack when he was five-months old. Rev. Steven Hight, director of the missionary organization Friends of Missions, was with us as the evangelist for our church's revival that week. Rex had known Brother Hight before that visit, but the rest of us had never met him. I felt tense since I wanted to be a good hostess to our guest, but had the extra burden of a sick baby needing a lot of my attention. Steve quickly put us all at ease, fitting into our family with no trouble and helping to make lasting memories that we treasure to this day. (Be sure to ask him about the dancing cows the next time you see him.) Our boys especially enjoyed his visit, which turned out to be the first of several that term, since, by mutual agreement shortly thereafter, Raymond Shreve and Evangelical Wesleyan Mission turned the work in Costa Rica over to Steve Hight and Friends of Missions. "Brudder Teve," as Jeffrey later called him, became not only our boss but also a close personal friend as well, a happy arrangement for all concerned.

For the next six months, Jeffrey was in and out of the doctor's office for frequently recurring flare-ups of his asthma. Then, I was invited back to the States for a tremendously exciting occasion. Jeffrey, Benjie, and I flew to North Carolina so I could deliver Priscilla's first child. We arrived two weeks before her due date and planned to stay for two weeks after, confident that the baby would be born somewhere within that very adequate range of time. Unlike his cousin Jeffrey, however, this infant did not favor an early arrival. In fact, he stayed tucked cozily inside his mommy for an extra two weeks, reluctantly making his appearance the very day I was scheduled to go back to home. Thankfully, the airlines extended our tickets for one day at no extra charge, and

I had the joy of welcoming Tyler Ray into the Jarry Oldaker home less than twenty-four hours before returning to Costa Rica.

Part of the purpose of our visit to the States was for Jeffrey to be evaluated by a Duke University Hospital pediatric specialist, who prescribed twice daily nebulizer treatments to keep his asthma under control. The nebulizer and medications were not available in Costa Rica, but we were able to take them back with us. Also, since Paraíso was just a few miles from a rain forest with the highest annual precipitation in the whole country, Jeffrey's doctor in Cartago had insisted that we get a dehumidifier to help decrease the dampness in our home. We took one of them back on that trip, as well, and the combination of the nebulizations and a somewhat drier house did help to reduce the frequency of his asthma problems.

Our cleaning lady was convinced, though, that *her* remedy was the determining factor in his improvement. She had heard wondrous stories of people who suffered with asthma greatly benefitting from a certain species of black beetles about a quarter-inch long. One had to be sure to obtain both a male and female bug so that many baby bugs would be born. We kept the bugs in a plastic container and fed them nothing but peanuts in the shell, so they were completely sanitary. They ate the peanuts and used the shells as bedding. They did multiply rapidly, but they never outgrew their accommodations, since each day, six to eight bugs sacrificed their lives by being whirled to death in our blender, liquefied in a cup of milk mixed with a spoonful of peanut butter, and slurped down with great pleasure by Jeffrey. His pediatrician had assured us that the bugs would not harm and possibly could help him. His lungs certainly seemed healthier not long after we introduced the "buggy milkshakes" to his diet. In fact, if we forgot one of his daily doses, he would remind us, pointing to the container of crawling insects on the counter and pleading, "Buggies, please? More buggies!"

## 20

## Did You Invite Them to Church on Your Way Out the Door?

*September 1994 – October 1998, Second Term ~ Paraíso, Costa Rica*

The Paraíso neighborhood where we lived upon returning to Central America had changed a lot in the six years since the church was first built. Instead of a single dirt road lined with a haphazard collection of shacks patched together from uneven strips of drab-grey tin and mismatched boards, the area had evolved into a community of cement-block-and-plaster houses painted cheerful shades of brilliant blue, vivid orange, sunny yellow, hot pink, and bold green. The road was still dirt, branching now in many directions to accommodate the growth explosion that had occurred since the early days of the free land grant.

People who had settled more recently in the outlying areas were pitiably poor, and a Peace Corps friend of ours told us that this section held the dubious distinction of having the highest rates of child abuse and teenage pregnancy in all of Costa Rica. Drug dealing was rampant. On one occasion, the police even used our church entryway as a stakeout point for a drug raid. Rexie watched from the living room window, nervously fascinated, as the policeman lurking in the shadows just across our carport ran out of hiding to converge with two other officers at the house across the street from us.

Mothers and fathers robbed whatever they thought they could resell for enough cash for their next fix, and children learned to fend for themselves. Our neighbors had a tiny grocery store in their living room from which they sold such staples as bread, milk, eggs, and cheese. They told us of the boy who came one morning, wanting to trade an expensive watch for a loaf of bread to take home and share with his hungry little sisters. The watch was one that his parents had stolen before they disappeared on another several day binge, leaving no food in the house.

We were not immune to the dangers of living in such an environment. Our property was broken into more than twenty times during our second term (we finally lost track of the number when it got that high). The thieves took anything they could hoist over the wall, including Rex's recently purchased bike, which he rode to call on our parishioners. One night when Rexie was in the back bedroom, getting on his pajamas, he heard muffled thumping and bumping from the restroom on the far end of the still-under-construction Sunday school building. He fearfully alerted his daddy, who went to investigate. Thankfully,

Rex had to unlock the restroom door with a key, thus forewarning the would-be thieves before walking in on them. This gave them time to squeeze back through the small, as-yet-bar-less window through which they had entered. To our amazement, they had tried to steal a solid, very heavy, wooden door that was stored in there. It was teetering half in and half out over the top of the re-stroom wall, a few inches below the tin roof. He retrieved the door, but did not arrive in time to keep the crooks from making off with one of the five-gallon buckets of paint intended to brighten the walls.

Before we got our dog, unwelcome visitors would stealthily scale our wall in the wee hours of the morning and scout out the laundry area between the front and back sections of the house. Reaching through the parallel metal bars, they pulled clothes from the lines where I had hung them to dry. After the first time that this happened, I took to hanging the clothes only partway down the lines, making sure to leave well over an arm's length of space between the last article of clothing and the bars. That worked for a while, until the night when someone got smart and bent a long, heavy-duty wire into a hook on one end, giving sufficient extra reach to snag hitherto-unattainable treasures from the clotheslines. They also dragged out several pairs of shoes which were sitting on the floor a supposedly safe distance inside.

Shortly after that, we purchased King. He was a mongrel of questionable bloodline, but he was perfect for our needs as he had a broad face, massive chest, and deep throated, menacing bark. Fortunately, we were the only ones who knew that his bark was much worse than his bite. He quickly developed a reputation as a fierce watchdog, and on the couple of occasions that he es-caped our yard to dash gleefully up the street, exulting in his liberty, children and grown men alike scattered, hastily scaling the nearest wall to perch out of harm's way.

On one of King's bids for freedom, he took off after another dog with Rex running pell-mell after him. When the other dog sought safety in the house of his owners, total strangers to us, King barreled through the open door after him and sped across the living room into the kitchen, leaving Rex no option but to follow. The startled housewife screamed and threw the pot of water in her hands at the two fiercely snarling, snapping dogs, effectively breaking up their squabble. A subdued King and his chagrined master slunk out of the house after Rex's fervent apology to the outraged homeowner.

"Did you think to invite them to church before you left?" I asked, when he arrived back home and told me the story. "They probably have never had a pastor call on them like *that* before!"

With King's reputation firmly established, the number of unwelcome nighttime visitors to our yard dropped dramatically. But there were still a few persistent hopefuls who tried a different approach, scaling a neighbor's wall and climbing from there onto our roof. I do not remember how many times we awoke to sounds like footsteps on the corrugated tin rooftop. Rex would slip on a pair of jeans, unlock the laundry room gate, and step out into the carport. He would then lock the gate and throw the keys back through the bars, so that if someone tried to grab him, the villain would not be able to get inside to the boys and me. He would stand on the bumper of our van and hold a small hand mirror high enough to see if someone was on the roof. This allowed him to stay in the relative safety of the carport instead of having to walk clear out into the yard to get a good view of whoever might be on top. Sometimes he saw nothing; either it had been an animal or the person had heard Rex coming and retreated immediately. On occasions when a culprit realized that he had been discovered, he would scramble over the edge of the roof and leave the same way he had come, not staying around to cause any further problem.

One night, I had gotten up to use the restroom, and on my way back to bed I heard King growling. I stepped around the corner into the laundry area and saw our dog standing on the edge of the carport, ears cocked, hairs on his neck bristling, peering intently into the dark back yard. Walking over to the bars, I called to him quietly, but he ignored me, gaze fixed on something I could not see. I stood still for another minute, straining to see what had bothered him. Abruptly, a man stepped from the grass onto the carport. I SCREAMED!!! King erupted into ferocious barking, while Rex and Rexie, rudely awakened from peaceful sleep, jumped from their beds and came running to see what was going on. That is, Rexie *tried* to run, but in his haste to rescue Mommy, he got his jeans turned around backwards and came hopping down the hall, one leg in and one leg out as he tried to cram himself into them en route.

At that moment, we heard the neighborhood guard blowing his whistle as he rode by on his bicycle out front. Rex hurried to unlock our front gate and ask him to come in and help us search for the intruder. He refused to enter until we took King into the house, by which time the man had long since disappeared.

King proved his worth on yet another occasion, one Saturday morning when Rex and Rexie were doing our weekly shopping. My cleaning lady, Cecilia, was with me, giving our floors her customary thorough mopping. A man was digging a ditch for water lines near our new Sunday school rooms, so Rex left the back gate open to allow him free access to the yard, securely tying King to a stake behind the church. Not long before I expected my guys home, King went crazy, barking wildly and incessantly for no apparent reason. I walked outside to investigate. Just as I stepped around the corner, I saw a man's hand, from *in-side* the church building, pulling a freshly cut section of the corrugated tin wall back into place. I was indignant! Whoever he was, he had no business tearing up our church or being inside that building. I needed to go get him out! Too focused on the audacity of someone who would so blatantly disrespect and destroy church property, I stupidly disregarded the danger, running into our house for the church keys so I could see who was in there.

Unlocking the door, I pulled it open sharply, taking a step or two inside to look around. No one was in the sanctuary. I walked across the back of the church and poked my head into the soon-to-be-replaced Sunday school room, dimly illuminated by the sunlight from two small windows on the side wall. Still I saw no one. I *knew* the man had to be in there somewhere. The only place he could be hiding was under the long, low table where the children colored their lesson papers each Sunday morning. Stooping down, I peered under the table—and he immediately started scrambling out toward me. I ran for the door, screaming "N-O-O-O-O-O!!!!!!" so loudly that my throat hurt for over an hour afterwards. He ran after me, talking fast.

"It's all right! It's all right! My grandfather used to attend this church."

I am not sure why he thought that gave him the right to break in. Maybe he was hoping to steal some offering money. Perhaps he thought he could filch some songbooks and resell them. At any rate, his attempt to make a little extra cash came to naught. Hands shaking so badly that I almost dropped the keys, I unlocked the gate.

"Leave. Just leave!" I managed to say. Hearing a commotion behind me, I turned to see Cecilia, waving her broom, charging toward us. Running right behind her was six-year-old Benjie, brandishing my biggest sharp knife, intent on helping to save me. The man fled through the gate, and five minutes later my market men arrived back home, twelve-year-old Rexie vastly disappointed at missing out on the excitement. To this day, I cringe when I think of the foolish chance I took. Even if I had not wanted to wait for my husband and son to flush out the trespasser, there were at least half a dozen strong men working on a clogged sewer pipe in the street just outside our front gate who would have been glad to come to my aid. And then there was the matter of Benjie, butcher knife in hand, running out to lend his support. That was probably the most dangerous part of the whole scenario. "Fools rush in where angels fear to tread" was certainly true in my case. I was so glad that God had overruled my reckless lack of foresight and protected us all from harm.

In the midst of such darkness, God used us to help shine the light of the gospel into sin-blackened lives, bringing them hope with the message of deliverance from sin. Carmen was one of our young people who needed that hope. During her early teens, she taught the children's Sunday school class, and no one was more faithful to attend services and participate in all of the activities of the church. Then she started taking the bus to a public high school in the next town, where she fell in with the wrong crowd. Church attendance was forgotten as more and more of her time was taken up with questionable activities. One day, her parents visited us in tears, telling us that Carmen had left home to move in with a young man who lived several hours away, and begging us to visit her. During the long bus ride from Paraíso to Turrialba, Rex and I prayed for wisdom to know what to say to the young couple. Our hearts were broken as we sat with them in their minuscule dwelling, a hastily constructed, windowless, extra room on his parents' house, barely big enough for a double bed and nothing else. Carmen and Rolando listened courteously to our words, but by the looks on their faces, we knew that our efforts were futile. They walked with us back to the bus stop, chatting nonchalantly, seemingly indifferent to their need of God. Feeling like utter failures, we hated to report the results of our visit to her parents.

Then God stepped in! Across the next few months as we continued to pray, Carmen and Rolando moved back to Paraíso and shared an apartment with Rolando's cousin and his girlfriend. Rex and I kept visiting them. In December, all four of the housemates attended our church Christmas program. They sat quietly, respectfully, watching with interest as the children and youth presented their songs and skit. Silently, we prayed that God would touch their hearts. I do not ever remember a greater touch of God's Spirit on Rex than there was that evening as he told the old, old story with a message that is ever new: For God so loved the world that He sent His Son Jesus to save us from our sins. At the close of the message, Rex gave a simple invitation to those present to accept the Christmas gift of eternal life that God wanted to give them. With tears overflowing our eyes and joy overflowing our hearts, we jubilantly praised God as both couples knelt in the straw of our manger scene, confessing their sins and asking Jesus into their hearts.

Carmen, now pregnant with their first baby, moved back home with her parents until she and Rolando could complete the necessary paperwork to make their marriage official. In Costa Rica, if a couple is married in the Catholic Church, only that ceremony is needed. Any marriage, however, that takes place in an evangelical church is not legal unless an additional step is taken. First, the couple must obtain a license and have a civil ceremony in the courthouse. After that, they can lawfully live together as man and wife. Some choose to get their civil license and enjoy married life for some weeks or months while saving up until they can afford a public wedding in the church for their friends and family to attend. Others plan and save so that they can have the church ceremony within a few days of the civil one. Rex and I felt pleased and honored when Carmen and Rolando asked us to be the witnesses for their official courthouse marriage, shortly before we left the country for our second furlough.

Not until over a year later did they scrape the money together to pay for a church ceremony, complete with a beautiful white dress for the bride (borrowed from a friend), a suit for the groom (also borrowed), streamers and flowers to decorate the church, and most important of all, a full meal for all of the guests. We were thrilled that they timed it during one of our visits back to Costa Rica and asked Rex to be the officiating minister. All of our years of ministry seemed worthwhile as we remembered the calamitous start of their relationship a few years earlier and the part which God had allowed us to play in the establishment of this fine Christian home.

In July 2014, I received a letter from Carmen. By then Rolando and Carmen were the parents of five sturdy sons and had been pastoring the church in Paraíso for six years. She wrote:

> *Hello, Mama,*
>
> *May God richly bless you. I have been wanting to write this letter to someone who is so special in my life. Remember that I love you very much. You are always in my prayers and in my heart. I hope you can see us some day personally and we can hug each other and share what's been happening, and you can see how big my boys (your grandchildren) have grown. Please give my greetings to Brother Rex and tell him that we love him hugely. He also is in our hearts like a father.*
>
> *We love you,*
> *Carmen*

As proud and thankful spiritual parents, we share the Apostle John's sentiments when he said, "I have no greater joy than to know that my children walk in truth." To God be the glory, great things He has done!

# 21

## Neighborhood Nurse

*September 1994 – October 1998, Second Term ~ Paraíso, Costa Rica*

In Nicaragua, I delivered babies because the maternity hospital in Managua had such a poor reputation. In Costa Rica, although the local maternity hospital was noted for a lack of compassion in the attention given to its patients, the actual physical care was adequate. I only attended births in Paraíso as a labor coach, monitoring an expectant mother's progress so she could remain in the comfort of her own home for as long as possible before going to the hospital for the birth of her baby.

I was also the unofficial neighborhood nurse for our community. That made home-schooling our boys a challenge, since someone might knock on our door at any hour of the day, asking me to remove the wooden bead a child had stuffed too far up his nose, or give a series of shots to someone with an infection, or take out stitches, or furnish medical advice for this or that set of symptoms. As always, I found that showing compassion for someone who was hurting was a wonderful bridge to sharing about God's love and care.

Raquel was a little girl who lived next door to us and attended our Sunday school. Her four older siblings were in their late teens and early twenties. She was happy to acquire playmates closer to her own age when we moved in, and she visited our home frequently. Her mother, Isabel, was a troubled woman who wanted to serve God, but struggled with her past. It did not help that her attendance at church was sporadic and that her husband was not a Christian. He enjoyed going to parties on the weekend where he would indulge in a glass or two of something stronger than Kool-Aid, and he wanted his wife to go with him to these affairs. Isabel, as well as her family, knew that alcohol, even in small quantities, had an enormously greater impact on her than it did on most people. As little as a partial drink would set her off, turning an otherwise sweet, gentle lady into a raging, uncontrollable, wild woman.

One night, while my parents were down visiting us so that Papa could teach a series of holiness lectures at our church, we were abruptly startled awake by violent shrieking and banging coming from—somewhere. Jumping out of bed, I stepped into the hallway to see if I could tell where the noise originated. From the volume of the ruckus, it sounded as though whatever was happening was close by. The commotion awakened my mother as well, who excitedly followed me into the living room, declaring that surely someone had broken into our neighbor's house (a mere twenty-five yards from us) and was attacking and killing its occupants. Furtively peeking around the edge of the living room curtain, I squinted into the dark night. A little girl sat huddled on the edge of the sidewalk, and with shock, I recognized Raquel. Cautiously unlocking our door, I softly called out to her. She turned a tear-stained face my direction and gulped out the news that her mommy had been to a party, and when she got home, she started seeing demons and was trying to fight them off. Raquel's older sisters had sent her out of the house so she would not be injured.

Beckoning the trembling child to me, I hugged her close while Rex went next door to see if there was anything he could do to help, as well as to ask if Raquel could wait in our house until the situation in her own home was under control. Her father was apparently still at the party, but her sisters gladly consented to having Raquel stay with us and asked Rex to please come in and pray for their mother. The sight that met his eyes as he stepped into the back bedroom was indeed bizarre. Isabel lay on her back on the floor, writhing and screaming, her two strong, teenage sons kneeling on either side of her, struggling to hold her down. She had punched a hole in the bedroom wall with her bare fist, and the chaotic appearance of the room testified to the fight she had put up in her efforts to ward off the unseen spirits who haunted her alcohol-fogged brain. Nearly shouting to make himself heard above her ranting, Rex began to pray, pleading the covering of the blood of Jesus. Isabel initially became even more violent, but as Rex continued to entreat God for a healing touch on this sorely distressed woman, she gradually quieted and stopped struggling. Her screaming changed to sobbing, until she finally fell asleep, exhausted.

The next morning, she was piteously embarrassed and apologetic. For a while, she attended church faithfully, but gradually her visits tapered off. Unfortunately, the next time we were awakened in the middle of the night by wild shrieking from next door, we knew what was going on. Raquel was not sitting outside, so both Rex and I went over to her house. Isabel had locked herself in the bathroom. We could hear her maniacal raving, accompanied by loud crashing and the ominous sound of splintering glass. When her boys finally got the door off its hinges so we could get to her, she had torn the sink away from the wall and shattered it on the floor. She was lying in a puddle of blood among the jagged shards of porcelain. I crouched beside her, appalled at the deep, five-inch-long gash on the front of her leg. Although by this point she was no longer thrashing and yelling, I was hesitant to try to suture the wound there in her home, since I did not know how long the calm spell would last. I explained to her family that we needed to take her to the emergency room so that they could give her something to sedate her if necessary while the wound was cleaned and stitched. At first, she adamantly refused to go, but when I assured her that I would stay with her, she finally consented and allowed herself to be helped into our van.

I was not favorably impressed with the emergency room doctor's cursory cleaning and rapid stitching of her wound. He did not put a deeper layer of sutures into the muscle and then close the skin with individually tied off stitches, as I expected. Instead, he did a continuous, shallow, running stitch back and forth to pull the two edges together, finishing the job quickly and dismissing her. My fears that the repair job was less than adequate were proven true a few days later, when Isabel sent for me. I stared in disbelief at the angry red color of her leg, which was swollen to nearly twice its normal size. The running stitch was still intact, but barely, since the edges of her wound had separated and the suture looked ready to pop through the taut, shiny skin. Putrid, yellow pus oozed from deep inside.

There was nothing to do but remove the stitches, thoroughly clean the nauseating mess, and let the wound heal without the benefit of being pulled closed. I showed Isabel how to carefully clean the area and apply a chamomile poultice every day, and I kept a frequent check on her progress. Amazingly, by the time we left for our furlough the next year, what was once a deep, jagged crater on her leg had shrunk to a hardly noticeable, flat scar.

At the going away meal given for us by the church, Isabel was one of the first to stand when the host asked if anyone wanted to say words of appreciation. She thanked us for being her spiritual parents and showing her what God's love was like. As my mind flashed back to the nights when we had been jarred from our sleep by her frantic screams, I thanked God for the change He had made and for the part that my nurse's training had played in touching her heart.

The most dramatic use of that training helped to save a little boy's life and gave us forever friends in his family. Micol was a neighbor boy who lived across the street and sometimes attended our Sunday school. Our family was at the supper table the night his older sister rapped on our door.

"Mommy says can you please come over and help Micol?" she asked. "He's not feeling very good." The sister did not look particularly anxious nor seem to be in a hurry.

"I'll be right over as soon as we finish eating," I replied. "Will that be okay?" The girl nodded and walked back across the street. I returned to the table where we were just getting ready to serve birthday cake to my nephew Tyler, down with his mommy, my sister Priscilla, to pay us a visit. Tyler blew out the two candles as we sang a rollicking rendition of "Happy Birthday" in a mixture of English and Spanish. Before I could slide the cut pieces of cake onto our plates, another knock came on our door, this one louder and more insistent than the one a few minutes earlier. It was Micol's older brother, his eyes wide with fright.

"Mommy says can you please come right away!" he panted. "Micol can't breathe!"

Remembering that Micol, like our Jeffrey, was an asthmatic, I rushed to grab the nebulizer and a premeasured ampule of Jeffrey's breathing treatment before running across the street to their house. Pushing through the half-open door, I instantly knew why the older brother had looked so anxious. Propped up on the couch beside his mother, Micol's nostrils flared as he fought to get enough air into his oxygen-starved lungs. The sound of his harsh, ragged breathing filled the room, and his dusky face and blue lips testified to a losing battle. Quickly kneeling on the floor beside him and plugging in the nebulizer, I held the mask close to his face, letting the cloud of airway-opening vapor billow in front of his nose and mouth. But Micol's lungs were so clamped down that he could not breathe deeply enough for the medication to get to where it needed and go to work. He slumped over, his face turning a deeper shade of blue.

"We have got to get him to the hospital NOW!" I urged his mother. "My husband will take you in our van." There was no ambulance service available, and at this hour of the night, finding a taxi in time would be next to impossible. Telephone lines didn't even exist in our section of the neighborhood, and the nearest payphone was across the street and up the road, three blocks away. By the time someone could run there to make a phone call, even if a taxi were dispatched immediately, it could be half an hour or more before one arrived.

I hurried back to our house to prepare an injection for Micol and to ask Rex to get the van backed out and ready to go. On more than one occasion, Jeffrey had needed a steroid shot to open up his airways. It usually seemed to happen at night or on the weekend when his doctor's office was closed, so we kept a vial of the medicine on hand for such emergencies. I knew that if Micol did not get some breathing relief soon, he was going to die. Thanking God that I had the medicine on hand, I quickly drew the correct dose into a syringe and ran with it out to the van. Laying Micol across my knees, I plunged the needle into his hip muscle, injecting the life-saving liquid. Rex put the van in gear, and we started on a desperate race for the hospital in Cartago, three miles away.

Now, three miles may not seem like a very great distance, and if one were traveling on a typical highway in the States, it would not be. But this road was generously scarred with potholes, necessitating watchful maneuvering back and forth across the road to miss them. As our van careened wildly through the darkness, dodging around and between the holes, flashing its lights at slower-moving vehicles before zipping around them, I tightly cradled Micol in my arms, bracing myself and praying out loud, begging God to help us make it safely to the hospital in time.

God answered that prayer. By the time we whipped around the final corner and up to the emergency room entrance, the injection had started to work. Micol was promptly settled into a bed and hooked up to oxygen. Now he was able to breathe enough for the nebulized medication to do some good, and after updating the ER doctor on what I had done and making sure that our small neighbor was going to be all right, Rex and I left.

"That was *fun!*" Rex exclaimed, as we climbed into the van.

"Fun?" I said in surprise. "I was scared to death!"

"Oh, well, of course, I was worried about Micol," he replied. "And I was praying for him too. But I've always wanted a legitimate chance to drive like that, and now I finally had it!"

Thankfully, Rex had no more opportunity to put into practice his ambulance-piloting skills. Time and time again, however, we were given a chance to reach into homes that would otherwise have been closed to the gospel, simply by showing people that we cared about their everyday concerns and problems.

I had no idea when we left for our second furlough that God would open a new door of missionary ministry a few years down the road that would bring me the excitement of several other wild ambulance rides and the thrill of using more extensively the midwifery part of my studies. As He has done throughout my life, he guided me along that turn in the path when I arrived there, letting me see no farther ahead than I needed to at the moment. One of my favorite hymns, by John W. Peterson, states it well: "Jesus led me all the way, led me step by step each day." Please join me in Part Two, as I share my memories of those steps.

# BABIES, BULLETS, and BEE STINGS

## MEMORIES OF A MISSIONARY MIDWIFE

### Part II

———

After two terms of full-time missionary work totaling nearly nine years in Costa Rica and Nicaragua, our family returned to the United States in 1998. In the fall of 1999, the Lord led us to Penn View Bible Institute and Christian Academy in Penns Creek, Pennsylvania. Rex was hired as an institute instructor and three years later became the head of the new Hispanic Studies Program in the missions division. I taught Spanish and health in the high school and worked as the Director of Student Health Services for both the academy and the institute. We felt blessed to still be involved in missions through helping to train a younger generation who were hearing the call to the whitened harvest fields. God also allowed us the privilege of traveling back to Costa Rica on various occasions to work with our people there. Rex II, Benjamin, and I were able to go on several tract team trips to Mexico as well, helping to fulfill my father's vision of distributing one million gospel tracts in Mexico City.

An exciting new area of ministry opened in August of 2001, when J. Stevan Manley, president of Evangelistic Faith Missions (with which Steve Hight and Friends of Missions merged that year), asked if I could go to Honduras for two weeks to help in their maternity clinic in San Luis. During my stay, I fell totally in love with the national nurses and the excitement of working in a setting where I got to use a set of nursing skills that I did not have many opportunities to practice in the States. Often, I was thrust out of my comfort zone. Frequently, I was reminded of my dependency on God and my sufficiency in Him alone.

During the thirteen years since 2001, I have made ten more missions trips to Honduras, three to Haiti, and three to Costa Rica, ranging from one-and-a-half to ten weeks in length. The remaining chapters of this book are taken almost entirely from the "Honduran Happenings" and "Helping in Haiti" e-mails that I sent back to relatives and friends in the States during those travels. They will give you the opportunity to feel firsthand the exhilaration, perplexity, anxiety, frustration, hilarity, exhaustion, and contentment that fueled my pen. They will show the faithfulness of our all-sufficient God, as His strength and grace proved time and again to be enough for my needs. I pray that they will encourage you to trust in the Lord with all your heart and lean not upon your own understanding. As you acknowledge Him in all your ways, He will surely direct your paths, just as He has always done and I am certain will continue to do with mine.

## 22

## Hello From Honduras: A Letter to Home

*August 14, 2001 ~ San Luis, Honduras*

*Dear Rex, Rex II, Benjie, and Jeffrey,*

*After two days of the oppressively humid warm welcome of San Pedro Sula, where I landed on August 1, I had no trouble adjusting to the higher altitude and more moderate (although definitely not cool) climate of the mission station here in San Luis, Honduras. In the twelve days of my stay, I have worked one hundred twenty hours. During that time I delivered six baby boys, took stitches out of a little fellow's head and a young man's hand, and treated a middle-aged woman in a severe asthmatic crisis as well as an elderly man with high blood sugar who both needed IV fluids, oxygen, various injection, and treatments. I performed pregnancy tests and stitched up two machete wounds. I cared for a man who had been hit in the face with a falling tree branch and came in with a terrible nosebleed, which dropped his blood pressure from 124/84 to 86/50. He had three bags of IV fluids, plus Vitamin K and other medications, in the five hours it took for his bleeding to finally stop. I gave intravenous rehydration to an older girl with nausea and vomiting and a baby boy with diarrhea. I wrapped and sterilized many packs of instruments, including the one that had to be resterilized after I opened it and found a nest of LOTS of little tiny ants inside. I sold numerous medicines from our small pharmacy. I gave a tetanus injection to a little girl who came in with a nasty dog bite on her leg, and I helped clean and bandage her wound. That is just a partial list of my experiences!*

*I thought you might be interested to hear details about some of my patients. For instance, Sunday evening a young woman in labor arrived, progressing rapidly. When I checked her, something seemed not quite right. However, I did not figure out what was wrong until Miriam, the night nurse, came on at 10:00 p.m. to relieve me. Then we realized that the baby was coming foot first instead of head first. A single footling breech delivery in this clinic, without sufficient backup emergency measures for a possible stuck head and suffocated baby, was not something that either of us wanted to handle. So we told her boyfriend, who has three or four other women as well and a whole tribe of children by them, that he needed to make arrangements to get her to the nearest hospital. Interestingly, that type of transportation is the family's responsibility, not the clinic's. He did not have the money that the ambulance required and asked if she could just wait until morning, I suppose thinking that he would be able to find more easily a willing friend to take her in a car then.*

*I don't know if he ever understood the seriousness of the situation, or how much he even cared whether the mother or the baby lived. Still, he did finally convince the Red Cross ambulance to come, even though he could not pay them. When they left at 11:30 p.m. on the dark, rough, two-hour-and-fifteen-minute ride to the nearest hospital, I was not at all optimistic for a good outcome. Miriam and I had prayer together for the girl, then I went to bed for a few hours before my next shift. Sadly, we heard several days later that at the hospital, instead of a doctor doing a cesarean section, they let the baby be born naturally. Of course, the head got trapped and the baby asphyxiated, which was the very thing that we were trying to avoid.*

*One morning I rode with resident missionaries Tom and Sharon McKnight and two San Luis health department nurses to some outlying villages for a vaccination campaign. We forded a stream four different times before arriving at a tiny, two-room, block-walled school in the jungle just a few miles from town. Even as relatively close as that distance is, it is a prohibitively long way for families without a vehicle to travel for immunizations. The health department nurses go every few months to take vaccines to these extremely poor people who would not otherwise receive them. One of the nurses and I stayed at the school while the others drove seven kilometers farther on to a second village. The two of us vaccinated fifty-five children and eight mothers in just a few hours. Among all of those, I only saw two people with shoes. Most of them wore simple rubber flip-flops on their feet; some were barefoot. I especially remember a thirty-year-old mother of eight children and wondered what her life must be like. Without a doubt, she lives in a small mud-and-stick-walled house with a dirt floor, cooks over an open fire, carries water from the stream for washing and drinking, and has no electricity. It is so easy to take for granted the luxuries that we think of as everyday necessities of life in America. Most of these women could not even imagine having such conveniences.*

*By the way, you would like the prices for medical services at the clinic. A baby delivery, including all materials and medications plus a twenty-four-hour stay with nursing care for mother and baby, costs 400 lempiras, which is right at $27.00. The charge for nonmaternity hospital admission and nursing care is $5.50 a day, plus medications and supplies. The clinic does not supply food, so family members bring in the patient's meals.*

*When I removed the sutures from the little boy who fell out of a car, it cost his family 65¢. The charge to have a minor injury like that repaired is $6.00. If the wound is deeper and more extensive, like the man's hand I sewed up a few days ago, it costs $12.00. On a Sunday afternoon, the single nurse on duty might have* *to stitch up as many as five serious machete wounds after an alcohol-provoked fight, all too common after a weekend of drinking.*

*The village children have regular problems with abscesses that form after a particularly nasty, biting* Torsalo *fly lays her eggs under their skin. By the time the hatched worms grow for several weeks, they can each be as big around as your little finger. At that point, the wound is full of pus and is extremely painful. Abscess drainage is normally $5.00. I don't know if removal of the worm costs extra.*

*The elderly gentleman who has been in twice for his series of penicillin injections, one every twelve hours, has not yet paid the 40¢ per shot that he owes, but probably will settle up his bill after all eight of the injections are given. The $3.20 charge may be difficult for him to pay with the drought this year that has caused a poor coffee harvest.*

*It is all a far cry from nursing in the United States, but I am thoroughly enjoying the experience. I stay in a house just behind the clinic, on the campus of the Bible institute with its twenty-one boarding students. The view of the mountain behind the institute is gorgeous! The McKnights here in San Luis and Dr. Don Smith's family in San Pedro Sula have been very kind and helpful. We have enjoyed sharing mutual missionary life experiences.*

*I need to close and get to bed. Thank you so much for your prayers during my stay. I am very conscious of my need of the Lord's help in my work here, and He has been faithful to meet that need. I love you and miss you!* Hasta luego *(So long),* Hannah/Mommie

\* \* \* \* \* \* \* \* \* \*

Thus read my initial "Honduran Happenings" e-mail, sent to my family back in the States two weeks into my first trip to the *Clínica de Maternidad Luz y Vida*. Over the next thirteen years, I would write dozens of these updates, chronicling more than a cumulative six months of time spent delivering babies, digging out bullets, sewing up machete wounds, tending bee stings, and experiencing other interesting escapades. But at that point, I had no idea that this visit would be followed by many. In fact, when I was asked to go to Honduras in 2001, it was a last minute deal. Rex already had a trip to Costa Rica scheduled for the same time, so that summer, our family of five was in five different locations: Rex and Hannah on separate mission journeys to Central America, Rex II working with a contractor in Lexington, North Carolina, Benjie romping in the woods with cousins at his Uncle Steve and Aunt Lois Hill's house in New Bethlehem, Pennsylvania, and Jeffrey climbing trees and going fishing with his adopted grandparents, Arizona and Edith Smith in Louisville, Ohio.

When he realized our scattered-across-the-country state of affairs, Evangelistic Faith Missions president J. Stevan Manley chuckled, "We generally try to keep our missionary families together; I'm not sure what happened this time!" Whatever had happened, it was the beginning of many happy summers of family ministry alongside Honduran missionaries and nationals who quickly became dear friends. With both the Bible school and clinic located on the same property, Rex and I were able to work in our respective areas of training, he with the students and I with the nurses.

I was both intrigued and gratified to learn that the clinic was mainly responsible for a drop in the infant mortality rate from nearly fifty percent to less than fifteen percent in San Luis and the surrounding areas. I felt privileged to join the ranks of the dedicated Christian nurses who had helped to make that a reality. In fact, the clinic's first-class reputation brought women from many miles away to have their babies there, knowing that they would be given compassionate, quality care at any hour of the day or night.

Of course, getting there from a great distance away could prove rather challenging, especially if it was in the middle of the night. I remember the jolt of adrenaline that I felt around three o'clock one morning when the front doorbell rang and I looked out the peephole to see a man with a pistol in his hand, standing on the porch. His very pregnant wife was bent over in the shadows of the yard behind him, rubbing her feet in the dew-dampened grass, trying rather unsuccessfully to scrape off the layers of mud that had liberally coated her shoes and ankles during their lengthy walk through the darkness. "I had to carry the gun to scare off the critters," the man matter-of-factly informed me, thrusting his weapon into his pocket. I thought it best not to ask him whether he had the two-legged or the four-legged kind of critters in mind. If *I* had been the woman in labor, the clinic would have needed an *extremely* good reputation to convince me it was worth trudging through the darkness over a perilous mountain path even for thirty minutes, let alone for two hours, as she had done.

When Dr. Don Smith arrived early in the afternoon of August the 14th to pick me up for the return trip to San Pedro and my flight out the next morning, I was in the delivery room, coaching thirty-eight-year-old Olivia Fernández through her last few contractions and the joyful birth of her fourth baby, a seven-pound, one-ounce, beautiful little boy, at 2:58 p.m. It was the fiftieth baby I had delivered since the long-ago days when the unexpected arrival of my niece Jamie in her parents' bedroom lit the fire of my interest in midwifery. I wondered what paths my fourteen classmates had traveled in the fourteen years since we parted ways after our commencement as the Medical University of South Carolina's Nurse-Midwifery Class of 1987. I was quite certain that none of them could top the satisfaction I was feeling with the path that God had chosen for me, and I could not wait to come back again! How true is the message of the chorus from "Submission," one of my favorite missionary songs, by R. R. Forman:

*Not what I wish to be, not where I wish to go;*
*For who am I, that I should choose my way.*
*The Lord shall choose for me! Tis better, far, I know.*
*So let Him bid me go, or stay.*

There is no satisfaction as great as being in the center of God's will and nothing sweeter than the rewards of doing His bidding!

# There's Been an Accident Up on the Mountain

*July 13, 2003 ~ San Luis, Honduras*

"You know it's going to be a hot, humid day when you wake up at 6:00 a.m., and just getting out of bed causes you to break out in a sweat," declared one of my students from the States. True as that was, not all of our sweating was connected with the tropical climate. Sometimes it had to do with the seriousness of a patient's condition when he showed up at the clinic for care. Such was the case on the Sunday morning midway through our six-and-a-half week stay during the summer of 2003, the first time that we went to Honduras as a family. Joy DeLong, a missions student from Penn View Bible Institute, flew down with us to fulfill her six-week internship requirement. Anita Kratz, who had graduated from high school with our son Rex II, joined us July 1-9, hoping to get in on some interesting clinic experiences.

I have said many times during our summers in Honduras that I do not *wish* for someone to have a major accident or illness just so they have to go to the clinic, but if anything *is* going to happen, let it be when I can get in on it! Plenty of things happened during those weeks; unfortunately for Anita's purposes, the most interesting ones took place after she left. She did experience the birth of one of the nine babies born on my shifts and had the fun of giving one her first bath. She became adept at cutting and folding gauze bandages, a mundane but nevertheless important chore. The clinic pharmacy sells individually packaged and sterilized 4 x 4 gauze pads, but all of the gauze that is used for inpatient wound care and baby deliveries is purchased by the yard. During the quiet spells between patients, the secretary and nurse on duty spend hours cutting the gauze into strips, folding it to the proper size, packing it into wide-mouthed, half-gallon-sized metal canisters, and sterilizing it in the little autoclave.

Anita learned the skill of taking vital signs: locating and counting a patient's pulse in his wrist, wrapping a blood pressure cuff and listening for the thump, thump of the heartbeat at the bend of the arm with a stethoscope, and finding the silver line of mercury in a glass thermometer after it has been under someone's tongue or arm for the proper amount of time. Calculating the correct dose of medication based on the patient's weight and age gave her a chance to keep her math skills sharp, as did figuring the exact number of drops per minute that a bag of IV fluids should flow when the tubing delivers one cc of liquid per twenty drops, and the patient needs, say, one liter in six hours of time. (Let me see, that's 1000 cc's divided by six hours, divided by sixty minutes in an hour, times 20 drops per cc, equals 56 drops per minute, or almost one a second. Did you do the math right? Great job!) Once she knew the number of drops per minute, the only challenge was keeping a vigilant eye on the trickling medication and adjusting the roller clamp on the tubing to increase or decrease the drip rate as needed.

Anita became an expert at the procedure for giving an injection, especially after multiple practice sessions with an orange. An orange can be stuck numerous times with the same syringe without any fear that you will contaminate or harm it. It can handle having a lot of liquid injected into it as well, but at some point it becomes waterlogged. When that happens, each time you push in another dose of water, the orange will squirt tiny fountains into the air from the other holes that have already been made in its skin. Thankfully, I have never seen that occur with a person.

Before letting her use her newly developed shooting skill on a real live patient, I wanted to be sure that she had the whole process down pat. I was the only available guinea pig, so just before our shift ended one afternoon, Anita drew some sterile saline into a syringe and injected it into my hip. Her technique was flawless. As we left the clinic, we decided to have some fun. Limping exaggeratedly, I crossed the yard to our house, rubbing my hip. We had gotten off work just in time to join Rex, Joy, and our boys for a visit to one of the local churches. I made a great show of struggling to lift my "sore" leg up into our vehicle, unaware that I had an extra person besides family in the audience. Luis, one of the two day guards, walked over and leaned in the window.

"What's wrong?" he asked me with concern.

"Umm, well, I had Anita practice giving shots on me," I told him, thinking to have a minute or two of fun before confessing that my limping was only an act, to play a prank on my family.

"Let me pray with you before you leave," he immediately offered. He bowed his head and proceeded to ask God to go with us to the service and give us safety on the trip. "And dear Lord, please touch Hermana Ana's (Sister Hannah's) injured leg, and make it well," he asked. Anita and I struggled to keep from snickering as he earnestly finished his prayer. The moment that he said "Amen," we both burst out laughing. He blinked his eyes and stared at us in surprise, a slightly hurt look on his face. I hastened to explain that I was not really in pain, and we were not making fun of him; my hobbling walk had just been a joke. In a moment he started to smile, but not very broadly. To this day, I do not know if he totally understood that the whole thing was a not-very-well-thought-out hoax. At any rate, I doubt that he would have trusted Anita to give *him* a shot after that.

Ironically, the nine days in the clinic after Anita flew home were the busiest of our entire stay. On Thursday, July 10, a pitiably poor couple arrived from a distant village with their five-month-old baby, the youngest of seven children. Sadly, they had waited too long to bring him for help. The little fellow's parched skin, sunken eyes, vomit-stained shirt, and foul-smelling, diarrhea-soaked diaper all bore mute testimony to the losing battle he was fighting with a stomach bug. When children come to the clinic for rehydration, it is a good sign if they have enough energy to put up a fight when we start the IV. Their child was so dehydrated that he neither whimpered nor stirred as one of the other nurses and I tried multiple times, without success, to slip a tiny, #24 gauge IV catheter into a vein. When his eyes rolled back in his head, we finally admitted defeat and sent him on the long ride to the nearest major hospital for a vein cutdown, the emergency procedure of exposing a vein surgically and then inserting an IV cannula under direct vision. I hugged his mother tightly as I prayed with the family before they left. There was no guarantee the baby would survive the trip, but there was nothing more that we could do for him.

Half an hour after I started my next shift, twenty-nine-year-old Lourdes Ixsabel arrived, her largely protruding abdomen attesting to a good-sized baby inside. Four hours and much pacing back and forth in the hallway later, she was completely dilated. As big as her baby appeared to be, it did not surprise me that he descended oh, so S-L-O-W-L-Y as she pushed. What was unusual was that her bulging bag of waters, which I tried twice to rupture with pincers to help speed up the process, stubbornly resisted my efforts to puncture it.

Lourdes strained once more. As my gloved fingers explored the perimeter of the bag of waters, something suddenly felt different. Puzzled, I ran my finger along the back margin once more. That was strange ... now it felt like *two* amniotic sacs, squeezed tightly side by side, with a ridge down the center between them. What in the world? Suddenly, I realized with dismay that the "bag of waters" I had been doing my best to pop was actually a smooth, shiny baby's bottom! This little one was coming seat first instead of head first, and I knew that we were in for trouble. No way did I want to do a breech delivery without an extra pair of hands (preferably experienced ones) available.

I grabbed the walkie-talkie on the corner of the counter and called the night guard. "Please go to Ana's house (the nurse who lived closest to the clinic) and tell her I need her *right away*," I directed urgently. "Tell her to hurry!" I am sure the fact that it was 4:00 a.m. helped Ana to realize that whatever the emergency, if I was rousting her out of bed at that hour, the need was indeed pressing, and she arrived even more quickly than I had dared to hope. Unfortunately, she had only been out of nursing school a short while and had no experience with breech deliveries. Nevertheless, throughout the next hour she helped immensely by checking the baby's heartbeat with each contraction, pulling over the oxygen tank and hooking up the mask and tubing for Lourdes to use when the heartbeat dropped briefly into the nineties, and assisting her to push effectively. And we both prayed ... many times.

At 5:13 a.m. the baby emerged into my expectant, nervous hands. One corner of my brain noted the fact that he was, indeed, a hefty size. The rest of my brain yelled a silent alarm as I rushed his white, limp body to the infant warmer where Ana worked feverishly to revive him. Five minutes of oxygen and stimulation later, he was pink and breathing on his own. "Thank you, God, that the baby is all right!" I praised aloud, immeasurably relieved and grateful.

When we weighed and measured him, it was no big surprise that he tipped the scales at eight pounds, four ounces. What did surprise me was comparing the statistics in the clinic logbook for the twenty-one other breech births in the past few years. Most of them were five or six pounders; this was the second largest. Almost certainly he would have been delivered by cesarean section had he been born in the States. I thought of the afternoon a few days before when I sat down with my old midwifery textbook and reviewed the essential steps for delivery of a breech baby. I had no idea at the time that I would need that review so soon, but our omniscient heavenly Father knew it and prompted my urge to pick up the book, making sure that I would be prepared when the need arose. Don't you love looking back and realizing the hand of God in such a circumstance?

The next morning, July 13th, I started my shift at 5:00 a.m. Another baby was born a mere five minutes after my arrival. I had just gotten the new mother and baby cleaned up and settled into the postpartum ward when the guard nonchalantly strolled in. "There's been an accident up on the mountain," he informed me. "A truck's brakes went out, and it rolled off the edge of the mountain. They will be bringing the wounded here." And with that, he casually walked back out, leaving me staring after him in dismay. My mind jumped into high gear, conjuring up vivid images and possible scenarios. An announcement like that would be nerve-racking any morning, but especially *this* morning, since it was Sunday and I would not have any extra assistance from our very capable cleaning lady and secretary, should I need it. With no details about how many would be coming or what their injuries were, I did not even know how to prepare. Fortunately, Joy was not scheduled to teach a Sunday school class that morning. I called Rex on the walkie-talkie, asking him to send her over. Shortly after, two trucks pulled up to the porch and discharged their cargo of seven battered, bleeding accident victims.

Four of the seven were children. A two-year-old had been sitting on his mother's lap in the truck cab, and both mother and child appeared to be all right. The others, an eight-year-old boy with a badly scraped forearm, a three-year-old girl with an alarmingly large knot on her forehead and blood oozing from both her ears and her nose, and a four-year-old girl with a jagged gash on her forehead and a terribly swollen jaw, had all been riding in the open pickup bed and were thrown out when the truck rolled. A seventy-two-year-old gentleman, grandpa to some of the children, had also been riding in the back. His grossly swollen ankle looked broken, and my probing fingers discovered three lacerations on his scalp. The twenty-five-year-old driver had his window down, and when the truck tumbled, his body slammed up against his door, throwing his left arm out the window where it took a nasty mauling as the truck slid along the gravel road.

What to do first? Thankfully, one of the drivers who brought the injured unfortunates to me was able to take those who needed it on to Santa Bárbara, site of the nearest hospital, for a more advanced level of care than our little clinic could provide. While I quickly sutured the four-year-old's head wound, Joy cleaned up the eight-year-old's scraped arm, and we sent all of the children and their mother off for further evaluation. At one point in my scurrying from one person to the other, I rushed past the chair where the elderly gentleman was sitting and tripped over his injured leg, which he had stuck straight out in front of him. He only groaned softly, but I am sure it must have hurt like crazy, and I felt terrible.

With the most critically wounded on their way to the hospital, the pace settled down considerably. Thankfully, no local patients had arrived in need of care, so I could concentrate on the two remaining accident victims. Painstakingly picking through his hair, I cleaned the grit out of the grandpa's head wounds and put in the stitches needed to close them. His ankle would need x-rays, but the most pressing problem was taken care of.

By this point, several hours had passed and church was long since out. I had saved the driver until last since his arm, although not actively bleeding, was so mangled that I knew cleaning and suturing it would be a major undertaking. Emotionally wrung out from the stress of his own injuries and his remorse over the fate of his passengers, he slumped against the wall, waiting his turn. Most of his lacerations were shallow, but nearly the entire top layer of skin from his elbow to his knuckles had been chewed up and spit out by the unyielding roadbed. It took a lot of meticulous probing and rinsing to remove the embedded grit before I could repair the places where a couple of sharp stones had ripped deep slices into his muscle. I was very thankful to have Joy there to hold the swollen wound edges together so I could properly stitch them. When he was finally patched up to my satisfaction, the driver pulled out his wallet to pay the entire bill for all seven people. Amazingly, his cost for everything, including suturing, antibiotics, and pain medication, came to only 630 *lempiras,* or $36.42. Too bad the truck could not be repaired so cheaply!

## 24

## Missions of Mercy

*June and July 2005 ~ San Luis, Honduras*

The walkie-talkie in our living room crackled to life with the voice of the nurse in the clinic just across the airstrip from the house where we were living during our current six-week visit to Honduras. "Hermana Ana, would you be able to start an IV on someone in the neighborhood? I can't leave the clinic, but it needs done before the end of my shift." Just eleven days into our trip, I was definitely experiencing the variety of occurrences that make missionary nursing so interesting. From my early-morning baby deliveries at 4:46 a.m. on Wednesday and 2:44 a.m. on Sunday, to the eighty-four-year-old man who suffered a heart attack and was brought in, hollering and thrashing with pain, to the ten-year-old little girl who sliced her hand with a razor blade and was so brave while I put in the six stitches that she needed yesterday, this was nothing like my part-time pediatric nursing job in the States.

I headed over to the clinic to gather my supplies and then followed the little barefoot guide who trotted ahead of us up the dirt road. Benjamin carried the plastic sack with alcohol-soaked cotton swabs, latex gloves, bag of intravenous fluid, tubing, tape, and several sizes of IV catheters. Accompanying us were Amanda Byler, a nursing student from Saginaw Valley State University in Michigan, and Jennifer Key, a student from God's Bible School and College in Cincinnati, Ohio. Amanda, who has gone on to become a Certified Registered Nurse Practitioner and serve on numerous two-week to six-month medical mission trips to the Dominican Republic, was working with me in the clinic to gain practical experience between her second and third years of nursing school. Jennifer was down to fulfill her six-week internship requirement as a missions major, and as such, she had been occupied more in the Bible institute under Rex's leadership. However, she had also spent time observing and lending an extra pair of helpful hands in the clinic and was happy to have this opportunity to share in what sounded as though it would be a unique cultural event.

Miriam told me that my patient was ninety-year-old *doña* Víctor, who lived in a tiny stick-and-dirt-walled house only a few hundred yards from the clinic. She had been spry and feisty until she fell and broke her hip over a year ago. Since then, she could not be out and about to beg as she was used to doing, but she was getting by with the kindness of neighbors and the help of a preteen granddaughter who lived with her and cooked her meals. Two weeks earlier, she had started vomiting nearly everything she ate and was now so dehydrated that she could not have made it to the clinic for help even if she *had* possessed the $4.20 that is charged per day for admission and nursing care.

As we stepped from the bright, sunlit street into the dimness of her home, my eyes gradually adjusted to take in the only furniture, a simple wooden table and two chairs, and the unpainted, cracked plaster wall behind them that was adorned with numerous pictures of the Virgin Mary. Some sheets of heavy, yellow plastic were tacked onto a bare frame of narrow upright slats of wood tied to horizontal cross pieces, which divided the one room into dining and sleeping areas. Glancing to the left, I noticed a chicken standing in the doorway of the dirt-floored cooking area attached to the house. Nearly a third of the space in the tiny kitchen was taken up by a large pile of sticks to fuel the "stove," a two-feet-wide, waist-high, cement slab in the far corner. A fire was crackling under the round "stovetop," a metal lid from the top of a fifty-five gallon drum. Sitting on the lid were a dented tea kettle and a two-quart pot, apparently all the cookware that she owned.

Two of the woman's daughters were waiting for us, and they motioned for me to push aside the flap of plastic and enter the bedroom area. A single naked lightbulb illuminated a shriveled figure lying on a wood frame bed with no mattress, only a thin piece of foam providing a slight bit of padding. A bright-pink plastic bedpan was tucked under the bed, definitely a necessity for this pitiful bit of a woman, since trips to the outhouse were without question not an option in her extremely weakened condition. As I looked at her emaciated arms, I knew that I would be using the smallest gauge IV needle in my bag. She nodded briefly as I explained what I was going to do, but kept her eyes closed the whole time I was working. Thankfully, Miriam had thought to include a two-inch-wide roll of bandaging material in the bag of supplies. I cut a long enough strip of the white cloth to thread through the top of the bag of fluid, then took my shoes off and stepped up onto the bed, straddling *doña* Victor while I hooked the improvised hanger onto a nail high in the wall, leaving the bag swinging at the proper height above her arm for gravity to carry the contents into her parched system. Before I oh-so-carefully eased the needle under her dry, fragile skin, Amanda and Jennifer helped me pray that I would get the vein on the first try, and the three of us sent grateful thanks heavenward when the Lord answered our petition. I rolled the valve on the tubing open and adjusted the flow rate to the correct number of drops per minute. Promising to return later in the day to check on her, I stepped out into the street, blinking back tears as I thought of the sharp contrast between what I had just seen and the general living conditions in affluent America.

That evening after Rex preached at the local church, he stopped by with me on our walk home from the service to see how things were going with my patient. Over the next few weeks as she continued to weaken, I went back ten more times, giving her injections, starting another IV, reading Scripture to her, and praying with her. She indicated on more than one occasion that she wanted to belong to Jesus. How I hoped and prayed that her pain-fogged mind was able to understand enough to turn to Him in repentance and faith!

On our last visit, we arrived around 11:00 p.m., after I finished my evening shift at the clinic. The street outside her door was filled with people, but this time there was no wasted form on the bed inside. The slats of wood with their plastic covering that had divided the room were gone, and a casket stood in the middle of the floor, with one of her grown grandsons crouched over it, wailing miserably. Another grandson, one of our Bible institute students, nodded a greeting and quietly ushered us to front row seats in the mismatched chairs that had been hastily gathered from here and there and grouped in front of the coffin. He smiled gravely at us and thanked us for coming. I could not help but compare the way he was handling his grandmother's passing with the wretched despair being demonstrated by the other grandson, who was not a Christian and could not have known of our hope that his grandmother had indeed repented and asked Jesus to live in her heart.

The last verse of W. A. Ogden's song, "Seeking the Lost," runs through my mind:

*Thus I would go on missions of mercy,*
*Following Christ from day unto day:*
*Cheering the faint, and raising the fallen;*
*Pointing the lost to Jesus, the way.*

I remember other "missions of mercy" during those six weeks. My heart still aches when I think of the sixteen-year-old boy who was going full tilt on his bicycle down the dirt road not far from us when his front tire slammed into a large stone, abruptly stopping his progress and flipping him with terrific force off the racing bike and down onto the road. He was brought in unconscious, his face smashed and bleeding, his nose so flattened that his respirations were loud snoring noises. After we stabilized him, I prayed with his father, who stood helplessly and unashamedly weeping as the ambulance volunteers loaded up his son for the trip to the Santa Bárbara hospital. Brokenly, the father thanked me for the prayer before he climbed into the back of the ambulance to accompany his son. Unfortunately, we learned the next day that the lad did not survive his crash. That evening, I gripped my own sixteen-year-old son

Benjamin in an extra big hug, overcome by gratitude to have him alive and well and by sorrow over the other family's loss of one so young and full of potential.

I was more emotional with Benjie than I might otherwise have been because of his accident shortly before that, on the afternoon that he took Jeffrey and Jennifer for a jaunt on a four-wheeler belonging to Daniel Melton, the resident missionary at the time. The young people liked to speed off at a fast clip down the runway, which stretches from the clinic gate clear to the end of the mission property and ends in an abrupt drop-off at the edge of a deep ravine. Benjie did not start slowing down soon enough and had to make a sharp turn to avoid shooting off the end of the runway. They flipped on the turn, and Benjie was pinned under the four-wheeler, with gas spewing out of the holes in the gas cap. He was able to turn the machine off, but he could not get his leg out. Jeffrey and Jennifer were thrown clear, Jennifer doing several spectacular somersaults and landing on the very edge of the precipice. Adrenaline surging at seeing his big brother in danger, Jeffrey hoisted the heavy vehicle enough for Benjie to free his leg. The commotion brought Daniel and some of the Bible institute students on the run, and they got another four-wheeler and transported all three of them to the clinic so I could check them out. Aside from some decent-sized scrapes and bruises, no one was seriously injured, although Jennifer stayed in bed most of the next day, saying that the only things that did not hurt to move were her eyes and toes. We shuddered to think of what could have been if they had dropped off the runway into the ravine and thanked the Lord over and over for protecting them.

Then there was Ricxi, another sixteen-year-old, who arrived at the clinic on July 3 at 2:00 a.m., seven-and-a-half centimeters dilated and having strong contractions. Her boyfriend thought the baby was due around the fifteenth of August, but they were not certain of that. There was no opportunity to transfer her to a hospital with an intensive care nursery just in case the baby was coming as prematurely as they surmised he might be. The baby's heart rate stayed well within the optimum 120- to 160-beats-per-minute range throughout the remainder of her labor. However, when their four-pound, eight-ounce little boy was born, he was limp and blue with gasping respirations and a heartbeat of less than 100. In spite of his receiving oxygen immediately via an Ambu bag (a ventilating device with a mask that fits over the baby's face, connected to a small rubber bag which is hand squeezed to force a mixture of air and oxygen into his lungs and help him breathe), his one minute Apgar score of three was not reassuring. (The Apgar scoring system is a means of determining a newborn's physical condition. It evaluates the baby's heart rate, respirations, muscle tone, response to being stimulated, and color. Each category is assigned a value of zero, one, or two. A nice, pink, active baby gets a ten; zero is a dead baby.) This baby's score dropped to one at five minutes because he had stopped moving and was not making any respiratory effort at all; his heart was still beating, but slowly, and we knew there was little chance that he would survive. However, after a dose of epinephrine and ten minutes of CPR (doing chest compressions while breathing for him with the Ambu bag), his heart reached the magic number of greater than 100 beats per minute and he pinked up and began breathing on his own, with loud, grunting respirations that could be heard all over the clinic.

Dr. Tulio Maldonado, the town physician who has collaborated with the clinic since the early 1980s and lives close enough to hop in his little green truck and dash over from his office to help with an emergency, came to evaluate the situation. He ordered a Dexamethasone injection to attempt to hasten the baby's lung maturity, as well as continuous oxygen and nebulized saline every four hours. Before going over to our house to sleep around 10:00 a.m., I did a gestational age assessment on the little fellow and was not too surprised to discover that he was between thirty-one and thirty-two weeks of age instead of the optimal thirty-eight to forty. Only a few short minutes after I had wearily crawled between the sheets, the walkie-talkie beside my bed squawked out the day guard's urgent request to please come back over to help the day nurse Rosmery, as the baby's heart had stopped again. Dr. Maldonado arrived as we were doing CPR. He stayed until the dose of nebulized epinephrine combined with the chest compressions and Ambu breathing had once more done their job and our tiny patient was pink and breathing on his own. We cautiously rejoiced together, knowing that the battle for life definitely was not yet won.

I was not surprised to receive another summons from Rosmery at 2:25 p.m. when, nearly eleven hours after his birth, the baby's heart stopped for the third and final time, and our best efforts at reviving him proved futile. I took photos of the perfectly formed little body dressed in the simple, white clinic onesie with rolled-up sleeves and the black, permanent-inked letters "CMLZ" (*Clínica de Maternidad Luz y Vida*) on the front. Not only was this the young couple's first child, it was Ricxi's parents' first grandchild as well. Rex printed out two pages with an arrangement of four photos for his parents and grandparents so they could remember their firstborn son and grandson. Along the edge of the bottom right picture, which he had cropped into the shape of a heart, were printed the words, *"Con nosotros pocas horas ... con el Padre celestial para siempre."* (With us a few hours ... with the heavenly Father forever.)

I was sitting at the desk, giving the grieving family some time alone with their little one, when the baby's daddy came out and asked me if we had a cardboard box that he could have. Puzzled, I looked blankly at him for a moment, and then tears sprang to my eyes as I realized the significance of his request. My heart was broken as I searched our storeroom for a box that would be the right size to serve as a coffin. Tenderly, his grandmother dressed the lifeless form in the lovingly chosen outfit that they had planned for him to wear home and then placed the body in the box. Throughout the anxious hours preceding this final moment, many prayers had been sent up. God in His infinite mercy had chosen to answer those prayers by taking this child home to revel forever in the joys of heaven instead of allowing him the opportunity to live on earth. Before carefully taping the box closed, I prayed once more with the parents, asking that they would be not only comforted in their grief, but also introduced to the One Who could show them the way to be reunited in heaven with their son someday. I watched the sorrowful father silently carry the box with its precious burden out the front door, on his way to the cemetery for the burial that must be done that same afternoon, before his wife was ready to go home. I could not imagine how I would feel if I were the baby's mother and could not be present while my child was buried.

On the evening of July 14, Rex and Daniel Melton were in San Pedro Sula to pick up Juleen Wilson and Linette Clough, two young ladies from our church back in Pennsylvania who were coming down to experience clinic life. Benjie, Jeffrey, and I were just finishing our family worship Bible reading when the nurse at the clinic called on the walkie-talkie, asking me to come over. A few seconds later, the guard called me on *his* walkie-talkie with the same request. I ran the whole way there, as it sounded pretty urgent. It was! A pickup truck had just brought in a gunshot victim, who was lying on the treatment table in the exam room with a nasty looking, small round hole on the side of his chest, halfway down his rib cage. His skin was icy cold, and when Elda, the on-duty nurse, tried to take his blood pressure, it registered exactly zero. She had already attempted, unsuccessfully, to start an IV on him, and wanted me to help. Between the two of us, we stuck him seven times, struggling to get a needle into a vein, but with all the bleeding going on internally, his veins were too collapsed. He was conscious, but barely, just enough to keep spitting out blood on the floor by my feet. The chief of police was there, along with two other police officers, a woman relative, several men, and dozens of curious neighbors gathered in the clinic hall, out on the porch and in the yard. When we had to give up on the IV, four men picked him up and hoisted him onto their shoulders, carrying him outside to a waiting pickup truck. They laid him on the bare truck bed and quickly rigged up a tarp to keep the pouring rain from hitting him directly. A police officer and three other men rode along to watch out for him on the trip to the hospital in San Pedro Sula.

After they left, I learned that he and a friend had successfully committed a robbery. Upon returning to the friend's house to divvy up the spoils, they got into an argument over who got what amount of the money. He pulled out a machete to settle the matter in his favor, but his friend was quicker on the draw with his pistol. Later that evening, the radio announcer said that the man was still living when he arrived at the San Pedro Sula hospital. They did surgery that night to remove the bullet in his lung, but by the next evening it was announced this that he was *agonizando* (in the last stages). Friday morning, the radio notified everyone that he was dead and asked that a vehicle be sent to pick up his body and take it home for burial. The saddest part about it all was that he is probably spending eternity forever without God. Elda was lamenting Wednesday night after we sent him on his way that we had not even had a chance to talk to him about his soul, what with his semiconscious state and the room full of anxious people. He was only twenty-five years old and probably never thought that he would be leaving this world so soon.

And so it went throughout those six weeks of June and July—so many people, with so many needs. Of course, not all of the memories are bad. I had the pleasure of coaching nurse Tiffany Melton, Daniel's wife, as she delivered half of the ten babies who were born during my clinic shifts, giving her a chance to become more comfortable with doing births and sharing in the excitement of her first five deliveries. Together with the other dedicated nurses who selflessly give of their time and talents, month in and month out, we were privileged to take part in missions of mercy, pointing people to Jesus, the Way.

## 25

## Splashdown

*June 15, 2006 ~ In the Air, and On the Road to San Luis, Honduras*

We left home at 1:12 this morning and made the connections for our 6:18 a.m. flight without any problems. Well, there were no problems if you do not count having to compact our already-compacted luggage even more, since the counter attendants were quite strict about weight and bag allowances. They refused to allow us to take the separate little bag with five packages of chewy Chips Ahoy cookies for the Meltons. Also, one of our six checked suitcases weighed one-and-a-half pounds too much. It is amazing what can be squeezed into an already-crammed-to-the-limit space when faced with the prospect of paying $50.00 for an extra piece of baggage. Minus a baby quilt for the clinic and one of the ten large rolls of extra-heavy-duty duct tape that we were taking to repair the big sheets of insulation in the Bible institute roof, the too-heavy suitcase made it. We stuffed the duct tape into Rex's carry-on, draped the quilt artistically over Hannah's shoulder, shoved the cookies into Jeffrey's and Hannah's carry-ons, and were on our merry way.

Our plane arrived at Miami around 8:30 a.m., and from then until Benjie's plane landed two hours later, we were doing plenty of praying that he had been able to make the connection from his missed flight in Ecuador. Two weeks earlier, he and some of his friends had left the States for a missions trip to Chiclayo, Peru. They flew to Guayaquil, Ecuador, staying the night with a woman who had known Nate Saint and had flown in his plane. In Peru, they helped with constructing a church during the day and held a week-long Vacation Bible School at night. Benjie was supposed to return to the U.S. alone on June 14, and we were all going to fly out on the 15th for Honduras. The group leader *thought* that he had made arrangements for a man from the Peruvian church to travel with Benjie on the bus from Chiclayo to the airport in Ecuador. Unfortunately, the *man* thought that he had only agreed to accompany Benjie to the Peru-Ecuador border; when everyone got off the bus for the border crossing, he said good-bye and left.

The computers at the border went haywire and started stamping incorrect dates in the passports, so everyone from the bus had to have papers processed manually and go through customs individually. Because of that delay, Benjie, now all by himself, arrived at the airport forty-five minutes before his plane was to leave. They told him he could fly, but only if he left his luggage behind.

Since it had everything he would need for the next six-and-a-half weeks in Honduras, naturally he did not want to fly without it. At that point, he called home to ask what he should do.

Of course, we had no previous idea that he had been abandoned at the border and was alone, and I panicked. Knowing he could not just leave his luggage there, we told him to stay put while I frantically started calling the airlines, trying to make arrangements for him. Meanwhile, sixteen-year-old Benjie, much calmer than his mother, connected with the woman they had met coming into Ecuador, and she arranged for her brother's family to pick him up. He spent the night with them, they saw him and his luggage safely onto the flight I was able to book for him that afternoon, and he flew into New York, landing at 1:32 a.m. on the 15th. Before his plane left New York six hours later to connect with us in Miami, he was so tired and stressed that he threw up the little that he had in his stomach in the airport restroom. Thankfully for our already worried minds, we did not know all those details while they were happening.

While Rex stayed with our luggage at the gate from which we would be leaving for Honduras, Jeffrey and I haunted the gate where Benjie's plane was to arrive and vied with each other over who would get to hug him first when he got off. Believe me, were we ever glad to see each other!

The boys and I were in the first row of coach seats on our flight from Miami to Honduras, but Rex was about halfway back, so he was unaware of how close we came to not being allowed to fly. Benjie was folded over in his seat, head down, all covered up with a baby afghan since he was still feeling chilled and nauseous. When the stewardess came by before we took off, I asked her for a glass of water and a vomit bag for him, since he was feeling sick. She brought back the requested items and, looking very concerned, asked how long "this person" had been sick and if "this person" could safely fly. She left, but came back shortly, saying that the captain was worried and thought it would be better for "this person" to get off and wait for the next flight. I told her he could not do that, as he was our son with whom we had just reconnected after he had missed his flight from Ecuador, and we were absolutely not going to be separated again. "Oh, he is your son!" she repeated, and then I realized she thought it was someone we just happened to be sitting with.

"Yes, and he is not eighteen yet, and we are not leaving him." She went back to confer and returned to say that the captain thought it best that we ALL get off and wait for another flight. If Benjie were to get so sick that they needed to land, there was no good place to do it on the way to Honduras, and they did not want to have to turn around and return to Miami partway into the flight. I assured her that Benjie's illness was due to exhaustion from a two-day-return-and-missed-flight ordeal and that I was a nurse and could take care of him. She was not convinced and went back to talk to the captain. I followed her to where the pilot, co-pilot, and two other people were in a huddle at the front of the plane, smiled (convincingly, I hoped) and repeated my assurances that my son was all right to fly. They finally decided that he (and we) could stay on. Whew!

The rest of the flight was uneventful, and we breezed through customs. Daniel was pulling a trailer behind his Land Rover to carry our suitcases, plus some tanks of oxygen he was taking back to the clinic. After grocery shopping for the things we would not be able to buy in San Luis, we headed out on the two-and-a-half hour trip to the mission station. We had barely started when it began to pour rain, and we commented on what a good thing it was that Daniel had thought to carefully and completely cover our suitcases with a large tarp so they would not be soaked. The dirt road is very rutted in places. As we jounced and splashed through numerous potholes with the muddy water spraying in sheets above the car, we were blissfully unaware of what was happening to the luggage in the trailer.

When we pulled up under the carport at our house next door to the clinic and started to unload, the men noted that, in spite of the careful precautions with the tarp, some of the suitcases looked damp along the bottom, and they suggested that I might want to check the things inside. You can imagine my dismay on opening each suitcase that had been in the trailer to find that not only water, but mud and sand as well had been forced in through the BOTTOM seams, where the tarp could not cover. So, for the next nearly six hours, I spread out and cleaned our wet, muddy things. It took load after load (a prewash to get out the grit and then a wash with soap) to launder not only our personal clothes, but baby afghans and clothes for the clinic. In between filling and emptying the washer and dryer, I wiped off what I could of the clinic supplies. Twenty-seven of the thirty-some books that we had brought for Jeffrey to read had varying degrees of wetness, and I spread them out in front of several fans. Rex was able to hose the grit out of the suitcases, and we propped them open in front of fans as well.

At 1:15 a.m., as I was looking for a Bible passage to help me go to sleep, I opened to Psalm 27: "In the time of trouble He shall hide me;... Be of good courage and He shall strengthen your heart." I thought again, as I had several times throughout the long night of mopping up the damage, how good God had been not to allow things to be worse. Except for a few disposable baby diapers which had to be thrown out, nothing was ruined completely. Many of the envelopes of sterile gauze bandages and gloves got wet, but only on the edges, not inside where the sterility would have been compromised. Five days later, the books, though wrinkled and stained, have dried out and are still readable.

It is as if the Lord said, "This far, devil, in your attempt to discourage and cause trouble, but no farther."

Partway through the tedious mop-up process, I was able to make a phone call to my sister Priscilla for an encouraging couple of minutes. It was immensely heartening to know that she was enlisting the support of the prayer warriors that I was not able to talk with myself. Thank you all, again, for being there and for loving us.

## 26

## We Squeezed Some Juice Out of Them
*June 17-18, 2006 ~ San Pedro Sula, Honduras*

It is amazing what a good night of sleep can do for one's outlook on life. Today is a beautiful, sunny, albeit muggy day. When I finish this, I plan to continue working on the songs I am illustrating for the children's services we will be holding this weekend.

Ah, yes, services. At least, these coming ones we are expecting. This past weekend, the surprise was our own fault; the seminars were right there on the schedule, but somehow, both Rex and I overlooked them. After getting to bed late the night, or rather, early the morning after our arrival, we slept in until about 9:00 a.m. Jet lag had caught up with us, and we were still not moving extremely rapidly when Daniel came over at noon to talk about the plans for going back to San Pedro the next morning.

"TOMORROW MORNING?!?"

"Well, yes, for the seminars, you know"

"WHAT SEMINARS?!?!"

"Why, the ones on the schedule Yaneth sent you." (Yaneth is the head of the Children's Outreach Committee, which had programmed the activities.)

"ON THE SCHEDULE?!?!?"

When we picked our dropped jaws up off the floor and looked at the schedule in question, sure enough, there it was. We were each to have two training sessions. I would be with the women's leaders in the morning and the children's teachers in the afternoon, while Rex would work with the youth teachers both of those times. Incredibly, we had both totally overlooked those assignments and were not expecting any training sessions until the following week.

I stayed up all but thirty minutes that night, pulling together the props for "How to Tell Bible Stories Dynamically" and getting my "Women in Leadership" session prepared. We left at 7:30 a.m., and from then until things wound down at around 5:00 that afternoon, we were again very thankful for the prayers of our family and friends, and for the help of our ever-faithful Lord.

Sunday morning, we went to a church we had not visited before, and Rex taught the youth group while I had a class of twenty-four children ranging in age from three to twelve years. Amazingly, for a group of that age spread, they all sat quietly, listened attentively to the story of Naaman's maid, and repeated the memory verse after me the dozen times that it took to have a different child come to the front and erase one or two of its words from the chalkboard after each successful recitation.

We attended another church that evening, where Rex was to preach. I was looking forward to the opportunity to hear him, since this time I was not scheduled for anything. Following congregational singing and other preliminaries, the children went out back to their classroom, and Rex got up to read his text. At that moment, an older girl came in, learned over the two people between me and the end of the row, and whispered close to my ear, "Hermana Ana, the children are waiting for you to tell the story."

"WHAT? ME TELL THE STORY?" I gulped, quickly scrambled to gather the teaching aids I had used that morning, and went to my class of twenty-eight eager youngsters. Rex and I looked at the schedule later and, to our relief, discovered that this time it truly was not an oversight on our part; I was *not* listed to teach a class that night. Oh well, as Yaneth said that evening, "We squeezed some juice out of Hermano Rex and Hermana Ana this weekend." Amen, Sister!

# 27

## Revenge!

*June 19, 2006 ~ San Pedro Sula, Honduras*

Following the Sunday evening service yesterday, Rex and I went to Pastor Víctor's house behind the church, while Daniel Melton and Víctor drove one of the ladies home. They planned to stop on the way back to pick up a stalk of bananas that someone had offered them, but even so, they were gone much longer than any of us expected. We sat waiting for their return, chatting a bit distractedly with Yaneth, Víctor's wife, as we worried about what could be holding them up. When the phone rang, Yaneth jumped to answer it, and from the look on her face as she talked, we knew the news was not good. Soberly, she hung up the receiver and recounted what was happening.

After Daniel and Víctor dropped off their passenger, they headed back for the bananas, an errand that led them down the street where Angel, the national church president, lived. As they passed his home, someone inside recognized the car and dashed out, frantically motioning for them to stop. They stepped inside the house to utter chaos. Moments before, Angel had gotten word that his uncle had been killed and the man's fourteen-year-old son was seriously injured in trying to defend his daddy. Angel's wife was inconsolably hysterical. Angel wanted to catch a ride to the hospital to see his nephew, but dared not leave his small children and wife while she was so emotionally traumatized. Long minutes and many prayers later, she calmed down enough for the men to leave.

Daniel did not arrive back until 3:45 this morning. He told us when we woke up that the killer was a former associate of Angel's uncle who had been in prison for a number of years for an earlier murder that he had committed. While in jail, he had ample time to brood over past grievances, one of which was the fact that Angel's uncle had stolen the affection of a girl that he fancied. His hatred and rage seethed under the surface, waiting the opportunity for release. His chance came last evening, only a week after being set free. Lurking in the shadows of his victim's home, he waited until dark to rap on the door. When the uncle answered the knock, he stared with shocked horror at the machete brandished above the hate-twisted face of his old acquaintance. Shouting a warning to his family behind him in the house, he turned to flee, but not in time to escape the ferocious swing of the blade which whacked open the back of his head from ear to ear. Hearing the commotion, his son ran to the rescue, but the murderer brutally struck him with a club. In the melee, a daughter was injured as well, but escaped before she could be seriously hurt.

Daniel and Víctor took Angel to the hospital to see the boy, who will likely be permanently blinded in the eye that took the brunt of the blow to his face. The three men were back at Angel's house when the morgue attendants brought his uncle home and dumped him into the hurriedly obtained coffin. When the family tried to change his stained shirt, blood from the recent head injury smeared liberally over the cloth lining on the inside of the coffin, causing even greater distress to his grieving relatives with the grisly reminder of their loved one's ruthless death. Daniel and Víctor stayed for part of the wake, leaving before the body was taken to San Luis later in the morning for burial in the family cemetery plot. In a country where little embalming is done, a corpse decomposes rapidly in the tropical heat. Interment had to be by noon, so the son who had so valiantly tried to save his father's life was not even able to attend the funeral. The saddest part of the whole tragic story is Angel's certain knowledge that his uncle left this world with no opportunity to be reconciled with the God he had ignored all his life.

On our way back to San Luis this afternoon, on a section of dirt road nearly halfway to our destination, we saw a large crowd of people milling around a house. More folks were running down the hill, and others were hurrying up a side road to join them. A lady waved us to a stop and leaned in the window, excitedly telling us that there had just been a bad accident and begging Daniel to please call the Red Cross. As is common here, a pickup truck, its bed crowded with people willing to grip the side rails and stand for a long time to get a ride to their destination, had been cruising along the narrow road on the mountain's edge. Unfortunately for his passengers, the young chauffeur did not have a license. In his inexperience, he misjudged either his speed or the sharpness of the curve, a fatal error which sent his truck plunging over the side of the mountain. Two were killed and many more injured by the time the tumbling vehicle finally settled to rest at the bottom of the ravine. With the ambulance on its way and nothing more that we could do, we continued our ride home, sobered by the second reminder in less than twenty-four hours of how unexpectedly life can be cut short and the importance of being ready to meet God.

## 28

## One Thousand Too Many

*June 23, 2006 ~ San Luis, Honduras*

It is Friday evening, and we are getting ready to leave for a second *culto infantil* (children's service). Rex and I both taught Sunday school lessons this past Lord's Day, but the service this evening is one of a series of special ones that the national church's education committee had been advertising over the radio for several weeks prior to our arrival in the country on June 15. They will be held in various churches throughout the coming weeks, and although some adults will be attending, the emphasis is on evangelizing the little people who are sometimes lost in the cracks during gospel outreach.

We start out with a belch of diesel fumes, a jerk of shifting gears, and the peculiar rumble of the nearly indestructible, decades-old, grey, converted army Chevy Blazer fondly known as "The Tank." We pause at the gate beside the clinic to wait for the guard to open the padlock. After a brief consultation with him, Rex reverses the Blazer back up the dirt road to the Melton's house to borrow a propane lantern from Tiffany. The electricity coming in from the town has been off for a good part of the past two days, and we have been on generator backup. The guard thinks it would be wise to take our own light source, since the little church where we are going on the edge of town probably does not have power, either.

Two young men and two girls from our Bible institute are waiting just outside the gate, along with the younger brothers of one of them. That makes eight of us in the vehicle. It is not bad compared to the eleven we hauled in here on the l-o-o-n-g ride back from the first marriage seminar we held. Even eleven is only a start to the number that can be crammed into anything with a more or less rectangular metal body mounted on four wheels, as we noticed at last night's service.

That one was supposed to start at 6:30 p.m., just like the one tonight. There were roughly a dozen children there on time, but no one seemed ready to begin. We sat around waiting for a few minutes until the pastor informed us that there would be more children coming, some from an outlying village, but we would be starting at 6:30 "old time." Honduras just recently implemented daylight savings time, but since many of the people in the country are used to ordering their days by the position of the sun and not by a clock, it has been a difficult adjustment for them. Many just keep doing as they have been used to, so although the clock said 6:30, by their figuring, it was only 5:30, and we still had an hour until service. During that hour the people, children as well as adults, kept trickling in, filling up the plain board benches. Meanwhile, the pastor kept announcing by means of the VERY LOUD amplifier aimed through the open windows that there would be a children's service "shortly." When we finally started at ten minutes till 8:00 p.m., there were at least fifty-six children and probably half that many adults. Twenty-two people had arrived from the neighboring village in a small pickup truck. As I said, our Blazer was not nearly filled to capacity.

We arrive at our destination this evening and repeat last night's experience. There, the pastor had said there would probably be around thirty, and nearly sixty children showed up. Tonight, when we begin at 7:35 (new time), we count sixty-eight—more than three times the number that this minister had predicted. I think there are a few more outside, as well. That number is just children; we do not know how many adults are present in addition.

Choruses are enthusiastically and LOUDLY sung and a memory verse learned, with the boys significantly beating the girls' time of arranging in correct order the scrambled poster board rectangles with the individual words and reference of the memory verse. Then the moment arrives to share the Bible stories about the lost coin and the lost sheep. I am keenly aware of my awesome responsibility. How many of these may be hearing the gospel for the first time I cannot say, but I realize it is important that I clearly present the message of salvation. I feel the Lord's presence and help, and at the end of the stories, twenty-five children come forward at the invitation to give their hearts to Jesus. No doubt several are there only to join a playmate, but we pray that they will all realize the reality and seriousness of the words they have just repeated after the Bible institute student who led them in prayer.

We sing another chorus or two, followed by the popular "Bonk" review game which elicits an enthusiastic response every time we play it. It is boys versus girls again, and although both sides answer the questions well, the boys win overwhelmingly, drawing the most points out of the bag without getting the dreaded "Bonk" slip of paper which erases all points earned for that round. They are thrilled with their prize: a brightly colored, two-inch-by-eight-inch poster-board bookmark, cheerily decorated with several stickers and tonight's memory verse. It is raining by the time we dismiss, but the cheerful grins of our congregation are not a bit dampened as the children scatter to their homes.

We arrive back at the mission compound at 10:00 p.m. Before the Blazer even rolls through the gate, the guard is at my window with an urgent request from the nurse on duty at the clinic next door that I come help her right away.

I jump out of the vehicle and rush in, my heart pounding fast with nervous excitement and anticipation. In the second bed of the general ward lies an elderly man, moaning and writhing in obvious pain. Surrounding him, covering his pillow, on the sheet on either side of him, and on the floor around his bed, are dozens, no, hundreds ... actually, make that *over one thousand* black specks. What in the world?!

Rosmery, the nurse, is bent over him, plucking more of the dark particles from his face and hair. I lean in closer to make out what it is she is removing. Realization strikes me, and overwhelmed with pity, I pick up a pair of small needle-nosed forceps and join her in extracting the torturing stingers from the bees that attacked him earlier this evening, viciously driving their venom-laden needles into his body and leaving him crumpled and helpless in the dirt at the edge of his yard. I learn that when his grown son ran to rescue him, he, too, was stung multiple times. The son received enough of the poison to drop him vomiting to the ground, but because he is so poor, he decided not to come to the clinic for help. The family felt that the father needed to be brought to us since he will be ninety-nine years old in August, and they were worried that the shock of the toxin would be too much for his system. They had good reason to be worried. Over one thousand bee stings are too many in a person of *any* age!

Doctor Maldonado has already been by to order IV medication and help remove as many of the stingers as possible by scraping the edge of his hard plastic *cédula* (a photo ID sort of like a driver's license) down the man's arms. But there are still hundreds of the sharp barbs, embedded in nearly every accessible spot of flesh on his face, arms, and neck, as well as on his chest where some got inside his shirt. Rosmery's shift ends at 10:00, and Esperanza comes on next, but her sight for the type of close-up work that this requires is not good enough. So, from 10:00 to midnight, I stay to help extract the several hundred stingers that still remain. The poor man's eyes are swollen shut; I gently pry them open to get out probably two dozen or more stingers from each eyelid and even along the very edge of the eye socket. I talk soothingly as I work on the sensitive areas where the bees got inside his nose and along his lips, but the combination of medicine and bee venom is making him groggy, and he is not rational. He keeps trying to bat my hands away. Esperanza and his wife grab for his arms so I can continue my work, but when they grip him, he yells in pain from the pressure of their hands on the many stingers still embedded there. So I switch my focus of work to his arms, and when those are cleared of as many stingers as I can see, he does not resist being restrained while I continue painstakingly removing the remaining spines on his face. When I leave after helping to put fresh sheets on his bed, getting him out of his stinger-filled clothes, and dressing him in hospital pj's, he is sleeping soundly. I pray with his wife, who hugs me with tears in her eyes. I think, as I have several times throughout the night, "What if it were my daddy?" I am glad for the privilege I have had to help make him more comfortable.

Thus ends our first full week in Honduras. I wonder what other adventures await us in the six weeks we have left of this summer's stay?

## 29

# 214 Bananas Later

*July 6, 2006 ~ San Luis, Honduras*

I am not sure where to place the blame. Perhaps it is attributable to spending so much time in a higher altitude than I am used to. Maybe it has something to do with the above average concentration of rice and beans in our diet. Whatever the reason, my creative talents seem to be especially shining during these humid tropical days in Honduras. I discovered that this morning after we finished taking care of the LARGE stalk of bananas that some friends in San Luis so kindly gave to us when they found out how much we enjoy them. In the United States, bananas are not as expensive as many other fruits, but at forty-nine to sixty-nine cents per pound, a nice bunch of eight or ten large ones can still cost $2.50 to $3.00 at the local grocery or farmer's market. Bananas are one of Honduras's chief export crops and therefore produced in sufficient quantities to be readily and cheaply available in-country. We can buy a dozen large ones here for fifty cents. The nationals are shocked when we tell them the price we have to pay at home. Although they are a healthy source of relatively inexpensive vitamins and minerals that we enjoy often on every visit, it is even better, of course, when someone drops a nice stalk by as a gift, such as happened this past Monday.

When I say "stalk of bananas," I am talking about the entire crop produced by a single plant, not just a bunch containing eight or ten, such as I mentioned above. The stalk is several inches in diameter at the top and can be two or three feet tall. It is harvested when the fruit is still bright green and hard, and the bananas will ripen gradually from bottom to top if the stalk is suspended vertically by a rope. Not having a good place to hang our gift, we left it lying on the porch.

Horizontal versus vertical does not work the same way, as we found out when the whole stalk—all 214 bananas—was ripe within three days. So this morning, before returning to San Pedro Sula for a weekend of conferences and services, we attacked the bananas. That is, Rex cut the stalk into manageable sections, he and Jeffrey and I pulled the bananas off and peeled them, and we mashed and froze enough to keep us in banana bread and banana smoothies for many days to come. Somewhere in the middle of the process is when my flash of inspiration occurred.

It is an original composition, sung to the tune of "100 Bottles of Pop on the Wall," but this version is even better, since there are so many more verses to enjoy. Everybody join in, please, as we all sing: "Two hundred fourteen bananas on the stalk, two hundred fourteen bananas. Twist one free, squish it with glee, two hundred thirteen bananas on the stalk. Two hundred thirteen bananas on the stalk, two hundred thirteen bananas,..."

Ah well, so I am not related to Fanny Crosby. The really good thing is that we did not have to sing all the verses before we ended up with zero bananas on the stalk. I trust that the translation I did of the "Jonah and the Whale" song that we have been using in the children's services was at least slightly more inspired. At any rate, the children seem to enjoy singing it, and they are certainly enthusiastic in doing the motions. Of course, they might like the "Two Hundred Fourteen Bananas" song, too.

Life has been moving rapidly along here, as it always does when we come on these trips. Daniel Melton went to the airport today to pick up the Titus Mowery family, joining us from Pennsylvania for two weeks of concentrated help with remodeling and fix-it-up projects. I am, as always, enjoying the chance to work in the clinic. During my first shift, I delivered the seven-pound, five-ounce baby boy of a fifteen-year-old mother. Although it is perfectly acceptable in this culture for a girl of that age to be having children, the thought that she was married when she was only thirteen boggles my mind. Despite my best efforts to encourage her twenty-two-year-old husband to be with her, the idea of the baby's father supporting his wife throughout her labor and the two of them experiencing the miracle of their child's birth together is something that is taking some time to catch on here. As is more common, her husband left a short while after bringing her to the clinic. Her father-in-law stopped by while she was still in labor to bring her some juice. He had been drinking, possibly to celebrate his first grandchild's soon arrival, but he did have enough respect to realize that he was not in any condition to hang around.

Not long after the little fellow was born, his daddy and grandfather showed up again, and when I was checking new mama's blood pressure, new grandpa asked if I would mind taking his, also. It was a very unhealthy high, which seemed to shake him up considerably. He asked me what he could do to get it lower, listened intently as I offered some advice, then asked if it would be helpful for him to stop drinking and smoking. That was the spring board to the wide-open door that I needed to witness to him of Jesus, Who could save him, help him clean up his life, and make him into the kind of man who would be a good example for a new little grandson to follow. He was quite receptive to what I said and seemed sincere when we prayed together after about forty-five minutes of conversation. Only God knows what took place in his heart, but even without all the many other things that occurred that shift, I felt that my time had been profitably spent.

That was my first *scheduled* work time, but the Saturday before, both Tiffany and I worked together to deliver not one but *three* babies, all born within about eight hours of each other. It was a great opportunity for her to get more practical experience, especially as each birth had some complication requiring more than the normal care. One mother had a major post-partum hemorrhage, and another had a retained placenta. The third baby had an Apgar score of three at one minute and six at five minutes, a state of affairs requiring immediate resuscitative efforts to help him adjust to the need to breathe on his own once he was outside rather than inside his mommy. All three situations turned out well, thank the Lord.

Unfortunately, that was not the case for the ninety-eight-year-old man about whom I told you in the last chapter, who received over a thousand bee stings. In spite of the best we could do, the shock was too much for his system, and he died the next day. I have no idea of his spiritual condition, but he was not anywhere close to being coherent enough to comprehend anything I might have said to him. I hope he was ready for heaven. The morning of his disastrous encounter, he had no thought that he would be ushered into eternity a mere twenty-four hours later. His story is yet another reminder that, even if you live to be nearly one hundred, at the moment of death, the only thing that matters is not what amount of money you have amassed, or whether you have made a great name for yourself or left a legacy of good works. In that instant, your personal relationship with Jesus is all that counts. And that is the reason for doing what we do. Any charitable organization can move into a poor community and open a clinic with the laudable intent of helping suffering people who would not otherwise have such services available. But only as God uses our efforts to help hurting souls as well as hurting bodies can we accomplish anything of undying value. We are asking Him to do that, and trusting that He will make this visit profitable for eternity.

## 30

# Forty-Three for the Price of One

## *July 21, 2006 ~ San Luis, Honduras*

It is 1:44 a.m. on Friday, and I am not quite halfway done with my night shift in the clinic. Shortly before I came on last evening, a first-time mommy delivered a beautiful baby girl, and they were settled into the second bed in the maternity ward, surrounded by happy family and friends. I helped the new little one as she learned how to get her first meal, then tended to an eight-month-pregnant woman who came seeking treatment for her high blood pressure. After that, I checked on another patient who was finally sleeping peacefully under the effect of two different medications and IV fluids to help ease her terrific headache. Forty-five minutes later, when new mommy got up to go to the bathroom, she took about five steps, said, *"Siento mareada"* (I feel dizzy), and promptly passed out. Thankfully, I was right beside her, grabbed her, and was able to ease her to the floor without a major crash. The look of surprise on her face when she came to was pretty comical. After getting her back into bed and cleaned up, she fell asleep quickly, and things have been quiet since then.

It is nice to have a chance to sit down and write to you. We have been going pretty much nonstop these last two weeks, and things will be zipping along at a good pace for a while yet. Tomorrow I am to give a training session for the nurses in the afternoon and join Rex for a talk to the youth at the local church that evening.

This past Sunday I worked the morning clinic shift and that evening had the last of the seven evangelistic children's services that had been planned for our time here. Benjie counted somewhere around fifty children and at least that many adults who listened attentively to the stories of the lost coin and lost sheep. One little girl prayed to be saved, making fifty-two children altogether in these special services who have asked Jesus into their hearts. We had enough of the brightly decorated bookmarks with the Bible verse from the lesson printed on them to give one to each child, as well as to many of the adults. The adults were, if anything, even more eager than the children to choose one with the color and stickers that they liked best. We trust that the verse will be a reminder of the truth of the lesson: the Good Shepherd wants to seek and save them.

Now it is 5:43 a.m., and for most of the past three hours, I have been trying to help little Miss Newborn learn how to eat. At this moment she is lying asleep on my lap as I type while we try to give Mommy a chance to rest. When one weighs only five pounds, eleven ounces, she doesn't have a very big tummy, and it needs filled more often.

Nearly two weeks ago, Titus and Julie Mowery and their teenage children, Brendon and Jaylena, flew down for an intensive, two-week "vacation" filled with dawn-to-dark help around the properties both in San Pedro and San Luis. We were excited to see them, not only because of the help that we anticipated their being, but also because of the luggage that they were bringing with them.

Before our own trip here, I had asked Miriam what was most urgently needed for the clinic. On every visit that we make, more than half of our suitcases are filled with medical supplies, most of them generously donated. These are a real blessing to a poor rural community where a good manual laborer may earn fifty cents an hour.

"Please try to bring us some new delivery gowns," Miriam's return e-mail had pleaded. "Ours are *really* getting worn out."

It "just so happens" that Julie is a labor and delivery nurse and knows the person in charge of ordering supplies for the hospital where she works. "Sure, we can order you some gowns," the supply supervisor promised. "Top-of-the-line quality costs $1,800.00 per dozen. How many dozen would you like?"

Gulp! "Well, Lord, what can you do now?" we prayed. "We surely can't pay $150.00 per gown. Please supply this need." A week or so later, Julie got a call from the gown company representative.

"I talked to our reprocessing center in Texas, and they have a proposition for you. How does $42.00 per dozen sound? They are not our highest quality, but they are new, and each gown should last through over one hundred washing and sterilization cycles. What do you think?"

"Wow! Thank you, God. That's ... forty-three gowns for the price of one! Tell him we'll take four dozen." Just happenstance? I think not, especially when a coworker from the hospital hosted a benefit concert to raise funds for Julie's ticket, all of which she put towards buying the gowns instead. Can you guess how much she was given? How about $175.00? That is right, just the amount needed to cover the cost of all forty-eight gowns, with even a tiny bit left over. What a joy it was to wheel a large suitcase into the linen room of the clinic and pile all of those gowns onto the counter for a delighted Miriam to inspect. Truly, our God had opened His rich storehouse and poured out an abundant blessing.

The Mowerys left here yesterday afternoon to go into San Pedro Sula and spend their last full workday putting up the cabinets for the kitchen in the missionary apartment above the radio station. Titus and Brendon were able to get some much-appreciated work done on the Bible institute buildings and

*Dating Days. Rex was not too sure about the joys of farm life when he visited my family a few months before our wedding in 1980.*

*Rexie joins other children from the Caballo Blanco congregation to spell N-A-V-I-D-A-D for the Christmas program our first year in Costa Rica.*

*Benjie, Rex, Rexie, and Hannah, behind our house on the outskirts of Nicaragua in 1991.*

*Rex's parents enjoyed being with us for a deputational service during our first furlough.*

Children from one of the mismatched-boards-and-corrugated-tin shanties in Paraíso, Costa Rica.

Woman selling meat at the market in Nicaragua. The round red bowl in front holds beef eyeballs, used to make soup.

Rexie helps plow our garden with the neighbor's team of oxen.

Benjie, after he fell down our front porch steps and Nurse Mommie stitched his scalp closed.

Holding Luis, the first baby I delivered in Central America, in front of the house where he was born.

Healthy, happy Baby Luis and his nurse-midwife.

Benjie kept getting intestinal bugs. I wonder why.

Rexie (in front) and Benjie, playing in the iguana tree beside our house in Nicaragua.

*Daddy reads aloud to Jeffrey, Benjie, and Rexie for Family Night.*

*Grandpa and Grandma Kaufman visit us during our second term in Costa Rica.*

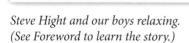

*Steve Hight and our boys relaxing. (See Foreword to learn the story.)*

*Rolando and Carmen Meneses Montero at their wedding.*

*Tiffany Melton and I delivered these three babies in less than eight hours at the Light and Life Maternity Clinic.*

*Giving some TLC to a fifteen-year-old during her labor.*

*Parents taking their new baby home in a moto-taxi.*

Enfermeras especiales *from left to right: Tiffany Melton, Miriam Orellana (clinic administrator), Rosmery Rodríguez, Esperanza Sabillon, and Maribel Aguilar.*

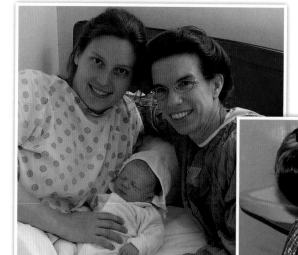

*Hannah with Tiffany Melton and baby Kenton, the first missionary baby born in the clinic.*

*Larissa Robberts meets her baby sister, Eleyna, delivered by "Grandma Hannah."*

*Hannah and Daniel DeLong hold their little sister, Joanna Brooke, who went to be with Jesus at birth.*

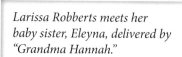

*A happy Honduran couple and their new baby, one of over 8,000 born in the clinic since it opened in 1979.*

A typical load of passengers in the back of a pickup truck. Practices like this help keep the clinic supplied with business.

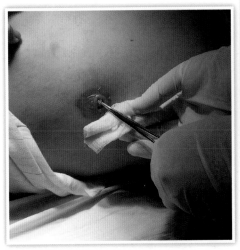

Extracting a dead-for-days Torsalo worm from a patient's abdomen.

We keep this shotgun in the clinic broom closet to scare off would-be troublemakers.

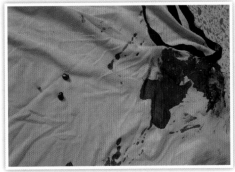

A gunshot victim's bullet-riddled, blood-stained shirt, and the three chunks of bullets that I dug out of his shoulder.

The shock of over 1,000 bee stings was too much for this ninety-eight-year-old man's system.

"Mommy wants the medicine that's written on this piece of paper. Do I have enough money to buy it?"

A little girl who nearly died from a severe asthma attack. Abandoned by her parents, her grandpa is raising her.

An elderly man waits for his every-couple-of-weeks catheter-bag change.

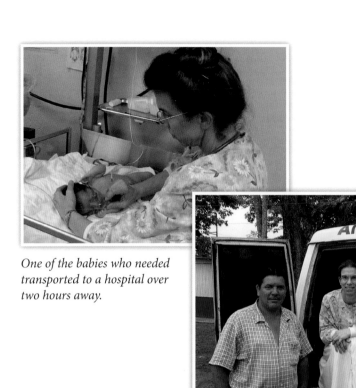

*One of the babies who needed transported to a hospital over two hours away.*

*The local Red Cross ambulance driver, his attendant, and I, after returning from taking my patient with a prolapsed cord to the Santa Bárbara Hospital.*

*The inside of a Honduran ambulance.*

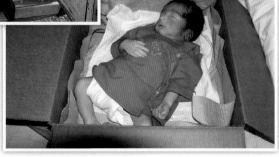

*A precious preemie whose lungs were too immature to survive. His parents buried him in this cardboard box.*

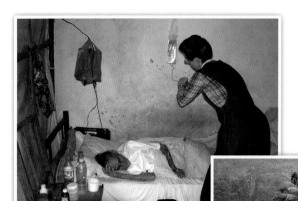

*Hanging IV fluids to treat an elderly woman in her home.*

*Edgar riding Estrella, before the accident.*

*Reviewing our notes during a break at the marriage seminar held in a cow pasture.*

*Some of the children who attended our children's revival services.*

*Four mothers and their sick babies in the clinic's pediatric ward.*

*"Light and Life Maternity Clinic."*

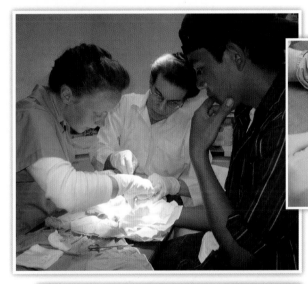

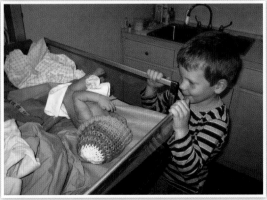

*Rachel Gregory learning to stitch a machete laceration. We had to clean out the tobacco leaves first.*

*Kenton Melton enjoys paying "Auntie Hannah" a visit at the clinic and seeing a brand-new baby.*

This man got shot through his hand, but told us a rock had rolled on it, so he would not get in trouble with the police. Benjamin helped clean and bandage his terrible wound.

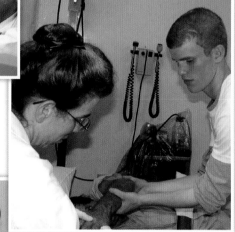

My future daughter-in-law, Jaylena Mowery, enjoys her class in cloth-diaper changing.

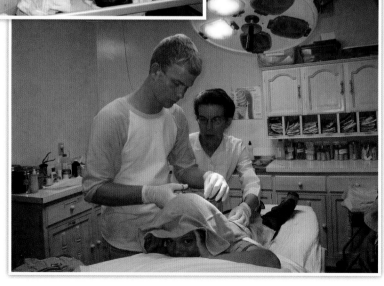

Jeffrey gets a sewing lesson from Mom while his patient plays peek-a-boo.

The Carrefour God's Missionary Church in Haiti had 1,279 people camping in its yard after the 2010 earthquake.

A common street scene in the days after the quake: a sheet-wrapped body awaiting burial in a mass grave.

Quake victims made shelters from sticks and cloth to protect themselves from the hot sun.

Dr. Bradley Moyer, Dr. Jack Devine, and I treating Enosh, one of the Bible school teachers. His family fixed him a bed in the street after his home was destroyed.

*Off on another motorcycle ride to care for victims of the quake.*

*Debriding a burned child's foot at an outdoor clinic.*

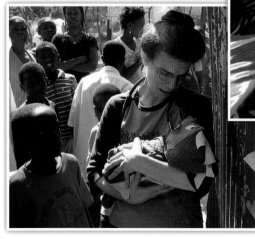

*The two-month-old baby who died an hour after our arrival at the clinic in a tin church high in the mountains.*

Jeffrey counts pills and fills orders for the nurses and doctors.

Deb Solley, RN, one of the Evangelical Community Hospital nurses who helped after the quake, enjoys her little patient.

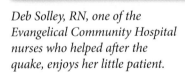

A pigtailed village mayor helps hold this child so I can bandage her burn.

A Haitian-born U.S. Marine interpreting instructions to a woman at our clinic in Leogane, Haiti.

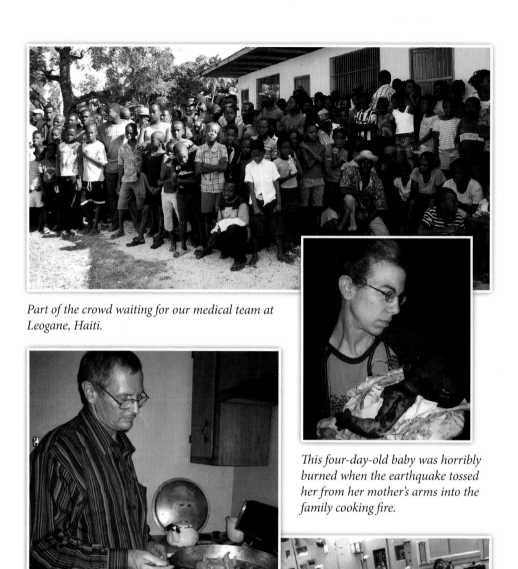

Part of the crowd waiting for our medical team at Leogane, Haiti.

This four-day-old baby was horribly burned when the earthquake tossed her from her mother's arms into the family cooking fire.

Don Mobley fixed a delicious soup made from dried fish when fresh food was unavailable.

Rev. Alan Walter, Dr. Rick Lapp, Hannah McDowell, and Vanessa Thompson seated in the cargo hold of a USAF C-17, the plane that carried us from Haiti back to the United States.

in the clinic as well during their time here. They power-sprayed and bleached property walls, scrubbed and painted many, many square yards of roofs, replaced worn-out gutters, taped up sagging insulation under the chapel roof, fixed leaky pipes and drains, installed a new emergency room back-up light that will automatically kick in if the mission generator fails to do its job when the town power goes off, and bounced and jounced over the rutted dirt roads to and from several of our children's services.

Julie sewed new curtains for sixteen of the eighteen windows in the clinic, cooked meals, helped her husband with the repairs, and even delivered a baby that was born faster than any of us expected, while Tiffany and I were drawing blood on a patient in isolation. Speaking of babies, this trip has proven to be different than the norm for when people come down to help in the clinic. Usually we have found that things seem to slow down when someone is here specifically for that experience. Not so this time! Julie and Jaylena have a variety of interesting tales to tell when they get home. It has been especially exciting for Jaylena, who got to be in on several births, give the babies their first baths, and learn how to pin on cloth diapers, something that young ladies in the States do not have much experience with in this generation of almost universal disposable-diaper usage.

One comical thing that happened the day before yesterday got Titus a good teasing, but thankfully did not leave anyone the worse for wear. The electric mechanism that raises and lowers the extremely heavy treatment table in the emergency room has not worked for two years. When there is an extensive wound to clean and suture or an abscess that needs excised and drained, the nurse's back is almost too stiff to straighten after she has bent over the low treatment table all that long time. Titus was able to take the table apart, discover the source of the problem, fix it, and put everything back together. Or so he thought.

Shortly after all the parts were in place and we could step on the nifty little foot pedal to raise and lower the table with great ease, an elderly gentleman came in. He was in a lot of pain from a large abscess on his side, midway between his arm and hip. Groaning, he carefully eased himself onto the table on his back. Whereupon, the head of the table promptly tipped down at a sharp angle, thrusting his feet into the air and nearly banging his head on the floor. I frantically grabbed for his shoulders, trying to keep him from sliding completely onto the floor, while Rosmery threw her weight into hauling down on the foot of the table. We finally got him on a fairly even keel. And that is how we discovered that the part taken from the keep-it-from-tipping-back-and-forth thingy, which Titus had used to replace the defunct part for the raise-and-lower-it-thingy, really was necessary after all! Unfortunately for the poor elderly gentleman, the spectacle of his almost flying off the table onto the floor was extremely funny, and Rosmery, Jaylena, Julie, and I nearly doubled over in gales of very unprofessional, but very human, laughter. Fortunately for us, the patient was one of our guards, quite a nice chap with a good sense of humor, and in spite of the pain he was in, he heartily joined us with his own guffaws of amusement.

# 31

## Wombs, Wounds, Worms, and Whatnot

### *July 24, 2006 ~ San Luis, Honduras*

I can hardly believe that we are planning to leave Honduras a week from to-day. During this visit, twenty-two babies have been born, but Tiffany and I have only attended nine of those, since a good many arrived while we were elsewhere for services and training seminars. We are praying for at least two more births while I am still here, preferably ones that will give her the op-portunity to do some suturing so I can talk her through the steps. I have a couple of chicken breasts thawing in the fridge on which we plan to cut and repair episiotomies this afternoon, using a spare packet of suture. That is how I learned to do it in my classes at the Medical University of South Carolina, so I think it will be great practice for her as well. The texture of the chicken gives a surprisingly close approximation to the real thing, but a distinct advantage to practicing with dead meat is that we can cut multiple episiotomies on the same chicken breast, putting in—and taking out—as many stitches as are needed to get a good feel for doing the job right. No matter how often the scissors snip it or the needle sticks it, the chicken will not utter one squawk of protest, something which would likely *not* hold true in a real-life stitching session on a new mother.

There are some experiences in delivering babies that we would just as soon neither of us has further chance to practice. Two weeks ago, a baby came so quickly that I only had time to pull on one glove and no chance at all to un-wrap a package of instruments before he was born. He slipped out in a rush, one loop of cord wrapped loosely around his neck. I was able to slide the cord down over his body without any trouble. The problem came after the placenta delivered. In spite of massaging the woman's uterus, giving her IV fluids with Pitocin, and injecting her with Methergine, Dicynone, and Vitamin K, she just kept pumping out the blood.

It is the first time in my life that I have had to take the last-resort measure of squeezing the uterus between both hands and maintaining enough pressure for the bleeding to finally stop. Believe me, there were plenty of prayers going rapidly up during those tense, scary minutes until the hemorrhaging was under control. When it had become evident that the baby would arrive soon, I had called Tiffany on the walkie-talkie to see if she wanted to come over and do the delivery. Things went much faster than expected, and she walked into the room just after the baby was born. Julie Mowery expertly started the IV on the mother, while Tiffany scurried around to draw up and inject the various drugs, since she knew where they were stored. I kept my hands clamped around the uterus, and they handled the myriad things that would have been impossible for one nurse to accomplish alone in that situation.

Shortly after that, in one of the training sessions that I am doing with the nurses, we discussed the steps in handling shoulder dystocia, or what to do if the shoulders get stuck after the head is born. All of us agreed that the Lord must surely protect missionary nurses by preventing what could, so many times, be a fatal situation when there is just one person to handle everything. It is God's work, so He watches out for His own, and "schedules" emergencies that have to have two pairs of hands.

Not long ago, a six-year-old came in with an order from the local doctor to have his finger sutured. The little fellow had been playing around a folding-frame bed when it collapsed, catching his hand and pinching off the end of his finger. Unfortunately, there was not enough left of the fingertip to suture anything. He was back yesterday to have the stump cleaned and dressed, and I was amazed at how quietly he lay on the treatment table, with just a little whimpering, during what had to be pretty significant pain.

He certainly was a lot different than the eleven-year-old girl who arrived that same morning to have a large abscess on her tailbone drained. It took over an hour of sweet talking and explaining on my part, and lots of idle threats, waving of arms, and a couple of ineffective swats from her mother, before she finally consented to lie on her stomach on the treatment table. Propped on her elbows, head twisted around, she peered at me anxiously over her shoulder. I picked up a syringe with local anesthesia. She surged up from the table. I tried my best to convince her that the incision with a scalpel blade and the pressure to squeeze out the infection would hurt a lot less if she would let me use the tiny needle with numbing medicine, but she adamantly refused to hear of that. I laid the syringe aside, and she plopped back down. Reaching for the scalpel, I poised it over the abscess. She kicked violently, connected squarely with my legs, and literally knocked me backwards off my feet, landing me neatly on my seat in the waste basket. I wriggled free and stood back up, straddled her, and finished the job, removing an incredible amount of pus, to my great satisfaction and to her great relief.

Although that abscess contained only pus, many that we drain have one or several *Torsalos*, the revolting, pasty-white worms covered with stiff black spines that entrench themselves in a host's subcutaneous fat layer, happily nibbling away. Seventy-four-year-old *don* Tonio is doing much better since we dug out the putrid, dead-for-four-days carcass of the VERY large one that was embedded in his abdomen. He has been back several times for us to clean and dress the hole that was left after he poured some liquid insecticide into the opening in his skin where the worm had burrowed. He killed the worm, all right, but instead of coming to have us remove it right away, he let it decay. It took many minutes of scooping and digging to extract the rotted remains that had grown half as big as my little finger. I think he will not try the do-it-yourself method of getting rid of an unwelcome visitor like that again.

Then there was the twelve-year-old girl who arrived at the clinic clutching a bloody rag around her hand. I was puzzled at the strange appearance of the wound and quite curious about the bright-green color of something peeping out from the bandage. Come to find out, her parents had liberally sprinkled cigar ashes into the deep, two-inch gash and topped it with coffee leaves. Before any stitching could be done, all of that mess had to be cleaned out, a process which did not make the job any more comfortable for the girl. I suppose they were attempting to stop the bleeding in the best way they knew how, and they had never had an opportunity to attend a first aid class and learn about putting direct pressure on a wound.

The week before last, I had just gotten back to our house after my evening shift and was nearly ready for bed when the nurse who had relieved me called on the walkie-talkie. *"Hermana Ana, ¿puede venir? Hay una grave herida."* (Sister Hannah, can you come? There's a serious wound.) The tone of her voice, plus the fact that, a few seconds after she gave her message, the night guard called on his walkie-talkie with the same request, sent me hurrying back into a uniform and racing next door.

She was not kidding when she said it was serious. In the treatment room sat a middle-aged gentleman with his hand tightly wound up in what looked like parts of a couple of shirts, all of it stiffly saturated with both fresh and dried blood. His story was that he had been working in a field, planting beans, when a large rock rolled off the mountain and pinned his hand under it. I slowly and carefully cut loose and unwrapped the layers of cloth around the hand to reveal a large, nasty, mangled-edged hole clear through the palm, with glistening slivers, fragments of protruding bone, and severed ends of tendon.

A wound which is that extensive is way beyond our capability to suture here, but we started a liter of IV fluid to run in wide open to replace the large quantity of blood that he had lost. While that was going, we thoroughly irrigated, bandaged, and splinted his hand, then packed ice around it for the ambulance transfer to a hospital with surgical facilities. Before starting the cleaning, I gave him an injection of pain reliever, but he was still moaning with agony while we worked as gently and quickly as we could.

We prayed with him before loading him into the ambulance a little after midnight and sending him on his way. While cleaning everything up after he left, we talked about the ways that his story and the clinical picture just did not add up, and it was no surprise to learn a few days later that the "rock" was actually a bullet that he had accidentally shot through his hand. *That* fit the scenario much better, especially with the relative sizes of the entrance and exit wounds. The gun was probably not registered, so he was afraid to have the authorities know about it, and he concocted the story about the bean field and big rock to keep from getting turned in to the police when he arrived at the clinic. It was another of those live-and-learn cases that make missionary nursing so unique and interesting.

# 32

## *Enfermeras Especiales*
### *Summer 2006 ~ San Luis, Honduras*

The EFM clinic in San Luis is staffed by dedicated nurses who have served the needs of over one hundred thousand people since the doors first opened on May 2, 1979. These services include things as simple as selling two Tylenol to the man with a headache, as serious as stitching up the machete-lacerated leg of the boy who stumbled while trimming grass in his yard, and as rewarding as ensuring the safe arrival into the world of thousands of babies.

During our family's visit this summer, I was again privileged to be a part of the clinic ministry by working Esperanza's shifts. She is a nurse who has been on the staff for twenty-four years, long enough to earn nearly a month of annual vacation. Our stay came at the right date to be able to give her time off with her grandchildren and afforded me the opportunity for more of the excitement and challenge of clinic work.

One afternoon toward the end of her vacation, Esperanza came by the clinic for a continuing-education class that I gave for all of the nurses. I accompanied her home for a visit afterwards and found out why she has stayed so trim and fit all of these years. A forty-five-minute-one-way walk every workday between her house high on the mountainside and the clinic in the valley is routine to her, but it left me huffing and puffing. Day after day, rain or shine, she has faithfully trudged the dirt path to give compassionate, skillful care to the men, women, and children who need her.

Esperanza is one of the four *emfermeras especiales* (special nurses) who cover the clinic shifts 24/7. Without a doctor on staff, they are solely responsible for making the split-second decisions necessary in an emergency and providing not only physical but spiritual care to the vast variety of people who walk, stagger, or are carried through the doors.

In addition, meet Miriam, our head nurse, who has given eighteen years of dependable, sacrificial service. She not only works regular shifts like everyone else, but if one of the others is ill, she fills in, assuring that the clinic doors are kept open. In addition, she orders the medicines necessary to stock the pharmacy shelves, keeps records, helps prepare the required government reports, juggles the monthly scheduling, and efficiently handles the other myriad tasks that her position demands.

Rosmery, the third longest on staff, divides her time among the roles of dedicated mom to the seven- and nine-year-old girls that she adopted as infants, active lay-teacher in the local church, and faithful nurse. Solid and steady in her commitment to the clinic, she is also an on-call nurse for her neighborhood, always ready to lend a hand or give advice when someone falls ill.

The newest nurse, Maribel, is a graduate of our Bible institute as well as one of a number of young ladies who have been helped with financial aid by EFM for their nursing education. She took her LPN exam three years ago at the age of thirty, and since then has proven to be a good investment of mission funds. She is kept extra busy between her full-time clinic job, care of an adopted daughter, and diligent attendance at the local high school, where she is working on finishing ninth grade. Interestingly, a candidate for one of the country's several nursing schools must only have completed seventh grade before starting two years of nursing studies leading to a "Grade One" nursing degree (equivalent to our LPN), or three years of classes needed to earn a "Grade Two" degree (equivalent to our RN).

The final nurse is Tiffany Melton, busy full-time missionary wife and mother. Though she does not generally work regular clinic shifts, she is on call to be an extra pair of hands whenever needed, as well as being responsible for important aspects of the office work. Together these *enfermeras especiales* supply a vital service to the community and the surrounding area.

\* \* \* \* \* \* \* \* \*

**UPDATE: Summer 2014.** In the thirty-five years since it was started, nurses and an occasional doctor have safely welcomed into the world close to nine thousand babies at the clinic, including dozens of pairs of twins and several sets of triplets. The first triplets were born in 1997 to a twenty-one-year-old mother with an eleven-month-old little one at home. Just imagine having no laundromat, washing machine, or diaper service available when you have four babies in diapers at the same time!

All of the nurses who were working in the clinic eight years ago are still faithfully tending patients. Rosmery has adopted another little girl, one that was born to an unmarried mother who did not want her. Tiffany has been blessed with two more sons, and Maribel recently married and now has an infant daughter. Busy as their lives are with caring for the needs of their own families, these nurses, and many others like them across the years of the clinic's existence, have been faithful to share the proverbial cup of cold water in Jesus' name, a service that Christ promised would not go unrewarded. As they put others' needs first, God's love is shown and His name glorified here in their corner of His kingdom.

# 33

## She Had Her Baby *Where?* Oh, There!
### *June 10, 2008 ~ San Luis, Honduras*

Muggy greetings from San Luis, Honduras. We arrived for our ten-week stay at the beginning of the rainy season, and the weather has cooperated as expected. In fact, our plane landed at the tail end of the worst storm that the locals can recall in over a year and a half. It is the first time I ever remember looking out the plane window and seeing huge sheets of lightning flashing *below* us as we flew above the clouds. That afternoon during the downpour, the water was running a foot deep in the streets and spewing four feet high from storm drains that were so inundated they could not contain the overflow.

We spent the night in the mission apartment in San Pedro Sula and did business in the city the next morning and afternoon, leaving for San Luis around 6:30 p.m. That is later than anyone feels comfortable with, since the dirt road that must be traveled for the last half of the journey is much safer by daylight. Just before we were ready to pull out, the wind kicked up and blew several heavy sheets of corrugated, tile-like roofing off the church which is next door to the apartment/radio station building. A couple of them crashed to the walkway below and shattered, though fortunately NOT when anyone was walking by. There were three good-sized pieces broken off but still lying loose on the roof, so Rex and two other men who were there got a broom, leaned WAY out over the wobbly second-story railing, and managed to pull the pieces to the edge of the church roof, then grab them and ease them down safely so they would not blow off with the next big gust of wind and wallop someone. It was one of those I-am-too-nervous-to-watch-but-I-am-too-nervous-not-to moments, during which I shot up several short, URGENT prayers that the railing would hold and the men not go catapulting over the edge to join the broken tiles on the sidewalk two stories below.

Thankfully, the trip out to San Luis was relatively peaceful. Partway there, we were forced to a stop by some large-sized boulders blocking the road. It took careful maneuvering and slowing w-a-y down to get around them and back onto the road. The whole thing seemed odd, since the road at that spot was not along a mountain. We wondered if someone had tried to set up a roadblock for an ambush, which is quite common after dark. In any case, we made it safely past the rocks to where we will be staying.

Thursday, during a heavy downpour and gusty winds, a big tree just outside the side-yard fence was uprooted and crashed down on the tin roof of the storage area beside the house. It snapped the line that supplies Internet service to fellow missionaries Zach and Sarah Robbert's house next door, pulled the other power lines down in a taut "V" halfway to the ground, and totally destroyed half the roof. We were grateful that no one was in the yard at the time, and the four-wheeler, large trampoline, and zero-turn riding lawnmower that are kept in that area were not damaged. A man from town brought his chainsaw the next morning and carefully cut off limb after limb of the downed tree. When he got to the main trunk, about a foot and a half in diameter, he straddled it and started chiseling it into sections. We were standing around with bated breath, hoping and praying that the power lines would withstand the tremendous strain of having had the tree's weight on them for twenty-four hours, followed by the sudden rebound we all expected as he cut through the last section. Amazingly, the weight of the roots and the dirt clinging to them slowly pulled the final section of trunk upright, and the roots thudded back into position, leaving the lines intact, though quite sagging. Someone lifted them from the garage roof, tied them back up to their proper spot on the pole, and we were in business once more. Rex, Jeffrey, and some other men and boys spent the rest of the day chopping, trimming, and hauling the wood up to the Bible institute kitchen, making the cooks happy with enough fuel to fire up their cookstove for weeks to come.

On this visit, I am once again having the privilege of working in the clinic. I never know what might happen, but I can always count on things being exciting and sometimes a bit scary—well, all right, sometimes REALLY scary! This morning Maribel called me just before breakfast to help with the delivery of a baby. The sixteen-year-old, first-time mama had arrived at 6 a.m., one-centimeter dilated. Shortly thereafter, the baby's heart rate dropped into the eighties, instead of staying between 120 and 160 beats per minute as it is supposed to. The girl was progressing so rapidly that Maribel was fairly certain there would be no time to transfer her to the hospital. Reaching for the adult-sized mask kept always at the ready in a bag hanging from the handle of the four-feet-tall oxygen tank, she slipped it over the girl's face and adjusted the flow, while helping her turn onto her left side to optimize the blood supply to the baby. The baby's heartbeat gradually inched up out of the absolute danger zone, but it stayed lower than ideal through a very fast labor—two-and-a-half hours from one centimeter to ten.

When Maribel called me, it was time for the delivery, and she wanted a second person on hand in case the baby needed extra help, which she most definitely did. At 8:49 a.m., she arrived into the world limp, white, and unmoving. Rapidly clamping and cutting the cord, I rushed her floppy body across the room to the infant warmer. Laying her gently on the heated blanket and snatching the infant-sized oxygen mask from the other bag dangling from the tank's handle, I quickly transferred the oxygen from mama to baby and adjusted the flow rate. Ten tense minutes of anxious effort and earnest prayer later, a pink, healthy, six-pound, wriggly little bundle of blessing was vigorously enjoying her first breakfast. Thank God!

Yesterday, I was there to help with the man who swung his machete the wrong way and connected with his wrist rather than the clump of grass that he was aiming for. He walked in the front door clutching his wound, blood dripping around and through his fingers as he unsuccessfully tried to staunch the profuse bleeding from the large blood vessel he had severed. Maribel prodded and probed with a hastily opened packet of hemostats, struggling to find and clamp the ends of the vein, but the unrelenting flow of blood made it impossible for her to see them. Grabbing a thick stack of gauze squares from the metal canister in the treatment room, she applied pressure to the nasty looking gash while I hustled to the front desk to make a STAT (immediate) call to Dr. Maldonado. Obliging as always, he left the patients in his office and hurried down to give us an excellent demonstration of tying off the two ends of the vein and repairing the laceration. I held the clamps that kept the edges of the wound apart so he could work, while I focused intently on his every move. I was especially grateful for the refresher course, as two years have passed since I last held a needle driver and studied the edges of an injury, deciding where to take my next stitch. It sounds as though I will get plenty of chances to refine my skills, because they tell me there have been a *lot* of suturing jobs lately.

Births happen the world over in unusual places, but not often by the choice of the mother. Two days ago, shortly before 3:00 p.m., Miriam had examined a new patient and found that she was dilated to five centimeters. The woman walked out of the labor room and stepped into the hall bathroom while Miriam went to the front desk to give report to the incoming nurse. Unfortunately, I was not that nurse, so I missed out on all the excitement. When the afternoon nurse had discharged a little pediatric patient, she went to check on the laboring mother. Glancing into the labor ward and down the hall, she saw no one. Then she noticed the closed bathroom door. Calling the woman's name but getting no response, she rattled the knob and knocked on the door. It was locked, and the woman refused to open it. Miriam had not left yet, so both nurses worked to force their way in. I do not know who was more surprised when the door finally swung open—the woman lying on the floor with her minutes-old infant sprawled on the tiles between her legs, or the two nurses gawking down at the sight. Incredibly, neither the woman nor her baby had made enough noise for anyone outside the door to have any idea of the momentous event taking place. Both mom and baby were fine, although I cannot say the same for either nurse's nerves.

## 34

## I Feel a Dog on My Head

*June 25, 2008 ~ San Luis, Honduras*

The forty-year-old man with a high fever whom I had admitted the day before shook his head from side to side, looked up at me and said, "I feel a dog on my head." Startled, I stopped counting the drops of the strong antibiotic that was piggy backed into his main IV line and shot a glance at his head. Nope, no dog there that I could see. In the next second, I realized my error. He really had said *"Siento un peso en mi cabeza,"* but I heard, *"Siento un perro en mi cabeza." Peso* means "weight"; *perro* means "dog." One letter's difference only, but what a vastly different meaning. Actually, I suppose if he truly did have a dog sitting on his head, he would feel a weight there as well. He and I chuckled together over my poor hearing before I gave him the next dose of medicine for fever and pain, a treatment that soon eliminated the heavy feeling. Later that morning, when our consulting doctor came to check on him, the presumptive diagnosis of malaria was changed to brucellosis, based on his fever pattern, lack of response to the anti-malarial medicine, and the fact that he had drunk raw milk several weeks before. Having a lab do a definitive diagnosis based on blood work would be nice, but is not even remotely possible. Fortunately for him, brucellosis is a lot less serious than malaria, and he should be well soon, if he takes the entire dose of antibiotic and gives his body time to recover.

I am at the end of my second week of working in the clinic, and as usual, the variety of nursing care has been interesting, to say the least. My patients have ranged in age from the seven-pound, four-ounce, brand new baby boy that I delivered last week, to the sixty-three-year-old man with postsurgical complications who was admitted the day before that. I have checked fasting blood sugars, one of which was 589 mg/dl. Normal is 80-120 mg/dl, so you can understand why that number gave me some anxious moments, especially when its owner said her vision was starting to blur. I have treated a couple of people with uncontrolled bleeding from molar extractions, performed pregnancy tests, started numerous IV's and figured out the drip calculations for them, injected MANY doses of antibiotics and pain medications, administered nebulizations and given oxygen for extremely asthmatic people, changed dressings and cleansed wounds, and helped extract from someone's index finger a splinter that had entered at the first joint and was poking through the skin at the very tip of the finger. (You are right—OUCH!) I have cared for patients with maladies running the gamut from scabies to sunstroke to scorpion sting.

Right now, it is 3:18 a.m., and I just finished making rounds for the umpteenth time tonight, checking on the newly delivered six-pound baby and her mommy and my five little pediatric patients, aged four months to sixteen months, who are all finally asleep. I hung a new bag of IV fluid for one, straining to see my watch in the dim light from the nurses' desk outside the pediatric ward as I adjusted the drip rate to the proper ten drops per minute. No modern IV pumps here! Even if we had them, I am not sure how well they would work, with the electricity situation as it is. At least three times tonight, the power has gone off, plunging us into total darkness for the half minute or so that it takes the generator behind the clinic to roar to life and give us back our lights. When the electricity from town kicks in again, the generator shuts off, ready to repeat the scenario as necessary.

In between shaking down thermometers and taking temperatures, giving injections and pushing IV meds, unpinning messy cloth diapers and pinning clean ones back on, wiping up vomit and changing sheets, getting pillows for the five mommies who are staying with their babies and helping each mom crawl up into a crib and get settled next to her little one for a few hours of sleep, I have had time to type five sentences. I actually started this letter three days ago …

… and now it is two days past that, and I finished that night without further opportunity to sit at the computer. Sometimes the night shift can be pretty quiet, but not so the last two times that I worked it. Sunday night, the afternoon nurse had only been gone a few minutes when I heard a great commotion outside the front door. The screen door is locked and the heavy wooden door is shut at night for safety's sake, so when someone rings the bell, we go to the window in the postpartum ward to see who is standing on the porch. This time, there were six or seven people there, one of them sobbing loudly. He collapsed onto the floor in a heap of misery, but the others dragged him to his feet and guided his stumbling steps through the door and down the hall to the exam table in the treatment room.

The nineteen-year-old young man was literally foaming at the mouth, his face all puckered up in pain, wailing that his stomach hurt. I took one whiff and knew without asking what at least part of his problem was. It was the last night of a two-week town party. There was plenty of beer flowing to keep things stirred up, and the boy had drunk a liter of the smelly stuff. One of the men with him thrust a stack of *lempiras* into my hand. "We took up a collection among all of us to pay for his treatment. None of us here is responsible for him, and no one else is either. Do what you can to help him." I stood there stunned for a moment, staring at the man who had spoken.

After checking the boy's vital signs, I called Dr. Maldonado, who outlined the four steps of treatment: 1) injectable Valium, 2) antispasmodic liquid, 3) antacid, and 4) "Tell his father to give him a good thrashing." The first three I could do. Unfortunately, although he probably needed the last thing the most, it was not a therapy I could administer. I drew the dose of Valium into a syringe and scrubbed with an alcohol-soaked cotton ball at a spot on his hip. Evidently the boy had fallen more than just on our porch, for his shorts were saturated with gritty mud. The men who had hauled him in stayed long enough to maneuver him to the bed in our isolation ward after his injection, but were all too glad to quickly exit after that. A town policeman who had stepped in with the others and stood quietly watching in the hall walked out with them. There I was my patients for the night: a very sick toddler in for IV rehydration following five days of vomiting and diarrhea, two new babies and their mommies, and a very drunk nineteen-year-old. As I was measuring out the antispasmodic liquid from the gallon jug in our little pharmacy, I heard a truck pull up outside. Patient number seven was just arriving: another baby needing IV rehydration.

This time, it was a sixteen-month-old boy. Fortunately, his veins were not as collapsed as some I have worked with, and I was able to successfully start the IV on the very first stick—which lasted for all of seven seconds as he jerked out the catheter before I could tape it down.

Ten minutes later, the IV was in place and running well. I had given him an antibiotic injection and was slowly pushing a dose of a different medication through his IV line when I glanced over at the other baby and saw that his IV was not dripping. His mother was holding him, watching me work on the new patient, and did not notice that in getting him out of the crib and settled on her lap, the IV tubing had kinked, cutting off the flow and allowing the blood to clot and occlude the needle. In spite of my best efforts, I could not get things flowing again, and my heart sank. I knew it had taken Miriam six failed tries that afternoon before a vein cooperated enough on the seventh stick to insert a tiny #25 butterfly needle, and he had not had enough fluids yet to make me hope that things would be much better now.

I had no chance to fret about the situation because just at that moment, an ambulance pulled up outside the door, lights flashing, and patient number eight arrived. It was another nineteen-year-old young man, unconscious, eyes rolled back in his head, pupils fixed and dilated. His anxious parents told me he had started complaining of chest pain around 8:30 p.m. It was now a few minutes until midnight. The ambulance attendants transferred him from the stretcher to a bed in our general ward, while I rushed to wheel in our big oxygen tank from another room. A quick finger stick and glucose check showed that his blood sugar was in the normal range.

Before starting an IV and hanging a liter of fluids, I prayed with the family, asking the Lord to touch their son for His glory and honor, and to comfort and sustain them. This boy was the nephew of Esperanza, the very nurse whose place I was taking that night while she was on vacation, and the family was a clean-living, Christian one. Minutes after the IV solution started pouring into his system, the boy regained consciousness, wildly thrashing in his confusion. I jumped to grab his arms, directing his father and some of the half-dozen others who were there with the family to help hold him so he would not pull his line out. I got right up in his face, holding his head with my hands while talking to him soothingly, explaining that he was in a clinic and we were there to help him. He lapsed back into unconsciousness a minute later, but his family was extremely encouraged that he had come to even briefly, especially given the fact that Esperanza had told them when the ambulance crew picked him up that she doubted he would make it to our clinic alive.

I turned to his mother at the head of his bed, taking her in my arms, stroking her back, and whispering words of comfort while she clung to me and sobbed for a long time. An hour passed while the boy lay there, unmoving. The last of the IV fluids ran into his vein. As though that were a signal, he again opened his eyes, but this time looked around calmly, with a puzzled expression on his face. I asked him what day it was, his name, and how old he was, all of which he answered correctly. Then I asked who the lady sitting beside him was. He glanced over, smiled, and said, "My mommy," reaching out both arms to give her a big hug. Believe me, we were all thanking the Lord! I told him I had one more question to ask to be sure he was well recovered.

"Look at me." He obediently did. "Do you think I am pretty or ugly?" I demanded.

He grinned and said, "Pretty!"

"Uh-oh," I responded, shaking my head at him. "Now I know for sure that you are still *really* sick!" We all laughed, enjoying the relief, and rejoicing at God's answer to our prayers. An hour and a half after being wheeled unconscious through the door, he walked out on his own two feet, with no signs of anything at all wrong with him.

Now I was back to the problem with the eleven-month-old with the clotted-off IV, a situation which had, of necessity, assumed a lower priority with the arrival of the unconscious boy. (Remember, there is only one nurse on shift at any time, day or night, no matter how many patients there are.) I tried twice, unsuccessfully, to restart the IV. He was still not hydrated enough.

The only recourse was to use the tube-through-his-nose-and-into-his-stomach trick. I explained to his seventeen-year-old mother (her husband had drowned during her pregnancy, so she was all alone in this crisis) what I needed to do and got her permission. Then, gathering my supplies, I carefully measured from his nose to his ear and on to the tip of his breastbone, to get the proper length of tubing needed to reach into the stomach. Everything went beautifully, and a few minutes later, tubing securely taped to his nose and forehead, the little one was back asleep, the life-giving fluids that he so badly needed doing their job.

Aside from the thirty-one-weeks-pregnant woman who came in at about 2:30 later that morning with signs of preterm labor, needing to be evaluated and treated, the rest of the night was *relatively* quiet. The drunken boy slept soundly the whole time, thankfully making no trouble. Rex was waiting for me when I got home a little after 7:00 a.m. and very patiently listened while I talked his ear off to unwind before heading for bed and some sleep.

# 35

## She Didn't Look Good in Purple

*June 30, 2008 ~ San Luis, Honduras*

It is 11:47 p.m. So far the night shift at the clinic has been peacefully quiet. A thunderstorm blustered through earlier this evening, dumping barrels of water down on the dusty roads, thirsty fields, and cement-block-walled houses on three sides of our mission compound. The only sounds now are an occasional drop of water from the tile roof plopping into a puddle on the gravel path below; the ceaseless, raucous croaking of hundreds of frogs jubilantly rejoicing at those puddles; and the periodic, harsh, clicking call of a lizard suspended somewhere close by on the branch of an overhanging coconut tree.

About an hour ago, I hurried to a window in the unoccupied isolation room, brushed aside the striped cotton curtain, and peered inquisitively into the blackness to investigate the crunching of tires and down-shifting of gears from a truck on the road leading to the clinic. Four years earlier, we had watched with astonishment as a crew of men armed with simple picks and shovels tackled the section of dirt road that wound from the center of San Luis, with its more than ten thousand residents, to our property located at the edge of town. Those final two kilometers that ended at the clinic gate were, hands down, the worst stretch of protruding rocks and bone-wrenching ruts along the entire ninety-kilometer route from the airport in San Pedro Sula to our clinic/radio station/Bible institute here in San Luis. In an unbelievably short number of days, the human backhoe had dug a trench measuring three feet wide and nearly four feet deep for new drainage pipes. The replacement tubing was sorely needed, since the old system was so deteriorated that some of the original pipes had completely crumbled away. However, it was weeks after the excavation was finished before the next phase was begun. Because it was the middle of the rainy season, the uneven piles of dirt and stones left from the digging were treacherously slippery, making our ten-minute walks to and from the local church rather challenging as we leaped awkwardly from one mound to the next. On this trip back for another summer of missionary work, not only were the pipes in place, but a beautiful concrete road had been poured, stopping abruptly just a few yards short of the compound gate.

More often than not at this time of night, any vehicle that creeps cautiously off the six-inch drop from the concrete onto the dirt road that continues past the clinic is headed for our front gate, bearing someone in need of medical attention. This time, the gutturally rumbling engine belonged to a cargo truck, carrying perhaps a load of green bananas to early morning market in a bigger city several hours away. I relaxed as I let the curtain fall back in place and returned to the front desk. Some of my most fervent prayers have been during the lonely predawn hours when I need God's help and wisdom while working single-handedly with a gravely ill patient. And yet, I am never truly alone. Time and again, I have been reminded that this is God's work, and He is right here with me, bringing to mind the things I need to remember in order to properly be "His hands extended." Still, there is always an extra surge of adrenaline that inevitably accompanies the arrival of anyone after 11:00 p.m.

I softly swing open the slatted-wood half door leading into the nine-feet by seventeen-feet pediatric ward. Five white-painted, iron-railed cribs in assorted sizes crowd along all four sides of every square inch of wall space. Bright-pink curtains with cheerful teddy bears hang jauntily at the one tiny window that is much too high and too small to invite in any significant light or air. A colorfully painted mural of Noah, his ark, and various pairs of lively animals flows invitingly across one wall and onto the adjoining one. It transforms the otherwise stark hospital room into a bright, inviting haven for the hundreds of children who spend time here each year, recuperating from the harsh realities of rural mountain life, with its lack of safe drinking water. In this area of the country where indoor plumbing is a luxury, it is no wonder that we see so many little ones with tummy troubles.

My lone pediatric patient is peacefully asleep, one leg draped over her mother, curled awkwardly beside her in the narrow crib. Now that the toddler has had a day of treatment with IV fluids and antibiotics, her frequent diarrhea and vomiting have stopped. It is good to see that both she and her worn-out mommy are catching up on some needed rest. I squint at my wristwatch in the dim light, counting the slowly falling drops of 5% dextrose and saline in the half-empty bag of IV solution hanging from the metal pole beside her bed. A slight adjustment of the rolling valve midway down the tubing slows the rate just enough to keep the fluid leisurely dripping at the prescribed rate into the slender plastic catheter secured in her foot with numerous strips of adhesive tape.

I exit the ward through the creaking half-door and take three steps to the pharmacy, smaller than a walk–in closet in many houses in the States. In spite of the fact that it can accommodate two people at a time only if both are very skinny or if one turns sideways, its shelves are packed with a respectable quantity and variety of medications. From its hook on the outside of the pharmacy door, I lift the frayed maroon hand towel. The nurse who worked the shift before mine used it dozens of times; it definitely needs to be exchanged for a clean, dry one. I head down the hall to the linen/utility room at the far end of the building. A water distiller hums on the counter, a rubber tube running from its depths into the small mouth of an ancient, brown glass gallon jug. We will use the distilled water to dilute iodine to a half-and-half concentration appropriate for cleansing wounds.

I notice the instruments air-drying in an orange plastic dish drainer beside the deep, square sink. Sometime before my shift ends, I need to wrap them in one of the well-worn pieces of cloth cut from an old sheet and hemmed to size for that purpose. There is no such luxury here as tossing a disposable instrument into the trash after a single use. Each needle holder, forceps, scalpel handle, and pair of scissors is carefully scrubbed and soaked in bleach, then rinsed and stacked in the drainer. Once dry, each instrument gets slipped into a special envelope made of heat-resistant white paper on one side and a clear, plastic-like film on the other, so the contents can be seen at a glance. Then they go through a two-hour sterilization process in our autoclave. Maribel used these instruments to suture the nasty gashes of the eighteen-year-old young man whose uncle violently attacked him with a machete this afternoon. The scars he will forever wear from the deep cuts on his shoulder, arm, and leg will fade with time, and the sling that supports his cracked shoulder blade will be removed in a few weeks. But the marks of the emotional trauma he carries inside will be raw for months and years to come. Oh, the tragedies that can be avoided by knowing and living for God!

I walk back up the hall to hang the fresh towel on its hook, enjoying for a moment the peaceful calm of the night. If this continues, I may even have some time to work on the class I will be doing with the nurses later this month. I cannot help but contrast the welcome tranquility with the happenings of this same shift slightly over a week ago.

I was tired from the start, having worked twenty-four of the previous forty hours (eight hours on, eight hours off, eight hours back on, and so forth). Rex's and my twenty-eighth wedding anniversary on July fourth had come and gone. It was not exactly the most romantic we had ever experienced, since my sweetheart was miles away that weekend, teaching a missiology course to national pastors. I had been spending every spare minute between clinic shifts finishing the research for a talk on menopause that I was scheduled to give to the women of the local church the evening of the fourth. Because of a terrific storm with subsequent power outage all over town, that service ended up being cancelled fifteen minutes before it was to have started. A few nights later, minus the booming thunder accompaniment and plus an ample supply of electricity, I gave the lecture to a large group of ladies and their interested husbands, and it went fine.

The evening of my twelve-hour shift on the fifth passed quickly with the usual assortment of people coming and going. The postpartum ward lights were not working again, but from the glow of the hall bulb through the open doorway, I could see that the not-quite-six-pound baby girl whose delivery I had helped with that morning was nursing well and appeared to be doing fine. I did not need a light to listen with my stethoscope, and I was pleased to hear that her lung sounds were nice and clean, in spite of her momentary breathing trouble right after birth.

By 11:00 p.m., the steady stream of walk-in patients had stopped, and mother and baby were sound asleep. A few minutes before 2:00 a.m., little Miss Newborn woke up hungry and nursed, but she kept crying even after she had eaten well and should have been satisfied. Her mother had been in labor for three days at home before coming to the clinic, and I knew she was exhausted. When she gratefully accepted my offer to take her baby for a little while so she could sleep, I carried the tiny girl back to our linen room for a diaper change. Imagine the heart-stopping shock I received when I unwrapped her blanket and discovered that her face was a deep, dark, ghastly shade of purple! Jerking open the snaps on her sleeper, I was dismayed to see that her entire body was the same horrible color. Snatching her back up in my arms, I ran down the hall to the delivery room, threw the lever to start the powerful bulbs in the infant warmer glowing with heat, and pulled the oxygen tank close. Quickly, I stripped off her sleeper and laid her in the warmer, sliding a small mask over her face and starting a rich flow of oxygen to her lungs. Rushing to the phone in the corner of the room, I hurriedly dialed Dr. Maldonado, who gave orders for a STAT intramuscular injection of steroid and assured me that he was on his way.

By the time he arrived a few minutes later, the baby's deep-purple color had gradually lightened to a dusky blue-grey. After a few more minutes of oxygen, she had *almost* returned to the much more attractive shade of pink that is so becoming to little girls. Although she was obviously struggling to breathe, surprisingly, I heard no heart murmur, and her lungs still sounded clear. I knew the doctor thought that I had overreacted, but he had not seen her in purple.

Over the next three hours, I discovered that as long as she was not crying, her color hovered around an unhealthy-looking pasty blush. The moment she started to fuss, she turned blue and mottled. I tried to keep her content by stroking her gently, singing and talking to her, and offering at intervals a bottle of glucose water to maintain her blood sugar at the very acceptable level that it was when I checked it earlier. I had no success in weaning her completely off the oxygen. Even a slight whimper changed her color from pale pink to purple with a rapidity that would have made any chameleon envious. I was extremely thankful for a nearly full oxygen tank that had been recently refilled in San Pedro and should easily last the rest of the night.

Early on, I had told the baby's mother what was happening, so when a woman in labor arrived at 5:00 a.m., I hurried to the postpartum ward and asked the new mother to come and watch over her daughter. She listened groggily to my rapid lesson in oxygen administration, caught on quickly, and took over efficiently, leaving me free to check on my new patient. From that point until the day shift nurse got there at 7:00 a.m., it got *really* interesting as I dashed back and forth between two rooms, juggling vigilance of the newborn with support and monitoring of the laboring woman.

When Rosmery arrived, things got a lot easier. She took over the care of the labor patient, and I stayed with the baby while her parents arranged for her transfer to a hospital where she could be evaluated by a neonatologist. What does the phrase "arranged for her transfer" conjure up in your mind? In the States, it involves a call from the attending physician at the referring hospital to a specialist at a higher-level hospital, and the specialist's consent to accept the child for treatment. Then, in the case of an unstable congenital heart defect such as this little girl appeared to have, an ambulance complete with monitoring equipment, oxygen, and an abundance of all imaginable needed supplies will be dispatched, along with skilled personnel trained to deal with any emergency that might arise on the trip.

Here in the mountains of rural Honduras, the only "arrangement" that needed to be made was how her parents were going to afford the trip to the nearest large hospital. Forget the collaboration between doctors. With the socialized medical system, her parents could seek the care of a specialist for their daughter without a formal referral. But they did not have the money for gas that the ambulance driver demanded to see before he would agree to transport. A four- to five-hour bus ride squashed among hot, sweating bodies seemed the only option. But the little one's critical condition made that totally unacceptable. Not only would she likely not survive the trip, I knew that arriving via any method other than ambulance would mean waiting tedious hours in a line that might stretch from the doctor's door clear around the block. If enough patients had gotten in line ahead of them, the baby could conceivably wait all day, only to be turned away at the end of office hours with the other unfortunates who were not close enough to the front to make it into the building before the doors were closed and locked.

What could we do? Thankfully, the clinic has a small fund kept for just such emergencies that can be dipped into when absolutely necessary. No question about the absolutely necessary part in this case! Three hours and various phone calls back and forth between the clinic and ambulance driver later, the sick infant and her mother were finally on their way to help. I breathed a long sigh of relief. However, my shift, which by now had stretched into fifteen hours, was not yet over.

During the snatches of time that I had been with the expectant mother, she had developed an attachment to me and insisted that I should do her delivery. Since I knew that it was her third baby and therefore likely to be a shorter labor, I did not have the heart to say no. I promised her that I would stay, but only after a break to prop up my feet for a few minutes and eat something.

Following a nowhere-near-leisurely late breakfast at the mission house with Rex and Jeffrey, I trudged back to the clinic once more. I was delighted at Rosmery's report that mama-to-be was eight-centimeters dilated and would surely deliver within the next hour. "Wonderful!" I thought. "Soon I can go home and crash."

So much for *that* optimistic idea. Another hour passed ... and another ... and another, and still the poor woman stayed persistently at the same stage of dilation, in spite of strong contractions three to five minutes apart. Every position change, comfort measure, reasonable intervention, prayer, and whatever else we could think of to help things along was futile. Finally, shortly before the afternoon-shift nurse arrived, things started progressing and delivery seemed imminent.

But she pushed ... and pushed ... and pushed. Over an hour and a half passed, and still no baby was born. By this point, her labor progress had fallen way off the normal/average chart and was definitely into the "we-have-*got*-to-do-something!" stage. We called the doctor, who came and examined her. His decision to transfer her to a larger hospital was not too surprising. What did startle me was the way he surreptitiously but urgently motioned for Maribel (who had taken Rosmery's place at 3:00 p.m.) and me to squeeze with him into our pharmacy, the only good place for a private conversation.

"Get her out of here as soon as you possibly can!" he hissed. "She and her husband are *bad news!* They never pay their bills. That woman has been into everything. She was a former prostitute, a police officer, a nurse, and who knows what else. If things don't turn out here as she wants, they are likely to sue the clinic!"

I gulped and glanced over at Maribel, who looked as shocked as I felt. She hurried to the desk to call the ambulance, while I went back to explain to the couple what would be happening next. "PLEASE go with me," the woman begged, desperately grabbing my hand in both of hers and fervently kissing it. "You are my angel!" Bone weary, but mindful of the doctor's dire warning, I figured there was no other choice if I wanted to keep her happy and prevent the trouble he had predicted. Bad credit record or not, the husband was able to convince the ambulance driver that he would take care of the gas, and in a much shorter time than it had taken for the baby that morning, the couple and I were on our way. Sure enough, partway through town the husband tapped on the window separating us from the driver and attendant in the front and gestured for them to stop. We rolled to a halt, and a man handed the husband a wad of bills in through the back window, more than enough to fill the ambulance tank when we stopped at the town's only gas station at the far edge of San Luis.

With that important piece of business attended to, we headed out of town and down the mountainside. Remembering my first such ride, I desperately hoped that I would manage to keep the contents of my stomach intact this time. I glanced furtively at the husband, wondering how he was faring as he crouched on the bench beside me, hands gripping it tightly on either side of him to protect his head from banging the ceiling when we hit a particularly deep rut. His thick, neatly slicked-back hair was falling over his forehead by now, and it privately amused me to see him pull a comb from his pocket a couple of times to force it back into place. Fifteen minutes of jerking and jostling into our journey, the dapper hairstyle was completely forgotten as he abruptly thrust his head out of the hastily opened window behind him. He miserably kept it there for the entire remaining two hours of the trip, periodically heaving his gastric offerings into the roadside bushes. I could both sympathize and totally empathize.

We finally made it to our destination in one piece. Rough as that ride is for the passengers balancing precariously on the bench in the back of the ambulance, it cannot begin to compare with the agony a woman in hard labor feels as she is jolted from side to side on the narrow stretcher. In this case, though, all the jostling served to do what nothing else we had tried could accomplish, and the couple's bouncing baby girl was born short minutes after we arrived at the Santa Bárbara hospital.

I was happy to sit up front on the way home, although I am afraid my somnolent conversation with the driver and attendant was not very stimulating. All I cared was that we made it safely back home, where I gratefully accepted my husband's sympathetic hug and stumbled wearily to bed, VERY thankful to have finally ended my more-than-twenty-six-hour shift. Just remembering it makes me tired!

## 36

## We Keep a Shotgun in Our Broom Closet

*July 3, 2008 ~ San Luis, Honduras*

That is correct! We keep a shotgun in our broom closet. There it stands, double barrels propped against the wall in the far left corner, sharing floor space with a couple of brooms, two bottles of bleach, and an assortment of empty gallon jugs that we use to safely dispose of used needles. I discovered it the morning I needed to sweep the floor when I arrived for my morning shift. The clinic has a wonderful cleaning lady who comes in six days a week and does a superb job of keeping things spick-and-span. Believe me, that is no small task, given our location at the edge of town on a dirt road which is alternately either very dusty or very muddy, depending on when it last rained. It takes several-times-daily sweeping and mopping to keep the tile floors adequately clean, and on the cleaning lady's one day a week off, that job falls to whichever nurse is on duty at the time.

Naturally, I was a bit startled at the odd addition to the normal arsenal of cleaning equipment that one might expect in a broom closet. Upon my inquiry to the guard on duty, he smiled, assured me it was not kept loaded, and confided that it had only been used a few times when one or another of the guards had carried it as a not-so-subtle deterrent to any would-be troublemaker who came around, or had shot it to scare away a stray mutt that persisted in sneaking onto the property and trying to kill the hens whose eggs helped bring in money for the Bible institute.

That is not the *only* difference in stateside-vs.-Honduran nursing. Something that never ceases to amaze me is the cost of clinic care here. The five-pound, eight-ounce, beautiful little girl whom I most recently welcomed into the world at 4:48 a.m. had a noncomplicated arrival, and she and her mommy were both able to go home twenty-four hours later. Their entire bill was five hundred. "Not too bad," you say? You are right, especially considering that we are talking about 500 *lempiras*, not dollars. At the current exchange rate of 18.9 *lempiras* for each dollar, that comes to $26.46. Of course, when either mother or baby needs extra attention, the bill goes up. If a bag of IV fluids is used, it costs $3.65, and oxygen at three liters a minute for an hour comes to an additional 95 cents. Intensive care for a newborn is another 110 *lempiras,* or $5.82.

If your child is dehydrated due to several days of diarrhea and vomiting because you failed to boil his drinking water, you can bring him to our clinic for IV rehydration and medication to get rid of whatever bad bug he got from the water. We will give him excellent nursing care for $4.23 per day plus the cost of his medications and IV fluids. Quite reasonable, especially compared to the $10.58 per five-minute visit that our collaborating physician charges to stop by and see how he is getting along and to make any necessary changes to his treatment plan.

If you are unfortunate enough to chop your hand instead of the tree limb you were trying to cut up for your wife's cooking fire, drop your machete, wrap the wound in a rag (hopefully a clean one), and hurry on in to us. We can inject it with a local anesthetic so the thorough cleaning it needs will not hurt, and you can lie back and close your eyes while one of our nurses expertly puts in the stitches necessary to neatly draw the gaping edges closed. If it is a small cut requiring only one package of suture, you will be charged $4.76 for the repair job and bandaging. If your machete was well sharpened and you were swinging vigorously, your wound will probably require two packages of suture, but in that case you will get a bargain; instead of paying double, your bill will only be $9.26. If you need a tetanus booster, the fee will be 21 cents for the syringe and 11 cents for one of us to give you the shot, since the Health Department supplies us with the vaccine itself free of charge.

Do be careful not to slow down too much at the crest of the hill on your way into town. I am told that it is a prime spot for gangs of hoodlums to leap from their roadside place of concealment, stop your car, and rob you. Just a week or so ago, that very thing happened to a sixty-year-old gentleman on his way to visit his elderly father. He arrived at the clinic mid-morning, clutching a blood-soaked towel to his shoulder. "I wasn't scared when they jumped out, I was mad!" he blustered, as I kept pressure on the wound while he eased down onto the exam table in our treatment room. "There were three of them. One fellow tried to grab my door, and when I swerved to run him down, another one pulled a rifle and shot me through the window!"

I gingerly slipped his bullet-riddled shirt over his head and carefully peeled away the towel. Pleased to find that the bleeding had stopped, I adjusted the brilliant overhead light to better examine the three-inch long and quarter-inch wide, blue-black tunnel that extended from his shoulder to his collar bone. With infinite care, I extracted one small and two rather significant-sized chunks of mangled bullet and tightly bandaged the gaping hole that was left. Twenty minutes later, his younger brother driving, he was on his way to a larger medical center for the x-ray he needed to see if his collar bone had been nicked and for their doctor to investigate the suspicious-looking bulge on his neck that I suspected might be another piece of bullet. He did not quibble a bit about the $2.65 he had to pay for my care, either!

There are a few occasions when we do not charge full price for our services. Twice now, I have been on duty when the extremely deaf, ninety-six-year-old man who cannot afford the surgery he has needed for two years comes tottering in for his every-week-to-ten-days Foley catheter change. Rheumy eyes blinking, he peers up at me and grins cheerfully as I give him a welcoming pat on the shoulder, then squat down to help him undo the thick black shoestring that he uses to tie the urine collection bag to his leg. When the pus-clogged, filth-encrusted tube and bag have been replaced and his dirt-and-sweat-stained clothing readjusted, he reaches into his pocket for the money he has tucked away and painstakingly counts out his stash. The normal cost of such a procedure is 80 *lempiras,* or $4.23. I accept the 40 lempiras his trembling fingers slide across the counter, smile, and loudly wish him a good day and God's blessing. He shakes my hand and thanks me before slowly shuffling out the door and up the dirt road. I turn to the sink to wash my hands, blinking back tears. How very blessed I am with so much that I take for granted! I silently thank the Lord for allowing me the privilege of ministering to "one of the least of these my brothers" and pray that His love will continue to shine through me into the lives of the many who walk through our doors.

# 37

# My Thirteen-Year-Old Patient Weighed 800 Pounds

### *July 24, 2008 ~ San Luis, Honduras*

The afternoon was another hot and humid one, and my head bobbed in a brief doze more than once as Rex and I sat in the study, translating material for our upcoming marriage seminar. I barely heard the tentative knock on the door above the soft whirr of the fan by the desk. Glancing through the screen, we saw Edgar, one of the Bible institute teachers, leaning against the door frame. "I'm sorry to disturb you, but could you please take the pickup truck and trailer to help me get Estrella home?" he apologetically requested of Rex. "She's terribly hurt and can't walk. I think maybe her left leg is broken." He grimaced as he shifted his weight, carefully easing his own left leg with its blood-stained-and-torn trouser into a more comfortable position.

"I'm all right," he assured me. "I banged up my knee pretty badly when we fell, but I caught myself with one hand and kept from slamming my face into the gravel as we hit the ground. I'm a lot more worried about how *she's* doing. We were running really fast uphill, and I still can't figure out whether she tripped over something or what, but her face and knees are all torn up. Do you think you could stitch her up for me when we get back?" he anxiously inquired. I gulped. "I'll do my best to help her," I promised, wondering what in the world I was getting myself into now.

Two hours later, Rex slowly pulled the truck and trailer to a stop by our gate, and I hurried out to get a good look at my patient: the thirteen-year-old, 800-pound, not-very-happy, Bible institute horse whose work of carrying various students and staff to their respective country churches throughout the week to hold services is invaluable. It was nearly 7:00 p.m. and dark by this time, so I had to inspect her wounds by flashlight. Edgar had good reason to be concerned. Both front knees were torn open, but the left one was so badly pulverized it looked like raw, albeit very dirty, hamburger. Peeping through the mangled flesh was a white glint of bone. I gulped again. "Well, Edgar, I know about suturing wounds on *people*, but I've never had to do it on a *horse* before. Let's see what we can do."

Understandably, Estrella ("Star") was not particularly enthusiastic about backing off the rattling, noisy metal trailer; and it took many minutes of coaxing, cajoling, and tugging on her rope halter before Rex, Edgar, the institute night guard, and two students finally maneuvered her down to solid ground.

Meanwhile, I had gone to the clinic to collect my supplies. "Your guess is as good as mine on how much local anesthesia to give her," the nurse on duty replied to my question. "I sewed up one of our chickens when she got caught on a wire and tore open her face and neck, but I didn't numb it any." Figuring it was better to be over rather than underprepared, I stuffed a plastic bag with a nearly full bottle of 2% Rapacaine, a 20-cc syringe, sterile suture instruments and cloths, a large bottle of iodine, a metal bowl, lots of gauze, disposable gloves, three packages of 0-0 gauge nylon suture (the thickest the clinic has), and one package of absorbable catgut suture.

Thus armed, I returned with some trepidation to the mare. "God, please guide my hands and help me to do this right," I silently pleaded. Holding aloft a flashlight, I examined more closely the gaping wounds on Estrella's knees, hind leg, nose, and above her eye as she stood trembling, refusing to put weight on her obviously extremely painful left front leg. "I don't think I'd better try to do anything to her while she's standing up," I decided. "Do you think you can get her to lie down?" Estrella was not as convinced of the necessity of that plan of action as I was, but as four men with ropes pulled her back legs out from under her, she did not have much choice. I winced as she dropped to the grass with a thud, and the watching crowd of students and fellow missionaries drew back slightly while she tossed her head and struggled to get back up. There was no lack of manpower to help hold her down, but I was still pretty nervous as I gingerly hitched my step stool close to her and drew up a full syringe of the local anesthetic. Edgar crouched beside her, his own injured leg held out stiffly at an awkward angle, and caressed her neck while keeping up a steady stream of reassuring words. I firmly grasped her left front leg and began slowly injecting the medication that I hoped would give her enough pain relief to allow me to thoroughly clean the worst of her wounds.

Thirty cc's of local anesthetic later, Estrella lay quietly as I washed her knee with copious amounts of diluted iodine and painstakingly picked out the grass and imbedded bits of dirt and gravel. To everyone's profound thankfulness, my probing fingers did not discover any bone fragments or obvious fracture. I carefully maneuvered the large sterile drape under her leg, spread out my instruments, and reached up for the pack of suture that one of my helpers dropped out of its envelope into my gloved hand. The first suture, deep into the lacerated muscle, went in smoothly, and I started to tie it off. At that moment, Estrella decided she was not comfortable with her restricted position and lashed out violently with her hind leg, in spite of the ropes that were tied to it and held by two students. She connected solidly with Edgar's stomach, sending him flying several feet backwards onto the ground. In my haste to jump up from my footstool and scramble out of range of her iron-clad hooves, I caught my heel in the hem of my skirt and ended up flat on my back in the grass as well. The frightened mare surged up and limped a few steps away, suture and needle dangling from her knee, as I felt around through the tall grass for my scissors and needle holder.

And thus it went throughout the remainder of the job. I would kneel in the grass, put in a couple of stitches, then jump back out of the way as she persisted in heaving herself up and moving to a different spot. She did not seem to be in pain from the suturing so much as she was jittery from having her head sat on and her feet pulled out from under her. I cannot say as I really blame her, can you? At one point, she opened her mouth, grabbed the by-now-no-longer-even-remotely-sterile drape in her teeth, and began vigorously chewing away, once more scattering all my instruments onto the ground.

Not only was she the most uncooperative patient I have ever had, she had the *toughest* hide I have ever had the misfortune to try to stick a needle through. Her skin was split open on the left knee from one side to the other with only a small intact portion in the back, necessitating sewing first one side closed and then the other, from back to front. I would take a "bite" of hide with the needle, putting all the strength of not only my hand and arm, but my whole upper body, into muscling the needle holder with its cargo through the incredibly resistant skin on one side of the wound and out through the equally tough hide on the other side. Rex did a great job of directing the flashlight beam where I needed it most, and a time or two he added his superior strength to the task of piercing the needle through. Twice I had to pause to bend the needle back into its normal "C" curve from the fish-hook shape it had assumed after a particularly tough insertion. As an extra precaution, I tied off each stitch five times, rather than the normal three. I was incredulous that the stitches were staying intact, in spite of the repeated times the mare had convulsively kicked with that leg in her attempts to get back on her feet.

Her right knee was not nearly as badly mutilated as the left, and I felt like a good cleaning, in addition to the heavy-duty antibiotic injection I had given her partway through the evening, would be all I needed to do for that injury, as well as for the cuts on her hind leg and nose. When I finally got to the repair of the deep hole on her forehead, she rolled both eyes alarmingly and nickered fearfully as I oh-so-carefully injected the local anesthetic, being extremely cautious not to prick the too-close-for-comfort eyeball itself. By this time, though, nearly three hours had passed, and she had had *enough*. I had only placed three of the six stitches that she needed, thankfully the ones that were most urgently necessary to close the worst of the wound, when she once again scrambled to her feet. This time, no amount of coaxing could convince her to let me finish the job.

About fifteen spectators had been closely following the proceedings, some of them helping hold the horse, others the flashlight, and one of the girls giving my by-now-aching back a good firm massage partway through the job. We collectively had prayer for Estrella's healing, asking the Lord if it could please Him to take over where human attempts could not carry on, and heal her terrible wounds so she could continue to be of service to His work. My very large patient limped away and began tugging off and chewing up mouthfuls of grass, the neat bandage on her knee gleaming white in the darkness.

Wearily, I gathered my equipment from the various spots on the ground where it had been scattered, and trudged back to the clinic to clean up the instruments. I also pulled off and smashed the three ticks that had taken advantage of my kneeling position on the grass and thirstily fastened themselves to my arm. When I was once more back in our house, a long, hot shower and hair wash had never before felt so good, and I tumbled into bed for a few hours of rest before my next clinic shift.

Where, I ask you, but on a mission field, can a nurse-midwife care for an 800-pound equine patient one night, and after four hours of sleep, deliver an eight-pound, two-ounce, beautiful baby boy the next morning? I am having a wonderful time, when I am not too exhausted to realize it!

## 38

# I Want to Throw His Diaper on the Roof

*August 11, 2008 ~ San Luis, Honduras*

She was just fifteen, still a child herself, yet she had given birth to her own child only a few hours before. Her baby's father had bowed out of the picture months ago, and she would be raising this little one without his ever knowing the meaning of the words "my daddy." I met her at the start of my night shift and knew I had only a few hours to help her start learning the multitude of things she needed to know for her herculean task of bridging the gap between young, carefree teenager and mature, responsible mother.

Her baby was a fussy one, and she was impatient with his insistence on her attention when all she wanted was some sleep. About midnight, he refused to obey her repeated snapped orders to shush up, and I went in to see what I could do to help her quiet his crying. The solution was a simple one: like any self-respecting fellow, he was not pleased to be lying in a soggy diaper. I figured a class in "Diaper Changing 101" was certainly in order, and I went to gather the needed study materials.

"Would you please give me his dirty diaper?" she requested. "I want it for a secret." More than a little startled, I nevertheless managed to keep from sticking my finger with the pin I was poking through the cloth and tried to be casual in my questioning. I had a hard time hiding my surprise at her shy confession. "I want to throw his diaper on the roof. That way, when someone comes by who wants to give him the evil eye and hurt him, they won't be able to." Years of superstitious training did not easily give way to my gentle assurance that Jesus could protect her little one from harm, and she tucked the plastic bag with its soiled diaper deep into her scuffed backpack, quite sure that her trust in its effectiveness was valid. My heart ached to think of the hopelessness of a life without knowledge of the One Who came to dispel such fears. I wondered, as I had done many times before, why God allowed me to be born into a Christian family and raised with the knowledge of how infinite and all-sufficient is the love of Christ. I thanked Him for the satisfaction of yet another chance to share that love with someone who is less fortunate than I.

At least, this was one belief that would not physically harm her baby any more than it would help him. Such was not the case with the proposed remedy for her newborn's colic that one mother asked me about. "Do you think that it would be all right to bathe him in his father's urine?" she wondered. "I've heard that it works well, but I want to know if you agree." I think I managed to convince her of the futility of such a practice—at least, I sincerely hope so!

Esperanza delivered the baby boy whose mother was from a more well-to-do home than many of the patients we see here, a situation which made no difference in the woman's strongly entrenched belief in the traditions that are passed down from generation to generation. I was there to help change the mother's gown and settle into her bed in the postpartum ward after the birth, and I could not help noticing the thin, bright-red cord tied around her abdomen. "I guess it's all right to take this off now, isn't it?" she asked. Esperanza assured her that it was and brought a pair of scissors to cut it. Once out of the room, Esperanza answered my inquiring look. "They believe that if a pregnant woman sees a lunar eclipse, her baby will have a cleft lip. We had an eclipse here in Honduras during the past nine months, so that woman wore her red cord the entire pregnancy to prevent such a calamity from happening."

Pregnancy itself supposedly confers unusual powers. For instance, a woman who is expecting her first child can massage someone's sprained ankle and instantly heal it. However, after her first baby is born, she loses that special touch, and the magic will not work during any subsequent pregnancy. Do be sure to stay out of sight of *any* pregnant woman, though, no matter how many babies she has had, if you are unfortunate enough to cut yourself, because if she looks at you before the wound is entirely healed, your scar will be a lot worse.

Of course, there are some situations with pregnant women that have nothing to do with superstition, but still manage to add some interest and spice to one's day. Such was the case with the mother who arrived not long ago with a hugely swollen abdomen, looking like she surely was expecting twins. To my surprise, a careful abdominal exam revealed only one baby. There was no doubt that it was a mammoth size, which spiked the chances of complications with the delivery, including shoulder dystocia, injury to the baby during the birth, and postpartum hemorrhage. She was a prime candidate for transfer to the Santa Bárbara hospital, but that plan entailed just one problem—there was no time. This was baby number twelve, and she was already eight centimeters dilated. Knowing that the baby could be born any moment, that none of the other nurses was close enough to get there in time to help, and that I could not handle everything that would need to be done all at once if she did hemorrhage, I called hurriedly over to our house. "Rex, can you please come to the clinic right away and help me out for a little bit?"

Only later, after the excitement had subsided and nobody had died, did I feel sorry for my husband. I still chuckle ruefully as I type this, remembering the astonished look on his face when he walked unsuspectingly through the back door of the clinic and I grabbed his arm, pulled him into the delivery room, and handed him two loaded syringes. "Here, hold these and stand right here, at the head of the table. As soon as the baby is born and I've delivered the placenta, stick this syringe in her left leg and inject the medicine that's in it, then do the same with the other syringe in her right leg. I'm expecting problems with this delivery, and I need an extra pair of hands. There's another emergency that just got here, though, so please stay here and let her squeeze your hand, and holler for me if she tells you the baby is coming. I'll be right back."

I dashed out the door and down the hall to the treatment room. You see, in the couple of minutes between my phone call to Rex and his arrival, a farmer with a severe machete laceration to his wrist had arrived. Thankfully, someone in the field had cinched a make-shift tourniquet around his forearm, so by the time he got to us, the wound was not bleeding heavily. I had grabbed some gauze 4x4's and showed him how to cover the injury and apply pressure to it, before I ran back to the delivery room to instruct Rex.

To my great relief, while I was in with the mother, giving Rex instructions, our efficient secretary had called Dr. Maldonado, who arrived in record time and was already at work on the machete injury when I walked back into the treatment room. It was much worse than even he felt comfortable trying to repair here, so after cleaning and bandaging it, he left, with instructions for us to transfer the man for a surgical repair. Meanwhile, amazingly, the laboring woman's contractions, which she had been having every couple of minutes, had completely stopped, and to my astonishment, she had gone *backwards* in her dilation, now measuring only six centimeters instead of eight. Wonderful! Maybe now we could transfer her as well, in time to avoid the disaster I feared.

That is how I came to take my third ambulance ride over the mountain, this time monitoring *two* patients with vastly different problems. After we pulled up to the hospital doors and discharged our cargo, I went to give a report to the doctor in charge. He glanced over at the woman lying in one of the cots in the emergency room, her protruding abdomen looking as though it could burst at any moment. "She is having twins, isn't she?" he queried.

"No, that is just one really big baby," I replied.

"It can't be!" he exclaimed, moving over and running his hands over her abdomen.

"Yes, it is," I insisted, more glad than ever that she was his patient now, not mine. He shook his head in disbelief while I walked back out to the waiting ambulance for the ride home.

"You'll see," I thought to myself. It was no surprise to hear the next day that the woman had her slightly over twelve-pound baby by cesarean section. How thankful I was that God had stopped her labor long enough for us to transfer her in time so that Rex's services were not needed. [Rex's editorial note: Me, too!]

Every bit as exciting, but in a much nicer manner, was the extra-special "handful on purpose" that God let fall my way with the opportunity to deliver two of my fellow missionary's babies within this last week before leaving Honduras. Daniel and Tiffany Melton's third son, seven-pound, fifteen-ounce Kenton Daniel, arrived into "Auntie Hannah's" welcoming hands at 6:03 Thursday morning. Zack and Sarah Robbert's second daughter, six-pound, five-ounce Eleyna Ruth, (the "Ruth" being chosen in part because it is "Grandma Hannah's" middle name) made her appearance at 4:25 Sunday afternoon. Both little ones were born in the clinic, which in itself made history, as they are the first missionary babies delivered there in the twenty-nine years the clinic has been in operation. Esperanza is tickled pink because she happened to be working each of the shifts when the babies arrived and was my assisting nurse for both deliveries. The town's people are bursting their buttons with pride and commenting with approval that *los gringos* are common, ordinary people, after all. It has been a wonderful means of bonding between the nationals and the missionaries, and a great advertisement for the clinic. I could not think of a more satisfying way to end this ten-week stay.

# 39

## Honeybees, Hitches, and High Winds

*July 12, 2009 ~ San Luis, Honduras*

Greetings, and a lovely Lord's Day to you. I am typing this while waiting for the whole-wheat mango coffee cake in the oven to finish baking. It has been wafting its tantalizing odors through the house for the past fifteen minutes, convincing Jeffrey that he will surely starve if he cannot have some of it soon. After all, nearly three hours have passed since he last ate, and the reserve of food in his hollow leg vanished long ago on our ten-minute walk to and from church this morning.

Speaking of food, we have been enjoying an ample variety of fresh tropical fruits every day: plantains, papaya, mangos, bananas, and pineapple. We have also had watermelon and cantaloupe, though those are not exactly tropical. Then there are the really unique things one can experience while living here, such as the stuff we have been pouring on our pancakes. Regular bottled pancake syrup is available, but it is imported and expensive. Instead, we purchased a four-by-five-inch block of *dulce*—sugarcane juice that is boiled down until it solidifies when poured into molds and cooled. Local housewives scrape or grate it to make a sort of brown sugar. We put ours in a pot of water and heated it until it converted back to its liquid state, making a deliciously different topping.

The only thing is, honeybees are tremendously attracted to sugarcane juice as well, and they congregate in droves when it is cooked in huge vats over open fires in the outdoor processing plants. As our block of would-be pancake syrup began to dissolve in the bubbling water, dead bees started popping to the surface. Half an hour later, the block was gone, replaced by a sweet, thick, sticky, yummy liquid—with lots of floaty things on top of the pot. Not having a strainer, I poured the whole potful through a colander. It was somewhat disconcerting when I counted them to discover that I had strained out sixty-eight bees. Of course, the colander could only prevent the *bodies* of the bees from washing through its holes. It did not keep out small bits like legs and antennas, so we had to keep picking bits of bees off our pancakes. But hey, bees are clean insects, and they had been boiled plenty long enough. John the Baptist ate wild locusts, and some people eat chocolate covered ants—on purpose.

We have been here for ten days. We were scheduled to fly down on Tuesday, June 30, but following ex-president Mel Zelaya's bid for power and the ensuing political blow-up earlier that week, we were not sure that it was safe to make the trip. When we called Daniel Melton Tuesday morning, he assured us it was all right to come. At Reagan International Airport in Washington, D.C., they gave us our boarding passes clear through to Honduras; but upon arrival in Miami, we found that our flight to Honduras had been canceled.

American Airlines put us up for the night at a ritzy hotel. It was so ritzy, in fact, that the least expensive thing on the supper menu was an $8.00 bowl of onion soup. Our tummies were way too empty for that to be enough, and our wallets not nearly full enough to handle the cheapest entrée: a fancy burger at $29.00. We trekked back to the airport on the hotel shuttle and ate at Burger King instead, returning to our room with tummies stuffed and wallets fatter than they would otherwise have been.

Wednesday morning, we landed in Honduras without incident, the only day that whole week and on into the next that the airport was open to commercial flights. God knew the window of opportunity we would need, even months before, when we bought our tickets! We crept through customs at an unusually slow snail's pace due to extra security, went grocery shopping, then waited—and waited—and waited—and waited some more for the big, heavy sheets of metal roofing that Daniel bought for the clinic *bodega* (storage building) to be loaded on his trailer. When we finally started for San Luis, hours after we had planned, it was dark and raining, and we had just enough time to make it there before the politically imposed 9:00 p.m. curfew, when all traffic and people were to be off the roads.

It *would* have been enough time without the heavily loaded trailer, that is. We whizzed along at a fairly respectable speed until we hit the dirt road halfway there. Less than a mile onto the slick, thick-mud track, and just before a fairly steep hill, Daniel stopped to check the load, feeling that something was just not quite right. He was correct. With all the jouncing and bouncing, the hitch welded onto the rear of his Isuzu pickup truck had bitten the dust, err, mud, quite literally. It had not pulled completely off, but the trailer tongue was dragging the ground.

By flashlight, Daniel and Rex jacked up the trailer, strained and tugged to pull the hitch back up, roped it to the back of the truck, and reattached the trailer. Then, with a prayer for protection and help, we were off again, at the terrifyingly dizzy speed of ten kilometers per hour. At the top of the long hill, everything checked out well; but before reaching home, the men had to go through the jack-up-trailer/pull-up-hitch/rope-to-bumper/reattach-trailer routine again. I think the speedometer might have hit twenty kph once or twice in there, but only briefly. It was well past curfew time before we finally pulled safely onto the mission grounds and headed for a short night's sleep, after first removing the bright-green tree frog from Jeffrey's bed that had decided to keep him company for the night.

We were extra-thankful that we had arrived when we did, since the next afternoon a storm moved in, swirling high winds and dumping heavy rain. Tiffany and I were fearfully watching the wildly tossing tree branches and ominous black clouds from the living room window when we heard a rending C-R-A-C-K and saw a large tree between the two missionary houses topple to the ground, uprooted by the force of the wind. What we did not realize at the time was that two other trees on the mission property had also lost the battle to the storm. We learned about the other ones shortly after the main part of the storm had blown over, when Tiffany turned on the water faucet, but nothing came out. She discovered that the pipe that supplies the house was broken in half. Suspended eight feet high in the tangled roots of the big mango tree lying on its side behind their bodega, it was pouring its supply of water into the hole left by the toppled tree.

Rex and Josh Carveth, a missions student from Penn View Bible Institute here for a six-week internship, scurried to find extra pipe and the supplies needed to fix the problem. In the meantime, Tiffany and I watched with great interest the unfolding drama of two urchins who had ducked through the fence and scampered up the hill behind the radio station, gathering downed branches to take home for their mama's cooking fire. Unfortunately, they were doing their gleaning on mission property, and our guard hurried up the hill from the other side to stop the thievery of the precious wood needed for our own dining hall's supply. The boys could not see him coming and were caught red-handed with the goods. They must have been pretty convincing in whatever story they gave, though, for a few minutes later we saw them trudge away with their haul, evidently having managed to soften the guard's heart.

So it goes. Not every day has been quite as eventful as those first two were, but as always, we are having some interesting times, and I am sure there are more to come.

## Breaking News

*July 24, 2009 ~ San Luis, Honduras*

It has been a different sort of week—at least, I hope we have no more like it. This past Sunday evening, our son Jeffrey said his left ear was mildly hurting. I was working at the clinic at the time and did not know about it until the next morning. When it still bothered him on Monday, I checked things out and saw that both eardrums were red and bulging, so I started him on an antibiotic. By that evening, he was in a lot of pain, but we were trusting that the medicine would soon begin to clear up the infection.

Around 1:00 a.m., he awoke with a yell at the sensation of something exploding in his left ear. Rex and I stood by his bed, praying, rubbing his back and legs, and trying to comfort him as he rolled back and forth, holding his ear. He was finally able to doze for a few minutes, only to wake up hollering again as a new explosion, in the right ear, jolted him from sleep. I was expecting the pain to ease off after that, but for the next hour, at least seven or eight times, he would get back to sleep for a few minutes, then startle awake with another huge "pop" and stab of pain in one ear or the other.

Around 2:00 a.m., when it became obvious that things were not getting better, I went over to the clinic and brought back an injection of Toradol for his pain. It made him throw up, adding to his misery, but at least the pain settled down enough to let him sleep for about three hours. Then, the same thing happened all over, with multiple sensations of one ear or the other exploding. By 1:30 Tuesday afternoon, after two more injections of Toradol throughout the morning, he was still in such extreme pain, with both ears continuing to drain large amounts of yellow fluid and pus, that I took him over to the clinic, admitted him, and started him on a strong IV antibiotic, an IV pain medication drip, and an IV anti-inflammatory medication. I added an IV sedative when all of the other medications still could not adequately control his pain.

When everything finally took hold enough to give him some relief, he fell asleep, exhausted, just before I started my afternoon shift. Rex had begun his week-long, intensive teaching course with the students here the day before, with classes from morning through evening, so he was not able to stay with Jeffrey as much as he would have liked. During the next two days, he stopped by a couple of times a day when he could snatch a few moments on a break, but this was his busiest week here. I spent the whole time in the clinic except for a few quick trips to the house for a shower and change of clothes, or to fix a bite to eat. I worked regular shifts each day, helped to care for Jeffrey, and caught sleep in the crib in his room when I could. He continued to have episodes of intense discomfort, vomiting, and bleeding from both ears.

Jeffrey was hospitalized from Tuesday afternoon until this evening, Friday. The town doctor, as well as Jeffrey's doctor back in the States, with whom I talked twice via telephone, both recommended the same things: IV Ceftri-axone and oral Cipro while he was in the clinic, followed by another week of Cipro and five days of Azithromycin. By the time he finishes all that, no self-re-specting germ in the world should dare get close to him.

Both doctors said today that if his eardrums are not completely healed by August 11 when we are scheduled to leave Honduras, Jeffrey will not be able to fly. Normally, that should be plenty of time, but as severe as the infection was, there is the possibility that the holes will not have completely closed. He is to follow up in a week with the local doctor and consult with an ear-nose-and-throat specialist in San Pedro on August 10. We are glad God is in control of this whole situation, and He knows what we need!

# A Kaleidoscope of Characters

*July 28, 2009 ~ San Luis, Honduras*

*men in white sombreros*

*horses with their foals, donkeys carrying milk cans—all sharing the road with little moto-taxis, trucks, and semis in various stages of rusting, and a sharp, new Mazda 6*

*machetes, machetes, machetes—well used, well sharpened, and carried in calloused, skilled hands*

*dress-up clothes and shoes that are too big or too small and filthy with the dirt of cooking fires, garden work, fishing in the sewage "creek," and perspiration*

*mothers proudly carrying their new infants wrapped in towels, and little boys running without pants*

*every house with a fence, every window with bars*

*green, craggy mountains covered with mist in the morning and barely supporting the small fields of* milpa *scratched into their surfaces*

*frogs—little frogs making big noises not unlike turkey calls, big frogs making little noises*

*mangy, skeleton-thin dogs whose hides jump with fleas*

*music and preaching from stereos, the louder the better*

*omnipresent cellphones*

*motors and horns*

*the wheeze of manual BP cuffs*

*the moan of a woman in labor*

*the refrigerator whose incredibly loud motor sounds just like the code siren at the hospital and gives a jolt of adrenaline every time it starts*

*the washer that spews oil and water, and whose agitator only works when pushed back into place*

*gates squeaking*

*the crunch of gravel in the front lot which usually means a new patient*

*the rapid, "talking-with-your-mouth-full" accent of the poor and/or uneducated*

buenos *without the* días

adios *as a both a greeting and a benediction*

("First Impressions," used by permission of Amanda Byler)

\* \* \* \* \* \* \* \* \* \*

It is 7:45 on a beautiful morning here at our mountain clinic. The diesel generator that supplies electricity to this building, three missionary houses, the AM/FM radio station, two dormitories, a dining hall, the classroom building, and the school director's home is roaring away out back, making it possible to conduct business as usual. Daniel Melton tells me that the 110 gallons of fuel we have in reserve should last for three to four complete days, maybe even a week if it is rationed. We have been using it since the terrific storm that blustered through last evening, the second such since our arrival, took out the power to the whole town. One of its victims was the forty-nine-year-old man who showed up for treatment after a lightning bolt struck the ground beside him. The resulting surge of deadly power left him with horrible third-degree burns and lacerations on both legs, from midthighs to feet. He had to be ... ooops, gotta run!

There, I am back. The interruption was to grab an emesis basin, thrust it into the hand of the young man who staggered vomiting through our front door a few minutes ago, help him crawl onto the treatment table, and hurry to prepare an injection to ease his nausea. He has refused the IV fluids I recommended and sprawls limply, face down, on the narrow cot, with his anxious young wife sitting in a chair beside him, wiping his face now and then with a cool cloth. Their three-year-old son huddles close to his mommy and stares wide-eyed as his daddy retches convulsively.

Now, an hour and a half and a steady stream of outpatients later, the nauseated gentleman is exhaustedly asleep in the four-bed general ward, IV fluids with more medication doing their job. In between frequent heaves of nothing but clear mucus, he kept insisting that he did not want an IV. When I showed his wife that the cost of IV rehydration and medicine was no greater than taking the pills by mouth that he could not keep down anyhow, he finally gave in; he has not vomited once since. Their total bill for that treatment is 130 *lempiras,* which translates to $6.88. A short while ago, I removed four stitches from the chin of a little boy who tripped and fell onto a concrete block last week. His mother paid fifty-three cents to have the stitches out, and I did not charge any extra for the damage to my eardrums as the kid screamed full blast into them at close range, with two other adults plus me holding him down so I could do my thing.

That lad's hysteria over something that he could barely feel is a far cry (quite literally) from the reaction of the eight-year-old who was carried in some days before by his mother, left foot and leg wrapped in a shirt and several blood-soaked rags. In a voice just above a whisper, he told me his name was Roger. He had been up in a small tree, chopping off dry branches for fire wood, when he lost his grip on both his machete and the branch onto which he was holding.

Boy and machete tumbled out of the tree and plummeted to the ground, but the machete landed first, blade up, seconds before he lit squarely atop its freshly sharpened edge and drove it into his ankle. Not sure how much he might still be bleeding, I gingerly unwrapped his foot and stared aghast at the gaping wound. His Achilles tendon was completely severed, and flesh hung down on either side of glistening white bone. This was WAY beyond my ability to repair, but I numbed, thoroughly cleaned, and bandaged the nasty hole, and then sent him off in the Red Cross ambulance to the Santa Bárbara hospital. The brave little fellow whimpered once or twice at the sting of the local anesthesia, but made no other sound the entire time.

So it goes again in EFM's *Clínica Luz y Vida*. Some days there is not as much going on, but most of the shifts have been lively and varied. Today, I could snatch a few minutes now and then to type a sentence or two, but I've been working at writing this now for eight-and-a-half hours, and you can see the tremendous progress. My latest event, a few minutes ago, was putting eight sutures into a gentleman's face to close the two-inch gash he got from falling off his roof this afternoon. He was up there to fix the damage caused by our storm last evening, but he got dizzy and toppled over the edge, catching his cheek on the edge of a broken-off piece of the tin. At least he didn't yell in my ear while I was working on him.

Yelling is something that twenty-two-year-old Eldin did not do much of either, for many days, after he tried to kill himself by drinking three ounces of pesticide. Perhaps he belatedly decided life was worth living after all once he had chugged the bitter concoction down, and voluntarily sought our help. Maybe someone in his family discovered what he had done and insisted he come in. However it happened, there he lay on the treatment table, surrounded by concerned friends and family, writhing and moaning in agony, alternating between gagging and vomiting out yellow poison every little bit, even after the gastric lavage Rosmery gave him to remove as much of it as possible while we waited for the ambulance to take him to San Pedro. I monitored his vital signs and helped with his treatment, not able to jump out of the way quickly enough at one point to avoid getting sprayed with spittle as his body tried desperately to rid itself of the caustic liquid. His suffering seemed to ease for a bit after we had prayer with him, but there was little other help we could give before he was transferred to the big public hospital.

To my surprise, he was back in the clinic as a patient when I returned for my next shift. He had been curtly informed in San Pedro that there was nothing they could do for him and sent right back home. By this point, everything from his lips down to his stomach was so raw that he could barely whisper, let alone swallow the copious strings of saliva that kept drooling from his blistered lips. For two days, we cared for him with stomach-buffering IV meds and fluids, antibiotics, and round-the-clock pain killers, without much improvement in his condition. I do not know what his final outcome has been, because his family decided they could not afford the $4.23 each day it was costing them to keep him in our clinic in addition to the much higher expense of his medications, and they took him home. I hope he survives. He needs the reason for living that only Christ can give. And he has an eighteen-month-old daughter who needs her daddy.

His is one of the many sad cases that arrive at our door as a consequence of sin. But in a land where grudges and arguments are resolved with slashing machetes, some of those involved do not make it here in time to do them any good. Hopefully, that was not the case with the man who was wheeled in on the Red Cross ambulance stretcher not long ago. It was only my second time in six summers of working here that the ambulance had ever *brought* me a patient, as opposed to the usual *taking* them from here to a larger facility. As soon as I got a good look at him, I knew we would just be stabilizing him, and the ambulance crew would wait to take him on. At least, I *hoped* we could get him stable enough to leave and not have him die on our treatment table. He was, without question, the most desperately wounded person I have ever seen. The stretcher was completely covered with a sheet of clear plastic, the size and thickness of a large tablecloth. Someone on either side held up the edges of the plastic so the copious amount of pooled blood would not pour off onto the floor as yet a third person carefully guided the stretcher with its gruesome burden down the hall.

The wounded man was praying loudly and brandishing his Bible aloft in his right hand. His left arm lay inert and helpless beside him, grit and splintered fragments of bone mixed with the mangled flesh of a nearly severed forearm. The ambulance attendants and I lifted him with infinite care onto the table, and with shaking hands I inserted a large-bore IV catheter into his right arm and started a liter of fluids infusing wide open to replace the lost blood. "Tell me what happened," I questioned while assessing his other wounds: a deep, two-and-a-half-inch gouge on the right side of his neck that narrowly missed his jugular vein, and another, longer one on his right upper back. I worked to dress and bandage his wounds while listening, horrified, to his story.

While walking down the mountain on the main dirt road leading to town, he had chanced upon a stranger and began witnessing to him of Jesus. The fellow listened with mounting fury, which was unnoticed by the gentleman intent on evangelism. That is, he did not notice his companion's agitation until the stranger suddenly jerked his machete from his belt, screaming, "Well, let's see if your God can save YOU," and took a frenzied swing at the guy's head, intending to sever it from his body. His victim reflexively threw up his arm to ward off the attack, catching diagonally across his elbow and the length of his forearm a blow of sufficient force to have rolled his head into the dirt. His upper and both lower arm bones were all three shattered, and half of his forearm sliced away. Thankfully, only the tip of the machete reached its *intended* goal, leaving the gouge on his neck. A second wild chop whistled down across the man's shoulder and upper back before his attacker fled.

By the time I had listened to his story and dressed his wounds, the man was silent and pale, drifting in and out of consciousness. I started a second bag of IV fluids and prayed aloud for God's healing touch and for safety in the journey. We loaded him carefully onto the ambulance once more, and the driver revved his motor, heading out with his fragile cargo. Tragic indeed! Yet, what comfort the viciously brutalized man had in the midst of his agony—the promise of a loving heavenly Father to go with him even through "the valley of the shadow of death." Whether he crosses that valley now or not, he has the hope of an eternity in heaven. How much better than the end awaiting his would-be murderer, who hates so intensely a God Who loves him so dearly that He died to save him.

# 42

## After You Tie His Two Big Toes Together, Then What?

### *August 6, 2009 ~ San Luis, Honduras*

Maribel recently needed a day off from her nursing duties to attend her cousin's funeral. He was only thirty-two years old, father to four children ranging in age from two to eight. In a savage dispute over land, he was hacked twice in the face with a machete and then decapitated. His body lay in the dirt beside the road not far from his home, in full view of his traumatized children, until the police could arrive to do their investigation. Once his remains were released, family and friends gathered to prepare him for the all-night wake. Sometimes a corpse will be injected with formaldehyde to offset its rapid decomposition in the intense tropical heat, but that is not commonly done, so burial is usually within twenty-four hours. In keeping with their custom, the simple casket lay closed on a table in the main room of the home, a fifteen- by twenty-inch window of glass in the lid providing a clear view of the dead man's face. Cotton protruded from his nostrils and ears to absorb the inevitable purulent discharge. The high collar of his simple white shirt skillfully concealed the fact that his head was not attached to his body, but nothing had been done to disguise the diagonal machete slashes and splintered facial bones that mutely testified to his untimely end.

Maribel did not want her last remembrance of him to be the horror of his mutilated face, so she stayed away from the casket. Even if she had gone up close to it, she would not have been able to see if the family had tied his two big toes together with thread, so they could find out who had murdered him. The way that works is actually pretty simple. If, as is often the case, the killer attends the wake, either out of curiosity or to throw off any suspicion, his guilt will be obvious in one of two ways. If the dead man's toes have been properly tied, when his murderer gets close to the casket, he will suddenly find himself immobilized, unable to move his feet to walk casually by. Everyone will be able to see that he is to blame. If the toes are not tied, another way that the corpse "speaks" is by oozing fresh blood from his wounds at the approach of his killer.

Too well-educated herself to put stock in these folkloric ideas, Maribel nevertheless recognizes the intensity with which the simple country folk embrace them and the futility of trying to persuade them otherwise. We *gringos* have beliefs and customs that to them seem just as odd as their tied toes and bleeding corpses do to us, but of course we know how perfectly sensible *our* methods are. It was interesting to be on the other side of the coin when our two younger sons were born in Costa Rica. I had a hard time justifying my practice of continuing to give them warm baths after they turned a year old, since doing so is guaranteed to give weak lungs. I was well aware that other mothers looked at me doubtfully and questioned my parenting skills. Of course, the fact that I failed to bury either Benjamin's or Jeffrey's umbilical cord under a mango or papaya tree was another strike against our boys and doubly doomed them to a childhood plagued with illness. Never mind that they are now both nearly six feet tall, hale, and hearty. I still made a big mistake in giving them those warm baths and throwing away their dried umbilical stumps!

Some of the customs, such as a strong sense of community and family unity, I admire. Time and again I have been amazed at the number of visitors someone who is admitted to the clinic will have. When Tom, Dick, and Harry (or Pedro, Juan, and Marcos, as would more likely be the case here) get the news that Great Aunt Mary (*tía abuela* María) is in the clinic on IV fluids and drop by to see her, they will likely know all the other people occupying beds in the general ward, as well as the new mother in postpartum, and the parents of the sick thirteen-month-old in pediatrics. So, of course, one has to stop and chat with each of them. Visiting hours do not really exist, and there can be a steady stream of people coming from 6:00 a.m., when a family member brings hot milk, tortillas, beans, and cheese for a patient's breakfast, to 10:30 p.m., when we close and lock the outer door, only admitting emergencies or women in labor after that.

The concept of close-knit family was made vividly real an hour or so into one of my afternoon shifts early last week, when I heard a car pull up outside and loud, excited voices chattering back and forth. I headed down the hall as the front door slammed behind the man known in town as "The Shooter," since he has at least two known murders to his credit. (He is the one who very kindly gave me a lift from the center of town once when I got caught in a heavy rainstorm walking back from buying a week's worth of fresh veggies and fruit.) The Shooter was supporting a younger man who was hopping on one foot, his face covered with blood. As he helped me get the wounded fellow up onto our treatment table, The Shooter vociferously declared, "It wasn't my fault! He cut right in front of me, and I couldn't stop in time!"

Not sure what he was talking about, I knew that whatever had happened, it had not been good. My attention immediately focused on the bleeding from the jagged laceration extending from the wounded man's hairline down the center of his forehead. I hurried around the table to the side counter and lifted the lid of one of the large, round, metal canisters of gauze lined up along the wall, reaching with my other hand for the tongs kept submersed in an antiseptic solution in a smaller canister so I could extract the 4x4's. Out of the corner of my eye, I caught a glimpse of the man's ankle and whirled around to confirm what I thought I had seen. Sure enough, the leg that he was waving in the air had a joint where God never intended for one to be. The broken-beyond-a-doubt ankle that he could not hold still kept flopping back and forth at a sickening angle, looking as though the protruding bone could pop through the skin at any moment.

"Please hold still, Sir," I begged, while applying pressure with the gauze to his forehead. I willed my stomach contents to stay in place as the grotesquely malformed "joint" continued its relentless flapping from side to side with his restless tossing and turning.

"My leg hurts," he groaned, clutching it and raising it off the table.

"I'm sure it does," I replied. "You've broken it badly, and you need to quit moving it until I can splint it for you."

"It's broken?" he queried in surprise, straining his head against my hand with the gauze and simultaneously lifting his leg to see for himself. "Flop," went the new joint, and I winced again. By this point, the room was jammed with concerned family and friends, and I enlisted one of them (his mother, I found out later) to hold the gauze to his forehead while I maneuvered through the rapidly growing crowd of people that was also filling the hall. From a lower shelf in the pharmacy, I chose one of the pieces of cardboard cut from the boxes in which our supplies are delivered. We wrap the varying lengths and widths of cardboard in strips of old sheets to make cheap, handy, disposable splints. Squeezing back into the room, I directed the people clustered around him to move aside so I could work on his leg. I had taken a few seconds while getting the splint to give a quick phone call to our house to enlist the help of Amanda Byler, a nurse friend of ours who had arrived just the day before to work with me in the clinic for two weeks. She walked in at that moment, and together we carefully applied the splint along his ankle and wrapped more of the torn strips of bed sheets around his foot and leg to fasten it in place.

With the floppy ankle finally at rest and an injection of pain killer starting its work, I could tackle once more the task of cleaning and suturing the laceration. Midway through mopping away the rivulets of sticky, drying blood so I could see better to know what needed done, our day guard's dog wandered in the room to be close to his master, the accident victim's father-in-law. Clapping my blood-stained gloved hands together and stamping my feet, I stormed after the animal, chasing him down the hall and out the front door. Back in the treatment room once more, I pushed through the mass of bodies to get back to my patient, shooing a couple of inquisitive children (cousins maybe?) away from my table of sterile instruments.

While waiting for the lidocaine injection to take effect, I glanced down just in time to see the father-in-law's dog trotting into the room a second time. Once more, the assembled crowd was treated to the comic relief of the foreign nurse's hand-clapping-foot-stomping-dog-chasing routine. This time, I hollered for someone in the crowd out on the porch of those who could not fit inside to please close the door and KEEP THAT DOG OUTSIDE! Two policemen who had stopped in to see the accident victim, after determining that he had indeed been at fault in the collision of his motorcycle with The Shooter's truck, stood in the hall, peering in over the heads of his aunts, uncles, cousins, grandmother, father, sisters and mother. In my focus on lining up and lacing together the edges of the wound that had exposed his skull, I never even saw them.

Amanda capably taped the gauze dressing in place when I finally finished my painstaking sewing job, while I stretched the kinks out of my back before calling the Red Cross ambulance to take him for X rays and surgery on his broken ankle. Not until the ambulance pulled up and the attendants began waving their arms and yelling at the mass of people packing the porch and hall to get out of the way so they could get in did I realize how rapidly the news had traveled and how large a crowd had assembled. Amanda counted over thirty in the treatment room and hall just outside the door, and more than forty others outside who were not lucky enough to arrive in time to have a ringside seat. No doubt about it, I found out what "family support system" means in a Latin country.

The unfortunate follow-up to the story is that, because the doctors and nurses in the public hospital where he was taken have been on strike to protest the political upheaval that has embroiled the country of Honduras since before our arrival, the young man still has not had his ankle set. That has been nearly two weeks ago, and as badly damaged as it was, it will be a miracle if he does not lose his foot. So much for the superiority of a socialized medical system. Have a healthy week, be grateful for your local emergency room doctors and nurses, and enjoy some time with your family.

# 43

## Trusting When We Don't Understand
*August 19, 2009 ~ San Pedro Sula, Honduras*

I am writing this on the plane on our way back to the United States. I wanted to contact you as soon as possible after the events of the past two days so you would hear firsthand what has happened. I know there have been a lot of stories flying around and thought you deserved to get something directly from me.

As you know, we have been in Honduras for the past seven weeks, where I worked in the EFM maternity clinic in San Luis. Rex taught classes there as well as in Guatemala and Costa Rica during this time. Jeffrey helped by mowing, weed eating, painting, and breaking up rocks on the runway to make it easier to mow.

We were only scheduled to be here for six weeks, but Jeffrey's ear infection prevented us from returning on August 11, as we had planned. We were surprised and disappointed at the delay, but were confident that God had everything in control. As Rex's cousin Marci said, "We will be excited to hear the purpose for God leaving you there an extra week."

Well, now we know why, although frankly, the events that happened are not what we would have chosen. In the midst of the questions and pain from the loss that has occurred, we are still sure that God does not make mistakes, and we choose to trust His loving care for His children.

Months ago, Stephen and Yvonne DeLong contacted me about the possibility of my delivering their baby while we were in Honduras. They are both former students of Rex and have been serving as missionaries in Honduras for the past several years after graduating from Penn View. We worked in Nicaragua with Stephen's parents when he was a boy, and he and his sisters are like part of our own family. Yvonne's baby was not due until after we were to have returned to the States, but we agreed to pray together about it, knowing that if God would be pleased to let them have the home birth that they wanted, then He would work out all the details.

By the time we were scheduled to leave, I had delivered seven babies in the clinic, giving me a total of forty-nine deliveries in Honduras in the six summers I have been there. When we knew we would have to stay an extra week, I was excited at least to think that maybe I would get to help one more little one arrive safely, making it my fiftieth Honduran baby in the year that I turned fifty years old. And of course, we wondered if maybe Yvonne's baby might be that one.

No babies were born at the clinic in the rest of the shifts I worked during our extra days there, and Yvonne's little one seemed pretty content to stay comfy cozy inside her mommy. Yvonne called me around 7:30 Monday evening, and we both agreed again that, though it would be nice if something would happen in the day that was left, all of us wanted the Lord's will to be done. If that meant I would not get to have a part in welcoming their baby into the world, we were sure that He knew best.

We planned to go into San Pedro yesterday afternoon to be sure we were there in time for Jeffrey's ear doctor's appointment this morning. I was still up, repacking the suitcases that we had packed and then unpacked the week before, when Stephen called me at 12:15 a.m. yesterday morning. "Yvonne's water just broke. She's having a lot of pressure—do you think you can make it in time?"

Yes, we could make it in time! I had the clinic's portable oxygen tank and a large storage container of delivery equipment and medications sitting by the front door. A quick call to Daniel Melton, who had kept his cell phone on beside his bed, brought him wide awake and ready to make the flying trip over the mountain. We arrived at the DeLongs apartment in a record one hour and twenty-three minutes.

For the next six-and-a-half hours, Yvonne alternated walking, rocking, and sitting in a warm shower while Stephen and I supported and encouraged her through increasingly stronger and more frequent contractions. Her blood pressure and the baby's heartbeat stayed well within normal range, and her labor progress was slow but steady.

Around 9:00 a.m., she felt an unusually strong pain, and for a minute it looked like the baby was all balled up at the top of her abdomen. I checked the fetal heartbeat, which was a reassuring 150 beats per minute. I checked Yvonne's dilation, which was all the way to seven centimeters. She had a small trickle of blood, but nothing more than sometimes happens at that stage of labor, and it only lasted a few seconds. I felt uneasy, even with the good heartbeat, and my mind flitted to several possibilities, one of which might be the separation of her uterine scar from her cesarean section four years ago with their first baby. However, their second child was born normally, at home, with a midwife attending, and things had gone fine, even with a twenty-five-hour labor and a nine-pound baby. About three minutes later, she had another small trickle of blood, and I again checked the fetal heart rate. It had been hovering between 130 and 150 every time before that, but this time it was around 100 beats per minute.

"We have to leave NOW for the hospital!" I said urgently, helping Yvonne onto her feet and practically pushing her toward the stairs. Stephen ran to get the keys and to tell his sister Lydia, who had arrived the week before to help them, what was going on. "I can't go like this!" Yvonne protested, gesturing to her nightgown, as we headed out the door. "That's not as important as getting you there as quickly as we can," I replied, jumping into the back seat of their pickup truck and helping her in beside me.

Stephen sped toward the hospital, weaving through traffic and fervently praying aloud. In the five minutes it took us to arrive, he had time to pull out his cell phone and call their doctor, asking him to meet us. We whipped into the emergency room entrance, he jumped out and ran inside to tell them we were there, and I grabbed a wheelchair for Yvonne. "I'm having another contraction, and the baby's really been moving a lot," she said as I rushed her into a curtained cubicle in the corner of the emergency room.

The ER doctor and several nurses converged on us while I rapidly explained why we were there. They asked all the questions about name, age, where she lived, etc. They checked her dilation: still seven centimeters, and she was not bleeding. "The baby's heartbeat was too low!" I reiterated, and the nurse started searching for it with the Doppler. "76...81...83...79...84..." the digital display read. "Where were you hearing it?" she queried, moving the wand around and probably thinking that she was picking up Yvonne's heart rate. "Right there," I indicated, touching the spot. "But that IS the baby. The heartbeat really IS that low!" Yvonne's personal doctor walked in at that moment, took one glance at the heart rate, and barked an order to get Yvonne up to surgery IMMEDIATELY! Another nurse started to check her blood pressure. "No time for that now," he snapped. "GET HER UPSTAIRS!" He dashed off to change clothes and scrub up. To their credit, the hospital staff shifted into high gear, starting an IV, transferring her to a gurney, and rushing her down the hall, around a corner, and up two long ramps to the operating room.

She clutched my hand as I trotted alongside the gurney. Stephen had been waylaid in the registration department, and I knew he was aching to be with her. "I'll stay with you," I promised, but when we got to the operating room's double doors, another nurse insisted I had to change into scrubs before going inside. I dashed into a tiny restroom and switched from my clothes into theirs with fumbling fingers, anxious to be back with Yvonne. When I ran back out, they were just locking the doors. I peered in through the windows and watched the flurry as first her doctor, then a pediatrician, then another doctor scrubbed their hands and forearms, donned masks and gloves and disappeared through another door.

I learned later that they tried to give her an epidural, but it did not work, and the doctor ordered the anesthesiologist to go ahead and give general anesthesia so he could get her opened up right away. Even so, it was still at least ten to fifteen minutes from the time we arrived until the surgery was in progress. Meanwhile, Stephen had finally finished registering Yvonne and hurried upstairs to where I was waiting. "How is she doing?" he asked anxiously. Just then a nurse unlocked a set of side doors and came through. "The doctor promised me I could go in with her!" he begged her, but she shook her head. I took his arm and pulled him into the room where the pile of clean scrub clothes was stacked. "Get changed, you'll get in," I promised.

A minute or so later he was back, tying the drawstring on the dark-blue pants, and asking the nurse once more to be allowed to see his wife. "No one can enter," she stated firmly. "She's having surgery."

"That doesn't matter," I said. "It's his baby, too; the doctor *promised* that her husband could stay with her, and he's going in!" I stripped off the paper shoe covers they had given me to put on, untied my mask, and retied it around Stephen's face as he struggled to fit the too-small covers over his tennis shoes. "Right through those doors," I pointed, and he headed through.

I leaned back against a wall and wearily closed my eyes, grimly waiting for news. The sliding door leading from the hall into the operating suite opened without warning, catching my arm and shoulder and knocking me onto the floor. I struggled to my feet as one of the attendants pushing another patient on a gurney turned his head aside, but not quickly enough to keep me from seeing his amused grin. My embarrassment was forgotten as I saw Stephen, shoulders slumped and face haggard, walking slowly toward me.

"They're working on our baby, but they don't know if she'll make it," he said dully. "The doctor told me he's doing his best to save Yvonne, but she's lost a lot of blood, and they're not sure about her, either." He broke into wracking sobs, and I hugged him tightly as he clung to me desperately and we cried aloud together to God for a miracle.

Managing to compose himself, he walked back into the operating suite. No one tried to stop him this time. I called Daniel Melton, who had gone to the mission apartment about an hour after dropping me off at DeLongs earlier that morning, to update him and ask for extra prayer support. I continued whispering earnest prayers while waiting, but when Stephen walked slowly back out a few minutes later, I knew without asking that he did not have good news. "Our little girl didn't make it," he whispered brokenly. "The doctor said Yvonne is going to be all right, though." I held him as I knew his mother would have done had she been there, as Stephen gulped out between agonized sobs, "Lord, I don't understand why this happened, but I know You know best. Thank You for sparing Yvonne's life and not taking her from me as well."

We waited together as people came and went, giving us sympathetic glances in passing. At last we saw a young nurse pushing a wheeled bassinet toward us. Through the transparent plastic sides we could clearly see a tiny form wrapped in a blanket. "Here's your little girl, Sir," she said softly. "I'm so sorry." She stood quietly, tears running down her cheeks, as we looked at the perfect, silent little body, then she gave me a hug and left us alone. I gently lifted Joanna Brooke and held her close for a moment before handing her to her father. He rocked her back and forth in his arms, gazing at her peaceful face. "At least we know she's safe in heaven with Jesus," he said at last, handing her back to me. I laid her into the bassinet, and we stood silently crying, looking down at her. The pediatrician came and talked to Stephen, offering his apologies. "I did every-thing I could, but I couldn't save her. Both the baby and placenta were outside the uterus when the surgeon opened Yvonne up. The baby bled out through the placenta." He hugged Stephen. "I'm very sorry." He left, and shortly there-after Daniel Melton walked in. Stephen turned to him. "She didn't make it," he stated simply. Daniel looked as though someone had struck him. "Oh, no!" he gasped, enveloping Stephen in a strong embrace and starting to cry with us.

Long minutes later, the nurses came to take little Joanna back. "We'll bring her down to your room after your wife gets out of recovery," they promised. "The hospital doesn't have a morgue, so you have twenty-four hours to decide what to do with her body and make arrangements to bury her." Stephen asked that they let him break the news to Yvonne, and they agreed to do so. He was in no condition to try to think about options for Joanna's body to be preserved, but Daniel, who is blessed with a gift of having friends in high places and knowing how to get things moving, left to make some phone calls investigating possibilities. Stephen and I went down to what would be Yvonne's room, and he began the sad task of calling their families to break the tragic news.

As he was dialing his mother-in-law, the doctor walked in. "She is going to be all right," he informed us, "but she was in very grave danger. Her uterus split open vertically, from top to bottom, in a huge jagged tear. She could have bled to death; not only will she recover, I was able to save her uterus as well."

At 1:00 p.m., Yvonne was wheeled into her room, smiling bravely. Daniel Melton was back by this time, and he and I waited in an adjoining room while Stephen and Yvonne had some time alone together. They called us in soon, and still smiling through her tears, Yvonne said, "We won't ever have to worry about her not making it to heaven now."

Midafternoon little Joanna Brooke, a pan of ice under the thin plastic pad in her bassinet, was brought to the room, and Yvonne got to cuddle her baby for the first time. Joanna's Aunt Lydia, big sister Hannah and big brother Daniel, Tiffany and Daniel Melton and their three boys, Rex and Jeffrey, and various

Honduran friends were in and out, offering prayer, sympathy and love. I went back to the mission apartment around 8:00 p.m. to get my first sleep in over 36 hours. Stephen and Yvonne both hugged me tightly and thanked me before I left, but I was feeling far from good, going over and over in my mind all that had happened and wondering the agonizing "what if's" that always accompany such an occurrence.

I can only conclude that God orchestrated everything, and we have to trust Him. Maybe if the surgery *had* been a few minutes sooner, Joanna would have lived, but she would almost certainly have had permanent brain damage from the oxygen deprivation. Maybe if I had already left the country, Yvonne would have been in the hospital when her uterus ruptured, but likely not. Had I not been there, she was planning to labor at home anyhow as long as she possibly could before going in to the hospital, because she was determined not to be tied down to a fetal monitor. It is very probable that she would have bled to death, since her hemorrhage was all inside. Her mother called me last evening, and through our tears we talked about what had happened. She and her husband both assured me that they believe God allowed me to be there to save Yvonne's life. Stephen and Yvonne had said the same thing the morning after it all happened when we stopped in again to see them before leaving the country. We will never know what *might* have been, but we know what *was*: God spared the life of a young mother with two little children and a husband who need her, and took to be with Him a precious, perfect, innocent baby who, although terribly grieved and greatly missed, will never suffer the pain of wrong decisions and sin, but is in a far better world, waiting to be reunited someday with her family. For whatever part He allowed me to play in that outcome, I am profoundly thankful.

# 44

## I Need 30,000 Pills, Please

*January 14–17, 2010 ~ Penns Creek and Lewisburg, Pennsylvania*

On Thursday, January 14, I sat at the supper table with my husband and sons, listening to the news broadcast with its horrific statistics from the worst earthquake to hit Haiti in more than two hundred years. Two days earlier, at 4:53 p.m. on January 12, the Caribbean and North American tectonic plates had pushed together along the Enriquillo-Plantain Garden Fault system line. The tremendous energy that was created fifteen miles southwest of the capital, Port-au-Prince, indiscriminately toppled buildings universally lacking earthquake-resistant designs. Hospitals, cathedrals, hotels, schools, the capital's main prison, the National Palace, and many government offices were demolished, as well as enormous numbers of the squat, cinder-block dwellings which were home to the lowliest of the lowly in this poverty-stricken nation. According to official estimates released months later, 230,000 to 316,000 people were killed, 300,000 injured, and 1.5 million displaced. The devastation included 97,294 houses destroyed and 183,383 damaged in the Port-au-Prince area and much of southern Haiti.

Earlier that day, I had made a fruitless call to the Red Cross to see if any teams from our area were planning to travel to Haiti to help with the relief effort. As I heard of the bodies of the quake's victims which still lined the streets, people scrabbling in the rubble with their bare hands seeking for loved ones, and the refugee camps where survivors were crammed in make-shift shelters without sanitation or clean water, my heart ached. "I want to go!" I exclaimed to my family. "I know I could help, if I just had a way to get there."

After we finished eating, I called my sister, Lois. "Please help me pray that if God wants me there, He will make a way," I asked her. I drove to my night shift at our local emergency room, my mind full of the tragic situation. Arriving back home Friday morning, I was just heading for bed when the phone rang. "Dwight Rine has been trying to get up with you," the caller said. "He's working to get a team together to go to Haiti to help the earthquake victims and wants you know if you can be part of it." I was astounded at this overnight answer to my prayers. "Tell him I would love to go!" I replied.

I learned that Dwight, director of God's Missionary Church's foreign missions department, had been contacted by Don Mobley, the GMC missionary in Haiti. "I have 1,279 people camped out in our mission compound," Don said. "Many of them are seriously wounded. Can you please send someone to help us?" Dwight phoned his friend, Dr. Timothy Slavens, who said he would be glad to help, but needed a few days to make arrangements.

"Can you be part of a team to go with Dr. Slavens?" Dwight asked me.

"Rex has already given his permission," I replied. "But if Don has that many people in need of help, wouldn't it be good to get a team there sooner? How about if I contact some of the doctors I work with and see if any of them could leave this weekend?" Dwight assured me that would be fine. It was Friday evening by the time we worked out this plan, and too late to make any more phone calls. Bright and early Saturday, I started to pack my bags, watching the time on the clock until it was a more reasonable hour to pick up the phone and see who could join me on this venture.

That same morning, Dr. Bradley Moyer had gotten up early to prepare for the start of his 6:00 a.m. emergency room shift at Evangelical Community Hospital, where we both worked. The ER was not busy that morning, so they called and told him to wait a couple of hours before he came in. He ate a leisurely breakfast while watching the news, which was still full of tragic stories from Haiti. "I want to go to Haiti," he told his wife. He, too, had checked into the possibilities of joining a team, but had come up with nothing.

"Just go," she told him.

"I can't just *go*," he protested. "I have to have someone to go *with*, some organization that will send me."

"If God wants you in Haiti," his wife replied, "He will get you there."

Minutes after Dr. Moyer left for work, I called his home to ask him if he would consider being part of a team to help in Haiti. His wife told me that he had already left, so I phoned the hospital and told the secretary what I needed. "Please have him call me when he gets there," I requested.

Dr. Jack Devine was already working when Dr. Moyer arrived. "Jack, I have got to get to Haiti," Dr. Moyer told his fellow physician.

"Just go," Dr. Devine said.

"I can't just *go*," Dr. Moyer replied, as he had answered his wife earlier.

"If you are supposed to be there, it will work out," his friend assured him.

Picking up a chart, Dr. Moyer headed toward a patient's room. The secretary glanced up and saw him. "Dr. Moyer, did Hannah get in contact with you yet?"

"No, why?" he asked her.

"She called here about ten minutes ago, wanting to know if you would be able to go to Haiti with her." He stared at her, incredulous, feeling almost as if a jolt of electricity had just struck him.

"All right, God," he thought to himself. "This has got to be from you!"

Finishing up with his patient, he walked back to the desk and told Dr. Devine what had just occurred.

"I would like to join you," his colleague told him.

And just like that, the details started falling into place for what would be the first of ten medical teams sent by God's Missionary Church to Haiti. Dr. Moyer called the hospital's president, Michael O'Keefe. "I realize that it is the weekend, Sir, but I am leaving this afternoon with two other Evangelical employees to help with the relief effort in Haiti, and I need 10,000 doses of Keflex, 10,000 doses of Bactrim, and 10,000 doses of Cipro," he told him. Ever gracious President O'Keefe may have gulped silently at the audacious request, but well aware of the huge need, he promised him the medications. He also gave him permission to go to the hospital storeroom and collect the wound-care supplies, as well as IV fluids, catheters, and tubing, that he would need for the trip.

Our team of four, including GMC pastor Rev. Alan Walter, left the next afternoon for the Harrisburg, PA, airport. When we arrived, we learned that our flight had been postponed, but the airline personnel loaded us and our supplies into a van and drove us the hundred miles to Philadelphia to get a connecting flight to Florida. At Philadelphia, we ran through the airport terminal to catch our plane, dragging our heavily loaded suitcases. When the agents at the ticket counter learned of our mission, they waved through our eight extra suitcases without any excess baggage charges. In fact, they even allowed Dr. Moyer to take his bulging hiker's backpack on the plane with him as a carry-on. It was over twice the normal allowable size, with an aluminum frame that extended from his hips to higher than his head. Also, someone had donated a number of one-liter bags of IV fluids at the last minute. They were ten times the normal one hundred-milliliter limit for liquids, but the doctors stuffed them into one of our carry-ons, and the agents OK'd that as well.

I did not realize about one of the last details of this mission that God so wonderfully pulled together until nearly a week into my sixteen-day stay on what would be the first of three trips to Haiti. On Thursday, the day before Dwight contacted me, I had visited an orthopedic surgeon, and he injected my left thumb with a steroid to decrease the extreme pain from an arthritic joint. For months, I had been having trouble using my thumb, and the pain from it woke me up at night. That steroid injection completely took away the pain and gave me free mobility of my hand during the entire time I was in Haiti. I had not known what would be needed when I scheduled the appointment weeks before to have the surgeon examine my thumb, but God did, and He timed the injection perfectly. "Great and marvelous are Your works, Lord God Almighty!" (Revelation 15:3)

## 45

## Helping in Haiti, Clinic Day One
### *January 19, 2010 ~ Carrefour, Haiti*

She died shortly before daybreak today, just a few feet from the door of the makeshift clinic we worked so hard to set up this morning. Her family was actually relieved; she had been slow mentally and a burden to them for the thirty-five years of her simple existence. Since the 7.0 earthquake that devastated Haiti and destroyed her home seven days before, she had not eaten, lying listlessly on a table in one of the classrooms here at the mission station. Her family refused to give her any care, so finally the resident missionary, Don Mobley, enlisted the help of some of the other women who were stranded in the mission compound to bathe her and exchange her filthy clothes for a clean T-shirt. He started an IV in a vain attempt to give her the fluids she was not taking voluntarily, but even with her arms restrained with soft strips of cloth, she pulled the tubing out, unable to understand that it was her only hope of life.

Our team consisted of Bradley Moyer and Jack Devine, both skilled ER doctors, Alan Walter, a pastor and the GMC World Missions treasurer, and me. We arrived at the God's Missionary Church Bible Institute at Carrefour, Haiti, at 5:16 Monday evening. We were close to exhaustion after the whirlwind of getting this trip pulled together, only two hours of sleep the night before, and the tension of not knowing for sure until the last moment if we would be among the fortunate few allowed on one of the two daily flights by Missionary Flights International from Fort Pierce, Florida, to Port-au-Prince, Haiti.

As we drove through the streets from the airport to the mission station, our minds had a hard time absorbing the shock of the horrendous destruction on every side. Even though we had all seen pictures of the effects of the earthquake, nothing could have prepared us for experiencing the reality firsthand. People who had lost everything milled through the rubble strewn streets—at least, the parts of streets that were not occupied with hastily improvised shelters of sticks stuck into the ground, with a sheet or curtain stretched over them to provide meager shelter from the relentless beating of a merciless tropical sun. An emaciated elderly woman, gaunt skin stretched over a bent skeleton, slowly shuffled her way past our truck, dressed in absolutely nothing but a stained pair of panties. In stark contrast to her shriveled figure, dozens of huge pigs, snouts snuffling through the mountains of garbage, appeared to be thriving abundantly. Helicopters clattered their way overhead, carrying wounded survivors of the violent tremor to help. The putrid stench of rotting flesh vied with the acrid sharpness of smoke from multiple fires and the suffocating fumes of the diesel trucks that bumped and wove their way over the curbs and around chunks of concrete, seeking a way to their destination that was not totally blocked by debris.

Don had told us that he had 1,279 people, whose homes had been destroyed, camping out in the mission compound, forty of them with severe wounds, and over one hundred others less seriously injured, but still in need of medical attention. Just reading those numbers did not give anything close to an accurate idea of what the situation is actually like. Fifty minutes after leaving the airport on the eight-mile trip to Don's home, our truck finally eased through the gate onto the mission property. People scrambled to drag the sheets and blankets on which they have been sleeping out of the way of the advancing tires, and dark bodies jostled each other to greet us. What was once an orderly, well-tended yard is now a sea of tents, some store bought, most nothing but sticks-and-sheets lean-tos.

A group of smiling Haitian young men, Don's students from the Bible institute, helped us unload our 830 pounds of luggage: twelve pieces that the four of us had checked, our carry-ons, and four garbage bags loaded with snacks, packets of sugar, rolls of toilet paper, paper towels, coffee, sanitizing wipes, and napkins that the friendly crew on our US Airways flight from Philadelphia, PA, to West Palm, FL, had donated for the relief efforts. For the next half hour, we looked over the schoolroom where we would be running the clinic, planning how to set things up. Shortly after 6:00 p.m., we joined Don for a delicious supper of rice and beans with sardine soup, cooked over a charcoal fire outside on his porch, since the propane he needs to use his stove is in short supply. After supper, we tackled the monumental task of sorting and organizing the mountains of medications and wound-care supplies that had been so generously donated by Evangelical Community Hospital, as well as other concerned agencies and individuals in our home area.

Two-and-a-half hours later, we had things divided into suitcases by categories: gloves, masks, and gowns in this one; IV fluids and tubing in that; sutures, lidocaine, and scalpels in the one on the floor by the door; lots and lots of rolls of bandaging materials in the green one on the chair; hundreds and hundreds of antibiotic and pain killer tablets in those two in the bedroom; and so forth. It was long past dark when we finished and time for Don to turn off the generator he uses to supply electricity to the compound, since there is none available from the city. I picked my way by flashlight across the crowded yard to a room behind the school library, across the compound from the classroom building that we would be using for our clinic. On the way, I passed a line of people with buckets, patiently waiting a turn to hold a container under the stream of water pouring out from a pipe stuck into an opening near the bottom of a 250-gallon tank on the roof of the second story of the guest house where the men would be staying. With so many pipes torn up and broken in the quake, the city water supply has been turned off, and the people here are among the fortunate few to have a supply of the precious liquid available from the well on the mission property. Don uses the generator to pump water from the well up into the tank, and gravity takes care of getting it down into the buckets held to receive it.

I was anxious for a shower and a bed, very thankful that I would not be making that bed up on the ground outside. This was the first night that anyone had felt that it was safe enough to sleep in the buildings, due to the continuing aftershocks in the days following the main tremor. I smiled apologetically at the family using the steps into my room as they moved out of the way so I could unlock the door, lit the kerosene lantern that Don had provided, grabbed my towel and washcloth, and headed down the hall to the shower. Unfortunately, the water supply to this building had not been turned on, so I had to be satisfied with wiping off the day's sweat and dust with some wet wipes before crawling between my clean sheets. Even as tired as I was, sleep did not come easily. For one thing, having over a thousand people in a seventy-five by one hundred fifty feet space, especially when that space is right outside your window, is not exactly soothing. For another thing, these people were not settling down for a peaceful night's rest. Although surrounded by overwhelming tragedy, they were still praising God, their sure refuge in time of trouble. The service that had started around 6:30 p.m. was still in full swing. A preacher on the church porch, using a VERY adequate sound system, was exhorting the largest congregation he had ever addressed, who enthusiastically supported him with loud cries of "Alleluia." It was quite disconcerting to me not to be able to understand any other words that were being said, but my Spanish knowledge was of virtually no use whatsoever here in a Creole-speaking country.

The service finally ended, and the sounds of children coughing, babies crying, and adults conversing or listening to battery-operated radios gradually dropped off. It was then that I heard the groans. They were not terribly loud, but the heavy night air carried them clearly into my bedroom. Over and over the heart-wrenching sounds were repeated, making me ache to do something to help. I thought of getting a flashlight and going out into the black yard to try to find the person in pain, but without being able to communicate, I would be helpless. The gates to Don Mobley's house and the apartment where the men from our group were staying were locked, and with no telephone available, I could not enlist their aid. The noises of distress finally stopped, and I drifted into an uneasy sleep.

Bright and early this morning, the compound erupted with singing as the refugees who were camping there started their day with another service every bit as loud as its predecessor the evening before. I rolled over to look at my alarm clock and stared in shock at the glowing dial which announced the time as 4:15 a.m. Oblivious to my fervent desire for another hour or two of sleep, the congregation sang on ... and on ... and on ..., giving no indication that anything unusual had happened. Indeed, from the joyful sounds of praise, one might imagine himself in a comfortable church building with an affluent congregation of people who had never been touched by suffering or heartache.

With that exuberant start to the day, you can imagine our incredulous responses to Don Mobley's announcement at the breakfast table that the population in our compound was down by one. The dead body of the woman whose groans had troubled me during the night was moved to a table outside the wall, where it lay all day in the intense sun, waiting for burial arrangements to be made. At one point, a group of men started digging a hole right beside the wall to bury her, but there was such an outcry from others who did not think it was a proper place that the grave diggers abandoned their efforts. By nightfall, a slow drip of dark-brown liquid from the edge of the table to the dust beneath testified mutely to the effect of the heat. Not until the next morning was her decaying body finally taken to a spot for collection and burial.

Our first clinic day ended on happier note that helped to ease the sting of our inability to help the poor, simple woman. One of the 120 patients that came seeking aid on Tuesday was a thin, four- or five-year-old girl, so terribly dehydrated and weak that she could not stand alone. Her blood sugar was low, so I started an IV of glucose water on her, and throughout the hours of the morning and afternoon, as the fluid dripped little by little into her veins, she made a gradual transition from near death to walking out on her own when we ended our day. All of us are positive that had her mother not sought our help, that little one, too, would have ended up a lifeless corpse on the street corner by nightfall. One life saved, and over a hundred desperately wounded and hurting Haitians given compassionate care. It was, overall, a very satisfying start to our mission of mercy.

## 46

## "WHAT WAS THAT SHE SAID?"

*January 26, 2010 ~ Carrefour, Haiti*

"CAN YOU ASK HER IF SHE FEELS THE BABY MOVING?" I hollered into Dominique's ear as we bent over the largely pregnant woman sitting on the bench at the front of the group of pushing, yelling villagers. Yesterday was the fifth afternoon we went into outlying areas around Carrefour to minister to pockets of people who had not been able to come to us at our clinic on the mission compound. The other four times, we set up our supplies in a church or school. Although the roof was gone from one place and part of a wall from another, crowd control was relatively easy. This afternoon, we were under a couple of large tarps hung over a yard at the edge of a heavily damaged village, and the 250 to 300 people who had quickly gathered to receive care were all wanting to be first to have us dress this wound or listen to that set of raspy lungs.

The local pastor, who had been ferreting out these people in need of help and organizing our visits, did his valiant best to maintain some semblance of order by waving his arms and shouting instructions to form three lines: pregnant women in one, wounded in another, and other illness issues in a third. We were still seeing a lot of nasty wounds that needed attention, but as the days stacked up for tens of thousands of homeless people living nearly on top of each other, sleeping on the ground and protected from the sun's burning rays by only a sheet stretched between poles, we saw more and more pneumonia, malaria, diarrhea and vomiting.

During the previous four hours, we had cared for more than 113 patients at the compound. I say "more than 113" because, although our doorman gave out that many slips of paper, at least a third of those who received numbers were family units, with a mother and one or two children included in the same admission ticket. Three of the many sick babies we saw that morning had to stay for an extended time for rehydration. One desperately ill little girl was so badly dehydrated that none of us, including the neonatal intensive care nurse who had joined our group Friday, was able to get an IV started on her. We decided to put a tube down her stomach and drip liquids into it, but discovered we had no such thing among our supplies. Enlisting the help of one of the compound guards to accompany me for protection, I hurried the two blocks to where the Doctors Without Borders hospital had been set up under huge tarps right in the middle of the street. We found out about their existence two days after our arrival and had been collaborating ever since, sharing medication and supplies. They were equipped to handle amputations and fracture repairs as well as complicated obstetric cases, but not to give the wound and illness care that we were providing.

Returning triumphantly with the only infant nasogastric tube they could find, I learned that the baby had started to take a few teaspoons of oral hydration fluid dribbled into her mouth with a syringe. Our team doctor wanted to continue with the oral fluids to see if the little tyke's veins would cooperate better in an hour or two, but before long, she vomited and had more diarrhea, so trying again to start an IV seemed like the best solution to replace the fluids she kept heaving back at us. This time, I found one good vein on the top of her hand, and the 24-gauge angiocath slid into it smoothly. In the meantime, two more babies with dehydration from nausea and vomiting arrived, thankfully not as seriously ill as our first one, but still definitely needing our help.

Before we left for the afternoon mobile clinic, all three babies, plus the young woman whose back had been injured when the quake hit and she was knocked off her feet by a crush of people falling on top of her, were stable enough for us to leave them in the capable hands of one of the national nurses for continued monitoring of their IV's and hydration status. Don Mobley was still at the airport, picking up the sixty-nine boxes of much-needed medical supplies and food that the second team brought with them. Nine Americans, two national interpreters, the pastor who arranged the clinic, and another helper all piled into two vehicles and headed up the mountain. Seven of the thirteen people, along with a big blue plastic footlocker, two suitcases, and a backpack of medicines and supplies, made a decent load for the bed of one small pickup truck, although by Haitian standards, things were not even crowded.

We laid our supplies out on a couple of chairs, a bench, and the porch wall of a damaged-but-still-standing house. Each doctor or nurse and his or her interpreter huddled down over their respective patients, heads close together as we tried to hear the symptoms they described. It was challenging to make out what they said above the noise of the anxious, shoving people crowded as close to the front as each one could possible get. Probably half of the patients I saw were expectant mothers, and by the end of the day, my interpreter knew the things to ask without my prompting: "WHEN IS THE BABY SUPPOSED TO BE BORN?" "CAN SHE FEEL IT MOVING?" "WAS SHE STRUCK WITH ANYTHING IN THE EARTHQUAKE?" "IS SHE HAVING ANY BLEEDING OR LEAKING OF FLUID?" "WHERE IS SHE HAVING PAIN?" After eliciting as much information I could via the interpreter, the next step was a belly exam. Imagine, if you can, lying down on a hard, narrow, wooden bench out in a yard in front of over two hundred people, and having someone whom you have never seen before today running her hands over your pregnant abdomen to determine your baby's position and how well it is growing. One by one, they stretched out and submitted to my probing, questioning fingers. Most of them left with the reassurance that, thanks to God's amazing protective design, the tiny life they were nurturing inside was safe and sound. I gave each mother-to-be a packet of fifteen vitamins, woefully inadequate to offset the nutritional deficits of diets that were sadly lacking even before the earthquake, and which now were maintained just above starvation level for many.

By the time we needed to pack up and head back to the mission compound, we were all dog-tired, not only from a long day of hard work, but also from the nervous strain of the situation. Every once in a while, the noises from the crowd had turned ominous as someone did not get his turn when he thought he should. Also, we were still seeing very nasty, infected wounds. The ones on children were especially hard to handle emotionally. One of my patients, a precious little tot about a year old, had been splashed with boiling water from the pot on the stove when the quake hit. I injected around the wounds with lidocaine before painstakingly removing the large areas of necrotic skin with a scalpel and tweezers. She was terrified, of course, and my heart was wrung as I firmly held her legs and did what needed to be done. The baby's mother gratefully thanked me with her eyes after the whole procedure was over, the crying finished, and the areas neatly covered with clean white bandages. I hope she could see God's love in my eyes as I smiled back and hugged her.

# 47

## Making Memories on a Motorcycle
### *January 27, 2010 ~ Carrefour, Haiti*

I sat with my feet in a basin of bleach water last night, shoes still on, hoping that the itching would go away. Early that afternoon, I had trekked up the mountain on one of the mission's motorcycles, sandwiched between the driver in front and my interpreter behind. Whizzing through the streets of Carrefour while straddling a two-wheeled conveyance gives a whole new perspective to the city, one not experienced by riding in the cab of the pickup that a local pastor has sent on several occasions to take us to outlying areas of need.

My mission was to debride and dress the badly burned foot of a little boy we had treated in one of the seven mobile clinics we have held so far. I loaded a backpack with the supplies I thought I would need, then added a handful of packets of various medications, extra gauze and dressings "just in case," and, of course, the all-important bottle of water to drink. In this heat, keeping hydrated is of prime importance.

Don had assured me that Sonson, my driver, was very responsible and careful. He did a remarkably good job of weaving our cycle through tight spaces between buses and dodging the rotting garbage piles, pedestrians, and dogs as we headed down the main street. I was thankful that my interpreter remembered which little dirt side road to turn into, since two days before, when our whole group had gone, I had dozed en route. I did remember the shallow stream that splashed down the mountain and washed our truck tires for half a mile or so as we drove through it. Navigating the same stream on the motorcycle did more than just clean the tires, though. I cringed as I felt the water hit my legs—water that had just splashed over the naked body of the little boy whose mother was giving him a bath upstream, and before that, had swirled around a dog that was cooling his flea-ridden hide.

Sonson gunned the motor as we jounced and bounced our way up the final steep stretch of hillside onto a level plain where yet another tent city had replaced the tumbled, cement-block-walled homes that still terraced the mountainside. We pulled up in a cloud of dust outside a yard enclosed with corrugated tin slats. The sandal-clad, pig-tailed mayor of this mostly destroyed village came bustling up with a plastic-covered, bright-red-upholstered chair for me to sit on while I waited for my patient to arrive. When his father carried him in through the gate a few minutes later, the two of them were directed to another chair that was placed in front of mine, and my outdoor treatment room was ready. He was not very happy with the lidocaine injection I gave him before I gently soaked and teased the two-day-old dirty dressing from his foot. In spite of my most careful efforts, the little fellow was a puddle of tears and his foot a raw, bleeding mass of outraged nerve endings by the time I got it uncovered to see what needed done. Whether he understood enough to appreciate it or not, the numbing solution did make a significant difference in his comfort as I gave the wound the thorough cleaning it needed. When the job was done, antibiotic ointment and Vaseline gauze dressing in place, and the foot securely wrapped with more gauze, he even had a smile for the camera as my interpreter snapped a picture of us.

For the next hour or so, my "just in case" medicines and extra supplies were pressed into duty by the crowd that had quickly gathered at my arrival. One after another, they lined up to have this chest listened to; that itchy, bumpy rash examined; or the other bloodshot, swollen, pus-encrusted eye inspected.

"Please tell her that her little girl has a bad lung infection and needs to take one of these white pills three times a day. Make sure she knows that it is very important for her to be giving the child water to drink many times throughout the day, and to make sure she takes all of the medicine."

"That is a scabies rash, and it needs to be washed in Tetmosol soap for three days in a row. You must leave the soap on for five minutes before washing it off."

"The redness and pus in your eye is from bacteria. Have your wife squeeze a half-inch ribbon of this ointment along the bottom eyelid twice a day for a week."

And so it went. My medicines were used up before I could check everyone, but I knew that my friends back at the mission would be worried if I stayed away too long, so I was just as glad I had not brought more pills. I set up a time to return in two days to tend the little boy's foot again, and then we headed back down the mountain.

A little later that afternoon, I climbed on again behind Sonson to visit Josette, the fifteen-year-old girl that we had found on our first trip away from the station. Dr. Devine was pretty sure the nasty wound on her back was an open fracture of her pelvis, but at that point, we had nowhere to take her to confirm or treat the break. She lay beside the road on a mattress, a piece of cardboard underneath her to protect the mattress from the feces and urine that had been leaking from her uncontrollably since the earthquake. Even though she knew that my every visit meant the pain of a dressing change, she still smiled when I peeked around the sheet that formed a wall of sorts to shield her from the view of passers-by. On this trip, a week after we had first found her, Josette's bowel and bladder functions had returned, but she was still unable to get up.

After finishing Josette's care, we ducked and dodged our way under the tarps and canvas that had been stretched across the street to form protective shade to families with no other homes. It was the first time I had ever ridden a motorcycle through someone's living room to get to work. We were on our way to visit Enosh, one of the Bible school teachers, whose wife was killed in the quake. When his home was destroyed, Enosh's legs were badly crushed from the knees down. His family somehow found a bed for him to lie on, so he is more fortunate than many, even though the bed is in the street. He, too, greeted us with a smile in spite of the severe pain he has to be suffering from his legs that are swollen like huge sausages. After three bags of IV fluids and antibiotics, he is doing better than when we first saw him over a week ago, but still has a L-O-N-G road to recovery. We are taking him nourishing food every day and Lidoderm patches to place over the areas of most extreme pain, so he can sleep at night.

The late afternoon sun was still plenty warm as we made our trip home, but I had absolutely no desire to go wading in the river we forded. This one was much deeper than the first one we had ridden through, and my feet were totally soaked with the murky spray flying up from the tires. To our right, half a dozen trucks were parked out in the convenient free car wash upstream while men busily scrubbed the day's grime off. Just a few hundred feet farther beyond, ropes stretched from one bank to the other, sporting hundreds of pieces of brightly colored laundry that flapped in the breeze, while their owners, stark naked, lathered the sweat off. At least, the huge pigs that fatten themselves on the garbage that is disposed of in the streams were gorging themselves *downstream* at this location, although I knew there were plenty of others upstream to add zillions of tiny, invisible bugs to the ones that had surely plastered themselves to me on our earlier crossing.

So that is why I gave my feet a bleach bath last evening. The itching did stop, although it was probably somewhat psychological. Did I mention that a hot, soaking tub bath is on my list of things to do as soon as possible after my arrival back home?

## 48

## Just Get Me Home, I Don't Care How!

*February 1-2, 2010 - Port-au-Prince*

**February 1, 2010**

*2:15 p.m.*

The line of people waiting to board the blue-and-white Missionary Flights International plane is getting shorter and shorter as one by one they climb the metal steps that lead into its pressurized interior. Unfortunately, I am not among them. Doctor Rick Lapp, Pastor Alan Walter, Registered Nurse Vanessa Thompson, and I have been sitting under the dusty shelter of a large military tent at the main airport in Port-au-Prince, Haiti, since 11:14 this morning. We are part of a varied crowd of Haitian-born U.S. citizens anxious to leave their disaster-struck native country and medical personnel and relief workers returning to the United States. All of us have one mission: GET OUT! But we will not be doing that any time soon. The mammoth C-17 USAF cargo jet that sits off to the side shows no signs of readying for departure, and we are told that it has been under repair for four days. The other plane of similar size that slowly taxied out of sight earlier took no one in our tent or the red-and-white-striped awning beside us, and the only thing we have been told is that no one knows anything to tell us.

We left Carrefour at 7:50 this morning, making the eight-mile trip to the airport in just over two hours. When we finally arrived, the people at the Missionary Flights International desk told us that our names were not on their list for the flight that was to leave at noon. So we all trekked back the way we had come and were directed around the back of the building to the area where the U.S. military has set up operations, since the large airport terminal is too structurally damaged to be used. There, we each stamped our left thumbprint in red ink on the back of a four-page emergency evacuation document and filled in the necessary information such as who to notify in case of death, to hopefully get us a flight out. About an hour ago, we were each handed a military rations Surepak meal and a bottle of water. The nifty little water-activated heater packet that was included with the food got my chicken breast and Mexican-style corn piping hot in minutes.

Too bad that the restroom stop I made around 7:00 this morning before we left Carrefour cannot last all day. The very nice soldier who not long ago escorted me to the row of four blue porta-johns just within sight of our tent stood well back to await my return. I certainly could understand why, after I caught my first whiff of the odor that smacked me in the face about twenty feet from my destination. It did not help me to feel any better about what I needed to do when the Haitian man who had preceded me to the same destination turned away in disgust, after investigating all four compartments. But when you gotta go, you gotta go, so I gingerly opened the first door and stepped in. One quick glance at the interior, and I decided to adapt to the culture. When I left a couple of minutes later, feeling much more comfortable, I had added my own set of dusty footprints to the multitude of others on both sides of the toilet seat. All Haitians are taught from childhood that the only correct way to use an outhouse is to climb up, plant one's feet firmly on either side of the hole, and aim straight. The fact that a straight aim does not always happen explains the deplorable smell and filth of the two outhouses I have used while here. At least, these portable ones provided by the military are cleaned every day. Unfortunately, that had not yet been done this morning before Mother Nature's call demanded that I answer.

It feels as though I have been here for several months, instead of the fifteen days that have passed since my arrival with the first group. Three other groups have come, and various ones have stayed anywhere from four to seven days before returning to the States. After seeing the needs during our first days here, I have called home twice and gotten permission from Rex for an extension of my time. We have been busy from before dawn to after dark every day, caring for the injured and ill, and the needs are still tremendous. During the first week, we were doing mainly wound care. Now, three weeks since the quake shook their world apart, although many who sustained ghastly gashes, burns, and breaks still need continued care, the majority of the people we treat are suffering the effects of crowded living conditions, poor sanitation, too little food, and impure water. Disease and malnutrition are taking their toll in ways that will continue to wreak destruction for months to come on people who were already the poorest in the Western Hemisphere.

*7:14 p.m.*

We have been sitting on the black tarmac under this black tent for nine hours and are still no closer to knowing when or if we will fly out of here today. Several hours ago, we gratefully inserted the wax earplugs issued to us, which help to deaden but cannot completely blot out the shrill whine of motors and the deafening roar of propellers on the military planes that keep coming and going. I curled up on my suitcase midafternoon to try to catch a nap, but the noise prohibited any sleep. The night shift of staff and soldiers has arrived to take the place of the ones who have been our guardians and providers throughout an interminably long day. Two of them came through our tent with a flashlight just minutes ago, checking our passports and crossing our names off on a list of people who are wilting in the heat while we wait ... and wait ... and wait. They tell us that there is still no definite word, but certainly no plane is scheduled to be here anytime soon. We are given the option of returning to wherever we came from to spend the night and trying again in the morning. The decision to stay and keep hoping is unanimous among our group of four. Most of our potential traveling companions opt for the same. None of us wants to lose our spot in line and have to start over. No commercial flights are coming or going, and this is our only hope of getting out.

## February 2, 2010

*12:39 a.m.*

Our fifteen-hour wait at the Port-au-Prince airport has finally ended. Nearly 200 Haitians and relief workers trudge up the steeply sloping ramp of our chariot home, a USAF C-17 ablaze with lights and swarming with soldiers. Before we could board, the two huge tractor-trailer trucks that were stored in her belly had to be disgorged and driven off. The twenty-five seats along each side of the interior have already been claimed by the elderly, parents with young children, and those fortunate enough to have arrived before we did. A soldier checks my bright-yellow armband sporting its #4-20 against the list and scans the red ink smear on my left thumb with a hand-held infrared device before giving me leave to claim my "seat," a spot on the floor about two-thirds of the way back. I crane my neck, trying to count how many rows of people are also sitting on the floor in front of me. Here we are, six or seven of us to a row, legs drawn up under us Indian fashion, as we wait to be seat-belted into place. The soldiers on either side of the rows roll out long canvas straps, hooking one end of each into a bar on the floor and then passing the other end down the row from one person to the next, across our laps, to be similarly bolted into place on the opposite side. I cannot imagine that any amount of turbulence will be able to shift us around very much, as tightly as we are packed in.

*1:52 a.m.*

We are moving. It still does not seem possible, but the cumbersome whale in whose belly we sit is slowly backing up, preparatory to swooping into the night-blackened sky with a grace that belies its size. Four powerful engines scream a challenge to gravity as we reach our cruising speed of 550 miles per hour. Exhaustion has made us kin, and as our plane levels off, we wearily maneuver ourselves into semicomfortable lying positions beside each other on the cold, bare, aluminum floor, trying to catch a bit of sleep. I am beyond caring that the person in the row behind me whose bare feet are inches from my nose is a total stranger. Sleep is fitful at best, but we are grateful for every precious moment of oblivion.

*4:07 a.m.*

We smile wearily at one another as our wheels touch down on home soil at Sanford, Florida. Too tired to be jubilantly exuberant, we are nevertheless profoundly grateful to have arrived. We have a thirty-mile shuttle trip to the Orlando airport for our flight to Charlotte, NC, from where we will take yet another plane on the last short jump to Harrisburg, PA.

*10:43 a.m.*

I am seated in the air-conditioned comfort of a US Airways Airbus 321, sipping the ice-chilled Sprite mixed with orange juice that Helen, our friendly stewardess, just offered me. When Alan commented to her that it was our first cold drink in over two weeks, she gave us each an extra serving and then bustled up to the front of the plane to speak with someone. Coming back, she leaned over the seat and in a conspiratorially lowered voice told us that they would be bringing us a surprise. It turned out to be a lunch-sized paper bag for each of us, stuffed to the brim with as many packaged snacks as she could squeeze in. It has been like this ever since we arrived. Everyone who learns that we were helping with the relief effort in Haiti has wished blessings on us and told us how grateful they are that we were there.

We are the ones who are grateful. None of what we were able to do could have happened without the uplifting strength we felt each day as friends and family in the States touched heaven in our behalf. In the midst of poverty and despair, to those suffering beyond imagination, God chose us to be His hands extended. What greater blessing could we have!

## 49

## Haiti, Round Two

*February 19 – March 2, 2010 ~ Carrefour, Haiti*

No sooner had Rex picked me up at the Harrisburg airport on February 2, 2010, than I wanted to fly right back to Haiti to continue helping the earthquake victims. The luxury of my life in the States was in such sharp contrast to their wrenching poverty that I struggled with feelings of guilt over our nice house and adequate food supply. I had terrible nightmares in which I dreamed that one of my loved ones was buried under the rubble, and I could do nothing to save him. In the middle of the night, I would wake up in a panic, hands frantically searching the bed beside me, to see if Rex was still really there. Four days after my return, I contacted Dwight Rine to see if he could get me on another team.

Two-and-a-half weeks later, our group of two doctors, a fourth-year Army medical student, three nurses, and my fifteen-year-old son Jeffrey flew into the Dominican Republic, where we rendezvoused with missionaries Doug and Kim Hoffman, who helped us make the necessary arrangements for the five-hour bus ride from the DR across to Port-au-Prince, Haiti.

Five weeks post-earthquake, there was very little noticeable improvement in the country's condition. Mountains of rubble still lay everywhere. Now, however, otherwise barren hillsides were splashed with great swatches of white and blue where an estimated 1.5 million people lived in makeshift tent cities. The *USS Comfort* medical ship lay at anchor in the harbor, continuing its ministry of mercy to the more seriously injured. I later learned that before it steamed back to Baltimore, Maryland, on March 14, its Navy doctors and nurses treated 8,600 patients, performing life-saving surgeries, amputations, and skin grafts for the many who had suffered debilitating crush injuries and major burns. The 20,000 U.S. soldiers and Marines who had been sent to help distribute food, care for the wounded, and keep order were gradually being withdrawn, although 8,000 would remain for some time.

It was dark when we arrived at the mission compound, but we had the luxury of unpacking by the aid of fluorescent lights rather than kerosene lanterns. The city electricity was back on sporadically, and this was one night that it happened to be working. The next morning, we had a good devotional time as a group, then set up clinic in the schoolroom and saw patients. Almost immediately, it became apparent that on this trip, the focus of care would not be treatment of injuries caused by falling brick walls and exploding propane stoves, but management of the myriad diseases that accompany a major natural disaster. Instead of splinting broken bones and cleaning deep wounds, we were fighting a battle against an invisible enemy: ailments such as malaria, pneumonia, and dysentery brought on by the crowded, squalid living conditions. I was appalled to learn that every twenty seconds a child under the age of five died from illnesses related to a lack of clean drinking water. Less than a third of the population had access to sanitation facilities.

That afternoon, Don drove us on a tour around the city. We got out to snap pictures of the National Palace, its three formerly beautiful white domes now nothing more than statistics, just another of the thousands of buildings destroyed by the powerful tremor. I noticed a lot of people running down the street past the palace and forming two lines behind a large, orange box truck. Curious, I walked away from our group and toward the excitement. Eight men were in the truck, passing down six-packs of one-liter-sized bottles of water. Six uniformed policemen stood on guard, swinging their billy clubs indiscriminately at anyone, male or female, who did not stay in line. Fascinated, I stepped down from the sidewalk and walked a few steps closer, snapping photo after photo of the jubilant grins on the faces of the grateful recipients who hurried back the way they had come, tightly clutching their precious gift. The crowd swelled rapidly as word of the free water was passed from person to person, and I suddenly found myself surrounded by sweating, shouting bodies, all eagerly shoving and straining to get to the front of the line before the supply ran out. A little nervous, I looked around for a way out. Suddenly, a strong pair of dark arms seized mine and propelled me firmly to the edge of the road, out of harm's way. Embarrassed, I thanked my unknown rescuer, who smiled and melted back into the crowd.

Safely back in Don's truck, I told the others about my adventure, and we marveled together at the conditions that made six liters of drinking water such a treasure. A few blocks later, we drove past a large cemetery, its headstones smashed and tumbled. Don obligingly pulled over so I could run back to take pictures. I gingerly pushed through a broken spot in the fence and snapped a few shots, but the smell was so horrible that I did not stay long. Not until I got back into the truck and looked at what I had captured on my camera did I realize the reason for the terrible odor. Headstones were not the only things crumbled by the quake. Broken caskets jutted from the ground, their contents flung unceremoniously about.

We stopped at a deep ravine whose vast hillside of cinder-block houses had been almost totally destroyed. Jeffrey stood looking over the edge, his face sober, and I knew that he, too, would forever be changed by this journey. As I write this four years later, he is an Emergency Medical Technician who is passionate about helping the sick and injured, doing so with a zeal that was initially sparked by his EMT older brother Benjamin, but fueled into flame by his trip to this tragedy-ravaged country.

The next morning, we treated nearly two hundred people in our morning clinic at the school. I was especially gratified to see the progress of some that I had helped care for on my previous trip and to receive their grateful hugs of thanks. That afternoon, we set up our supplies in the large yard of a house owned by an American. He was put out with us because he had not been given much notice of our coming.

"We could have had 1,000 people here if we had just known in time," he scolded. Frankly, we were quite happy that he was *not* informed of our visit any sooner. The 245 people who patiently waited in line, inching forward slowly as one after another was examined, kept us plenty busy.

Twice that night, we were jolted from sleep by tremors strong enough to provoke near panic in one of the ladies in our group who had never experienced the like before. I did not know if these could be properly termed aftershocks five weeks later, but I was amazed at how much the ground and building shuddered. I learned the next morning that one of our doctors had been knocked clear out of his bed and onto the floor by one of the tremors, but on a cot in the hall just on the other side of the wall, Jeffrey had slept undisturbed through the whole thing! At least, we women had not all dashed for the door at the same time and gotten stuck in it together, as the guys in the guest apartment had done during my first visit, when an even stronger tremor shook our nerves as well as the building.

The number of people we were seeing each day kept growing. On Wednesday, we held our usual morning clinic at the school before going to yet another location after lunch. I think that place held the record at over 400 patients evaluated and treated in one afternoon. No matter how long they had to wait in line, or how much they might have pushed and shoved among themselves, each person who sat in front of one of us to be examined was courteous and grateful for our services.

I will never forget the beautiful sound of the group of twenty-six pastors and community leaders who formed a circle around us at the close of one mobile clinic visit and sang hymns of praise to God for sending us to help them. Their lovely a cappella harmony soared above the shattered walls and collapsed roof of the church where we had just spent the afternoon caring for their broken and hurting countrymen, bringing tears to our eyes. In blessing them, we were blessed. In helping them, we were helped, perhaps not in a way that could be measured like the correct dose of a medicine or noticed like the clean whiteness of a bandage, but in the deep satisfaction of knowing that, by ministering "to the least of these, my brethren," we were pleasing God, our heavenly Father. His smile was reward enough.

## 50

# Thank You, James Herriot

*July 8-18, 2010 ~ La Croix, Haiti*

My third trip to Haiti took place six months after the earthquake. This time, our purpose was not to give aid to its victims, but rather to work at a clinic in La Croix, many miles to the north of Port-au-Prince. God's Missionary Church had operated the clinic there some years before, but it had been closed for several years due to lack of personnel. Our team of five included Dr. Russell Gombosi, his daughter Elizabeth, my nurse friend Deb Solley, and Jeffrey and me. We arrived in Port-au-Prince at 11:00 a.m. Friday morning, very glad, indeed, to see the smiling faces of two of our Haitian interpreters after a frustrating time of haggling with the three pushy porters who wanted $60 to wheel the three luggage carts (that we rented for two dollars each and loaded ourselves) out to Don's truck. Thankfully, the cart pushers were satisfied with the $10 that Don said to give them.

We drove straight to La Croix and set out our supplies in the clinic's two rooms so we would be ready to start seeing patients bright and early the next morning. Jeffrey, Deb, and I had all been in Haiti in February and thought that it was hot then. Now we realized what hot *really* meant! I was grateful that I had purchased a small, battery-operated fan, on the advice of another nurse who had worked in the clinic the month before.

People started gathering at 4:30 the next morning; by 6:00 a.m., the gate-keepers had given out ninety-five numbers. As usual, most of those were not single patients. At an average of three persons per number, we figured that we saw between 275 and 300 people that day, with a myriad of complaints ranging from abscesses to lung infections to tummy troubles to *lots* of skin rashes. Jeffrey and Elizabeth were kept busy packaging tablets and creams, and by the end of the morning, they had the Creole phrases for "Take one tablet, one (or two, or three) times a day," well memorized.

Since we were not giving emergency care as we had done after the earthquake, we did not open the clinic the next day, but attended Sunday services at the mission church next door. In the afternoon, I wandered up the dusty road a short ways, fascinated with the peaceful rural countryside so different than the bustling, hectic streets surrounding the mission station in Carrefour. Fences of loosely spaced, tall, spiny cactus plants divided one yard from the next. Herds of goats wandered freely, every animal sporting a cumbersome neck yoke made of three sticks, each about eighteen-inches long, bound together with string at the ends to form a triangle. With such a contraption in place, the goats could not push through the thorn hedges to invade a neighbor's yard and eat precious garden produce. If a persistent goat without a hindering yoke managed to get in where he did not belong, the neighbor could demand two hundred Haitian dollars, between $25 and $30 U.S., for any damage it caused. Or he could just kill the goat by cutting off its head, a perfectly acceptable means of justice in this community. On our way out of La Croix the following week, we saw two beheaded goats lying by the side of the road; their unfortunate owners apparently had not tied on their yokes tightly enough.

On Monday, we gave out ninety-six numbers and saw another 275 to 300 patients. Many of these were pregnant women, and I was glad that we had brought 17,500 vitamin and iron tablets with us, enough to give each one a three month's supply.

Pregnant humans were not the only ones in need of care that day. Around three o'clock that afternoon, two men pushed their way to the front of the waiting crowd, begging the gatekeeper to let them come in and talk to the medical people.

"Is there anyone here who can help us with a cow?" they questioned anxiously. "She had a calf yesterday and her uterus prolapsed. We've been trying and trying, but we can't get it put back inside. If she doesn't get help soon, she will certainly die." We looked at each other blankly. As the midwife in the group, I was the logical one to go with them. But we had probably sixty more patients to see, and Dr. Gombosi was reluctant to send me off to tend an animal when there were still people needing my attention. Yet we recognized the urgency of their request; in a poor rural community such as this, the loss of a cow would indeed be a tragedy.

Suddenly, a scene from the life of the beloved storyteller, James Herriot, popped into my mind. As a teenager, I had been fascinated by his warm and joyful tales of life as a country vet in the Yorkshire Dales. Now I remembered how he told of struggling for lengthy periods of time to replace a cow's prolapsed uterus. He would soap up his arm, grasp the uterus, and forcibly attempt to shove it back into place. Invariably, he would get it nearly all in, and then the cow would give a single, seemingly effortless push, and pop it right back out. This scenario could be repeated numerous times, until the veterinarian was sweating and exhausted, before the task was finally accomplished.

Then he learned a trick from an old veterinarian who had a rather unorthodox but surefire method of replacing a prolapsed uterus. Enlisting the help of the cow's owner, he would get the beast kneeling on her front legs with a bale of hay propping up her hindquarters, so she could not strain and push the uterus back out just when it was nearly stuffed into place. Then, sliding the displaced uterus onto a wooden tray, he sprinkled it liberally with sugar to shrink its by now grossly swollen mass down to a near normal size. With the cow tipped forward and unable to resist, the experienced vet deftly eased the uterus from the tray, helping it back inside with a few gentle pushes. Once the organ was back in its proper location, he used a glass soda bottle filled with soapy water to rotate the two uterine horns back into place so that the whole thing would not easily slip back out.

Hurriedly calling my interpreter, I went over the steps of the procedure with the two men, having them repeat everything to make sure they understood it well. They hurried off, eager to try my suggestions, while I returned to my human patients, wondering if I would ever know the outcome of what was surely my most unusual midwifery consultation. My mind wandered to their dilemma more than once throughout the rest of the afternoon, hoping that the poor cow was all right.

To my delight, they showed up at our house that evening around 8:30, both of them beaming with satisfaction as they vigorously pumped my hand, telling me how grateful they were that I had been there to help them save the cow's life. They had followed the instructions to the letter, and the cow, uterus back in its correct abode, appeared to be doing fine. I was tickled that everything had worked out, and happy that they had returned to let us know the results. It was doubly satisfying when Don informed me that he knew the men, who were both from the church. In fact, one of the two was the local vet. Now he would be armed with knowledge that could potentially benefit other farmers in the community, thanks to the long-ago reminiscing of one of my favorite storytellers. Thank you, James Herriot!

Once the men had left, we all dissolved into gales of laughter at the incongruity of a nurse-midwife from the United States traveling all the way to Haiti to help save a cow. Still, all of us were glad things had turned out as they did.

The next day, we had our largest number of patients yet—giving out over one hundred numbers, which meant actually treating 300 to 325 people. The worst of these was a three-year-old little girl, nothing but skin and bones and the grossly protruding abdomen of a severely malnourished child. We had cans of powdered formula and cereal to give her, but wondered if her mother, who was amply padded, would indeed give them to her starving daughter or sell them to make a little extra income.

On Wednesday, July 14, we loaded our supplies into Don's truck and left at 8:10 a.m. to hold a mobile clinic higher up in the mountains. We thought we had arrived at our destination when Don parked the truck beside the dirt road over which we had been jouncing and bouncing for forty minutes. But we still had a fifteen-minute walk, carrying our footlockers and suitcases full of supplies and wading across three streams, before arriving at a church completely filled with probably two hundred people. We worked without a break until a few minutes before 3 o'clock, running out of medications before we ran out of patients.

The next day was our final one in La Croix, only a half day at that, since we needed to pack up after lunch and drive to Carrefour for two days of clinic at the mission school before returning to the States on Monday. That morning, we tried to treat a woman with a painfully swollen abscess which needed to be lanced and drained. I say tried, because she adamantly refused to let Dr. Gombosi puncture her skin with either a needle or a scalpel, sure that if she did, the spirits would be unhappy and something dreadful would happen to her. It was a sad case that pointed out the deception and misery caused by deeply entrenched and blindly followed false beliefs in a country where approximately half of the population practices voodoo worship. But the darker the night of sin, the brighter the light of salvation shines. Thank God for the opportunity He gave us to spread that light by means of medical missions!

## 51

## Wrapping It All Up
### *March 2, 2010 ~ Carrefour, Haiti*

*Although chronologically preceding Chapter 50, this account
fits better here as a reflection on my entire Haiti experience.*

His wiry black hair was liberally sprinkled with grey, his steps no longer as firm as they had been in his prime. He was only one of more than a thousand whose lives God allowed me to touch during my two trips and twenty-three days of helping in Haiti following the January 12 earthquake which snatched up to an estimated 316,000 souls into eternity. He had patiently waited in line for nearly three hours in the sweltering heat, to be seen at our final mobile clinic before my return to the States. My interpreter translated the questions I needed answered to know where to focus the physical exam that would tell me what problem(s) needed treated. I shut my eyes to better concentrate on the sounds being carried through my stethoscope, wishing for the hundredth time that I could as easily shut out the noises that swirled and collided around me.

Surrounded by eight U.S. medical personnel, my son Jeffrey, four Haitian interpreters, the gate keepers who registered patients and did their best to control the crowd, and several hundred men, women, and children vying for the next spot in the long line of those wanting to be seen, it was no wonder we struggled to hear. I finished the exam and pushed my way through the dozen or so bodies clogging the small area between my patient and the two tables at the edge of the patio. The table surfaces were covered with thousands of antibiotic and pain tablets, vitamins, worm pills, diabetes and blood pressure regulating medications, and scabies and fungus creams, all donated by hospitals, pharmacies, and friends in the States. Jeffrey efficiently filled my request for a week's supply of the needed antibiotic, and I handed the gentleman a small, red-and-pink striped plastic bag of pills to treat his lung infection. He grasped it with one hand and with the other, raised my hand to his lips and gently kissed it.

His grateful response was not the only time I was given cause to gulp down a lump that rose in my throat. Working with such desperately needy people as our disaster-stricken Haitian brothers and sisters has been a life-changing experience for every one of the sixty members of the ten teams who have donated time and talents to the God's Missionary Church relief effort. Memories flood my mind and tears sear my eyes as I struggle to find the words that will help you to feel the raw emotions that so moved all of us as we collectively treated between 12,000 and 13,000 people in the forty-six days of clinics since the quake.

My ears ring again ... with the scream of despair from the young mother whose two-month-old baby took his last, agonized, gasping breath only an hour after our team's arrival at the blisteringly hot, tin-walled, tin-roofed church perched high on the mountainside above Carrefour. He had been sick for three days, and in spite of our best efforts to rehydrate him and treat the massive pneumonia that ravaged his tiny body, the toll on his heart from his desperate fight to breathe was too overwhelming. I snatched his limp, dead form seconds before he would have hit the floor as his mother threw up her arms and kicked her chair over backwards, thrashing and wailing in her grief. Friends carried her down the hill, while I tenderly re-dressed the still-warm, lifeless little body in the bright-green-and-purple sleeper trimmed in yellow that he had been wearing on his arrival. How I wish I could have had a few moments to tell her about the loving heavenly Father Who knew the pain of His own Son's death, and Who could give her the hope of spending all eternity with her child. Someone else carried her baby to her while I choked back sobs before turning to the next of the multitude of other sick patients needing treated. I never saw either of them again.

I feel once more ... the pats on my cheeks from the hands of the woman whose leg had been horribly burned when her propane stove exploded during the earthquake. We called her "the Gecko Lady," because the clicking noises she made with her tongue sounded just like a gecko lizard each of the many times I caused her pain in the necessary debriding and dressing of her wounds. Her burns were too deep to heal properly without skin grafts, but all of the local hospitals that could have done them had been destroyed. Shortly before I left the first time, a Red Cross group from Finland set up a tent-hospital in the stadium just two blocks from us, complete with an air-conditioned operating room. We transferred her there for the grafts, but I had not heard how things went.

You can imagine my delight when, just minutes after my arrival back in the yard on my second trip, the Gecko Lady's teenage daughter rushed up to me, grasped my hand, and pulled me around the perimeter of the yard to the classroom where her mother and some of the other more seriously wounded people had been recuperating. It was totally dark in there, but a flashlight ray directed me to a familiar beaming smile and reaching arms that pulled me down for a tight hug and more pats on my face from their owner, sitting on a blanket on the floor. The next day when I changed the dressing on her finally healing burns and the large raw areas on her thigh from where the grafts had been taken, my efforts were again rewarded with cheek patting and a lovely smile of gratitude.

The Sunday morning before we left, I sang along on the hymns whose sound was carried from our church service in progress next door, while I spent an hour and a half with numerous basins of water, soap, a soft brush, and gauze, carefully scrubbing off as much as I could of the six-weeks' accumulation of flaky, itchy, dead skin from around her burns and grafts. After rubbing in lotion, re-dressing the wounds, and wrapping her entire leg in a large Ace bandage for protection, I received an extra-long session of hugs, pats, and smiles. I am going to miss that.

I see the trembling lips ... of the woman who came seeking help for her spinning head, heart palpitations, and stomach pain. We treated so many with these symptoms, understandable after all the emotional trauma that people have suffered, not only in the initial quake, but also in the dozens of aftershocks since. Already-damaged buildings are continuing to collapse as the shaking persists. I remember too well the pure terror that I felt the morning after my first arrival, when a 6.2-magnitude quake jolted me awake and sent me leaping from my bed. The moments that I spent frantically searching in the darkness for my flashlight, so I could find my glasses, so I could find the keys, so I could unlock my door, so I could escape, seemed like forever. I cannot imagine what it must be like for the multitude of those who lost homes and family in the 7.0 quake. Any sizable aftershock occasions a few heart-stopping moments as everyone pauses to wonder if THIS ONE will be even worse than the first. This woman stared straight ahead as she tonelessly related to me the horror of searching for her infant daughter for three days before finally finding and digging her bloody, lifeless body from the wreckage. It was another two days before her nine-year-old son, trapped in the crumbled ruins of their home but miraculously still alive, was freed from his prison and rushed to a hospital in another part of the country. She had not been able to visit him since.

When she finished her story, I did my exam, then walked to the medication table and surveyed the bottles of pills. The intensity of her pain was so great and our human ability to treat the source of her heartburn and headache so obviously inadequate, that for several minutes I could only lean against the rough block wall and cry. My mind could not wrap itself around the magnitude of such suffering. Desperately begging God for the right words to say, I went back and sat in front of her once more, handed her a supply of pills to treat her symptoms, and softly asked if I could pray for her. My often-joking and boisterous interpreter, sensitive to the moment, was himself brushing tears from his eyes as he translated my earnest prayer. I took her in my arms and held her close as she clung tightly to me and we wept together, two mothers living oceans apart in both distance and circumstances, yet brought together by a God Who loves us equally, and Who is the only One able to heal her broken heart.

My mind recoils in horror ... from the thought of the agony the four-day-old little baby must have suffered when she was tossed from her mother's arms into the family cooking fire during the forty-five-second eternity that the quake savagely shook their home. I gingerly cuddled her close, careful not to brush her charred, black head and arm against my blouse, on the trip to the hospital ship in the harbor for the operation she needed.

I smell the sharply metallic, musty scent ... of the mingled blood and amniotic fluid that puddled invisibly in the darkness on the floor under my feet as the wet, slippery body of one of the two Haitian babies that I delivered in January slipped into my hands. The tiny girl's lungs expanded with her first breath of air, and a reassuring cry rent the night. I tipped my head to focus the beam of the headlight strapped to my forehead and checked out the perfectly formed little body. What a nice contrast to all of the wounds and fractures that we had been seeing! In the midst of death and destruction, life goes on.

My nose pricks ... with the acrid, sour stench of vomit. My stomach recoiled as my flashlight beam picked out the unconscious form of the man lying on the ground in a pool of slimy, partially digested food, body writhing with convulsions. Don Mobley tapped on our door that night at 10:30 p.m., saying that one of the night guards had just called to tell him that someone was very sick. What an understatement! We moved the man to a table in the clinic where, for the next three hours, another team member and I fought desperately to save the life of this diabetic who had inadvertently taken a double dose of his long-acting insulin, bottoming out his sugar and putting himself into a coma. He is still alive today because God put us in the right place at the right time.

I taste the raindrops on my lips ... and remember the welcome coolness of fresh-washed night air from the first rain since the earthquake, two nights before we left at the end of my second visit. My shoes sloshed through water and mud as I walked the short distance from the clinic to my room. I ducked under the tarp near the door that I needed to enter, where several dozen of the hundreds of people still living in the yard were trying to sleep. The bright moonlight played over bodies lying on soaked blankets on the muddy ground. My heart was wrung at the sight. I felt guilty lying down on my dry mattress covered with a dry sheet, sitting on a dry cement floor, with a water-proof tin roof overhead.

* * * * * * * * *

All the teams are home as I sit at my computer and record memories of my few weeks in a world so vastly different than ours here in the heartland of America, which we so casually take for granted. I flipped a switch on the wall this evening as it grew dark and did not waste a second's thought in wondering if the light would come on. The candle flickering on the table is burning solely for the luxury of its scent and romantic touch, not because it is our only means of illumination. In a few minutes, I will open my refrigerator and from its abundantly stocked shelves collect the makings of a warm, well-balanced supper, to be added to stomachs that have already digested two other adequate meals this day. This morning, I ironed a week's supply of shirts for my husband, and that did not begin to exhaust the number of them still hanging in his closet. A pile of laundry in the hall needs transferred to my washer downstairs, where the touch of a button is all that is needed for the load to be washed and rinsed with no further effort on my part. I hear the sound of my son taking a shower as I write. He did not need to stand in line with a five-gallon bucket this morning to get our family's water ration for the day from a well, nor worry that there will be none left for the person who follows him if he uses more than a small basinful to bathe.

I am so blessed! I pray that God will keep fresh on my mind how truly trivial are the petty things that so easily irritate me. May my life be one that He can use, wherever He chooses, to show His love to as many as possible, in whatever way He sees best.

I wonder if it is raining in Haiti tonight ...

# 52

## Kidnapped in Costa Rica!
## Ransom: One Dollar and Five Cents

### *September 28, 2010 ~ San José, Costa Rica*

I glanced back four rows behind me to seat 20E of American Airlines Flight #868 and smiled at my son Jeffrey. At 7:28 p.m. on this Tuesday evening, he should have been halfway through his weekly trumpet lesson at a local college near our home in Pennsylvania. Instead, we were extremely thankful to be well on our way back to PA after what was *supposed* to have been a two-week visit to Costa Rica to help welcome into the world the newest EFM missionary. Jared Lee McDowell, son of Rex II and his wife Missy, had arrived two weeks earlier. Both of his grandmas were blessed to share in the joy of that momentous occasion, and happy to cook meals, wash dishes, do laundry, change diapers, and cuddle our grandson so his mommy could rest. Jared's big brother, three-year-old Devin, was delighted to spend hours tussling on the floor and kicking a ball with "Uncle Jeshy," who had the energy necessary to keep up with him.

Fourteen days together flew by so quickly, and all too soon we were standing on the curb with our suitcases at the San José airport Saturday morning, sharing final hugs and tearful good-byes. Rex, Missy, and their boys drove off, and Jeffrey, Mom Susan, and Mom McDowell headed to the booth at the far end of the airport to pay the requisite $26.00 exit tax apiece. Receipts in hand, we casually chatted as we approached the roped-off area near the American Airlines check-in counter for the mundane routine of ticket verification and baggage weigh-in. Instead of waving us through to the desk, the crisply uniformed official who scrutinized our passports directed me to the immigration office at the opposite end of the concourse, since one of us, fifteen-year-old Jeffrey, was *menor de edad* (a minor). Rather than lug our suitcases the whole way to the office and back, Jeffrey stood guard over them while Mrs. Susan and I headed briskly across the airport.

Blissfully unaware of the adventure that awaited us, I handed our exit tax receipts, customs forms, and passports to the lady at the second window. Glancing briefly at Mrs. Susan's and mine, she handed them back. "Where are your son's papers?" she queried.

"You have them right there," I replied, indicating Jeffrey's documents in her hand. She rifled through them again, not satisfied.

"I need the permission from his father for him to leave Coast Rica," she insisted. Mystified, I glanced at Mrs. Susan, and the first niggling thread of fear wormed its way into my mind.

"My son and I came here together two weeks ago on round-trip tickets from the United States, and we are returning there to his father today," I assured her with my best "of-course-I-know-what-I-am-doing" look. She did not buy it.

"Since your son is a Costa Rican citizen, we cannot allow you to take him out of our country unless we are sure that his father knows and approves. Our law prevents one parent from kidnapping a child from the other that way," she matter-of-factly informed me. I stared at her in shocked disbelief.

"You are telling me that I, his mother, cannot take *my child*, who came here *with me*, back to our home in the United States, where he is *also* a citizen?"

"No, Ma'am," she affirmed. "Not without the authorization of his father."

Our minds reeling, Mrs. Susan and I returned to Jeffrey, patiently waiting with our luggage near the ticket counter. "We can't leave," I told him. He stared down at me, puzzled, and it struck me how ludicrous the idea of my "kidnapping" this six-foot-tall, 155-pound "baby" of mine out of the country actually was! But like it or not, the officials were adamant that we would not be leaving that day. The next hour sped away in a haze of fervent but ineffectual pleas with still other officials, one of whom told me, "Pardon my country. It's a stupid rule, but I can't help you." Sandwiched among these entreaties were frantic phone calls to Rex II, telling him of our predicament, and Daddy Rex, who assured the lady with whom he spoke that it was *fine* for his wife to bring our son back home to him.

Complicating things still further was the fact that the McDowells were not the only ones with a frightening, unexpected situation to deal with. Missy's mother, Drema Susan, had been very eager to go to Costa Rica to help her daughter, but she had never flown internationally before and did not speak any Spanish. Since I had traveled into and out of several Latin countries various times and could communicate with the foreign airport workers, we went together, with the idea that Drema would not have to try to understand the Spanish-speaking personnel in Costa Rica nor find her way around the mammoth Miami airport and go through customs by herself. Now, she was faced with the choice of either paying a substantial ticket-change fee to wait behind with Jeffrey and me until the mess surrounding his paperwork was cleared up, or going on by herself. She decided to wing it alone, so after hurried last-minute words of advice about navigating customs in Miami, she disappeared through the doors leading up to the boarding area, and Jeffrey and I continued our attempts to move the hearts of the officials. They remained utterly unyielding.

Two hours after dropping us off, Rex II loaded us back up at the same spot, and we returned to a surprised Devin, elated to see his Uncle Jeshy again.

Over the weekend, I spent several hours doing computer research on the requirements that we needed and tracking down phone numbers to the U.S. embassy and the Costa Rican consulates. Bright and early Monday morning, I made the first of thirty-three phone calls from Rex and Missy's house: nine to Rex in Pennsylvania, fifteen to the Costa Rican consulates in Washington, D.C. and New York City, three to the U.S. embassy in Costa Rica, and six to family and our pastor in the States, asking them to PLEASE PRAY! On his end, Rex kept the phone lines humming as well, finding out what he needed to take and where he needed to go before setting out on his three-and-a-half hour drive to the consulate in Washington, D.C., where he could give his official permission for Jeffrey to return to the United States.

As soon as I had finished collecting all of the information via phone that I could, Jeffrey and I took a bus to downtown San José and walked the many blocks to the Civil Registry, where the statistics from his birth at *Clínica Bíblica* fifteen years ago were on file. The problem we were facing had actually begun a few years before he was born, when Franklin Chang emigrated from Costa Rica to the United States and joined our space program. In order for him to be a U.S. astronaut, he had to first become a U.S. citizen. At that time, Costa Rica did not allow adults to have dual citizenship; one had to renounce his Costa Rican "birthright" to become a citizen of any other country. However, when Chang gained widespread notoriety as an astronaut, Costa Rica wanted the recognition that he was "theirs," so officials passed a law granting both retroactive and future lifetime citizenship to any person born within their borders, no matter if he later left to live elsewhere.

Jeffrey had been three when our family returned to the States twelve years before this current trip. Both parents had been with him then, and we had done all the appropriate paperwork, so there was no issue with taking him out of the country. He had not accompanied us any of the various times that Rex and I had gone back to Costa Rica for ministry during the intervening years, and he was now traveling with a U.S. passport, so the thought that we might have need of a document from his father to allow me to leave with him this time had never once crossed our minds. The frustrating thing was that nothing had been said to that effect when we had entered the country and gone through customs two weeks earlier. Had someone mentioned it then, Rex would have had plenty of time to get the necessary paperwork before we tried to leave. But none of the "if only's" made any difference in the situation. There was nothing now to do but come up with the documentation they were demanding.

After Jeffrey and I arrived at the Civil Registry, we got in a nice short line and paid five cents for the two required *timbres* (official stamps); then we stood fifty-nine minutes in a much longer line to exchange the *timbres* for his official birth certificate. It was well past noon when we completed step one and called Rex II to find out if Daddy Rex had had any success with his mission. Son Rex reported that there was no word from father Rex, but we could not wait to see if he had made it to the Washington, D.C. consulate before they closed at 2:00 p.m.

We caught a taxi and hurried on to step two: getting Jeffrey's photo taken. The cab driver, to whom I had explained our predicament and the need for speed, braked to a quick halt at the curb beside the open door of a tiny shop, rolled his window down and yelled in to the shop proprietor, asking how long it took to get pictures done. "Ten minutes," he hollered back, so out we hopped, dashing through the by-now-heavy rain to the curb. I plunked down $1.00 for the regulation-sized passport photo, while Jeffrey managed a half-hearted smile for the camera.

Twelve minutes later, we were back on the sidewalk, huddled under our umbrella and waving down another taxi. To my great relief, it was the same helpful driver who had guided us to the photo place. No sooner had we scrambled in and closed the doors than he rapidly and efficiently started dodging through the heavy afternoon traffic toward the final destination in our quest: the immigration offices on the outskirts of the opposite side of the city. En route, I got a phone call from Rex II with the welcome news that Daddy Rex had been able to officially give his permission for Jeffrey to leave. The consul told him they would e-mail the authorization to immigration in Costa Rica immediately, so it should be there waiting for us.

It was forty-five minutes until closing time when we arrived, so I heaved a sigh of relief to see only three other families ahead of us in line at the office where we were directed to wait. However, as the minutes marched relentlessly on, the steady rain turned into a heavy downpour, and we stayed in the same spot, my stomach churned into tighter and tighter knots. Finally, two minutes before the scheduled closing time, a lady poked her head out the door and asked the remaining family ahead of us, as well as Jeffrey and me, if we would like to come in out of the wet. Jubilant to at least be on the right side of the door, we all crowded into the small office, umbrellas dripping into widening puddles on the floor.

It took sixteen minutes to dispatch the needs of the family directly ahead of us, but our turn finally came. "I need to take my son back home to the United States," I explained. "The official permission from his father was sent from your consulate in Washington, D.C. earlier this afternoon." The woman shuffled through a stack of papers on her desk and then scrolled down a long line of e-mails on her computer.

"Nothing has come from Washington," she declared. "Let me see what you have with you." I handed her Jeffrey's birth certificate and pictures. "Where is his *carné?*" she demanded.

"What *carné?*" I asked.

"The photo identification badge with his personal information that you should have had done when you got his birth certificate," she explained. "We can't give you permission to leave without it. Besides, we have not received anything from his father." I could not believe my ears.

"Ma'am, we have fulfilled every single requirement that our embassy here in Costa Rica and your consulate in Washington, D.C. told us we needed to do," I politely but firmly informed her. "My husband told me that your consul e-mailed the official permission here to you, and no one said anything about a *carné* until now, when it is too late to get one. I am *not* leaving this office until I have whatever I need to take my son with me out of the country tomorrow!"

She stared at me for a moment, shocked, and then hurried from the room, saying that she would check with her supervisor. Trembling, I sank into the nearest chair, buried my face in my hands, and started to cry. Wild thoughts flitted through my mind about what the inside of a Costa Rican jail looked like, whether the police would handcuff me first to drag me off to it, and what would happen to Jeffrey when I refused to leave here without his exit permit. He leaned over and gave me a hug, not having understood what I said, but knowing that tears were not a good sign. "Please God," I silently pleaded, "get us out."

Long minutes later, the lady bustled briskly back into the room and sat down in front of her computer. "My supervisor said we will go ahead and do it, even though you don't have everything that you need," she announced, starting to type out Jeffrey's information. "Probably the items from Washington, D.C. will arrive tomorrow."

I thanked her effusively as she pulled the completed page from her printer, stamped it, and handed it across the desk. Suddenly, the splashing rain and our wet feet were unimportant. Never mind that the plane-ticket-change fee, plus the taxi, bus, and gasoline cost for all the running around, were nearly three hundred times the $1.05 "ransom" that the photo and *timbres* had cost. We had the paper to release Jeffrey from his captivity!

The next morning, we repeated our trip to the airport, but this time Rex II waited in the parking lot for my call that we had successfully cleared security and were at our boarding gate before he left. Things went without incident, and as our plane lifted smoothly from the runway with both "kidnapped" and "kidnapper" on board, I rejoiced that God had once again heard and answered prayer, and "let [His] people go."

# 53

## What Was That About Not Too Many Patients?

*June 28, 2011 ~ San Luis, Honduras*

It is two minutes after midnight. Outside the *Clínica Luz y Vida,* a dog is barking somewhere in the darkness up the dirt road behind us. Inside, a fan is whirring in the large room behind me where a thirty-something-ish man sleeps exhaustedly, a vitamin-complex IV solution dripping slowly into his arm. He stumbled through the front door this afternoon ten minutes before my day shift ended at 3:00 p.m., arms draped limply over the shoulders of two friends who shuffled awkwardly sideways to get him around the corner of the nurses' station. Their story was that he had gotten very dizzy and vomited twice at work, for no apparent reason. I grabbed the nearest trash can and thrust it under his chin not quite in time to catch all of the third upheaval of what was left in his stomach before he flopped down onto the second of our four general ward beds.

A quick check of his vital signs puzzled me, for his blood pressure was a nice, healthy 120/80, his pulse was strong and steady at sixty-four beats a minute, and he did not have a fever. The afternoon shift nurse who was to relieve me was ten minutes late, so I had time to start the IV fluids indicated via telephone by Dr. Maldonado, our always-on-call town physician. He gave orders for several other medications and said he would stop in tomorrow morning to see how things were going.

The IV was to run in over eight hours, so it should have been mostly infused by the time I came back on again for the evening's 10:00 p.m. to 7:00 a.m. shift. I was not at all surprised to find well over half of it still in the bag. With no IV pumps to assure a steady, constant rate, if things are *really* busy, it can be quite a challenge, for example, to keep eighty-one-year-old Tío Juan's frail arm positioned in just the right way so that the drops keep falling at the necessary fifty-six-per-minute the whole shift. Even more fun is assuring that restless fifteen-month-old toddler María's foot with its tiny IV catheter stays strapped to the torn-sheet-wrapped piece of cardboard to stabilize it and does not get tangled up in the IV tubing.

Wait; did I say "really busy"? I was told a week ago today when I started my first shift that things would probably be rather slow, since a seventy-person medical brigade from the States was in town for seven days. Many who would normally come to the clinic for help were going to the school just down the road from us to be treated there by the American doctors and dentists, so I could expect fewer patients.

In spite of the brigade's presence, when I walked into the clinic the next morning, it was to the sight of Rosmery, up to her elbows in bloody towels, bowls of disinfectant, and multiple used syringes of local anesthetic. It is the annual fiesta week in San Luis, and two brothers had been taking advantage of the occasion to party enthusiastically. When they got on their motorcycle sometime in the wee hours of the morning to go home, the combination of bad brakes and a none-too-steady driver resulted in a trip to our clinic to repair the damages. To the brothers, that is. The motorcycle was beyond repair, from what I understand. Anyhow, Rosmery had been stitching the twenty-year-old driver's face together for two-and-a-half hours when I arrived, and she still was not done. It *is* kind of hard to sew skin together that has been gouged out in chunks here and there from its sudden and unexpected encounter with a cobblestone street.

While she was finishing up, another *herida* (wounded person) arrived: a woman who had been hanging clothes in her yard when a sheet of metal roofing fell onto her foot, slicing deeply just behind her big toe. So there we were, Rosmery with her face job on the exam table under the big light, and me with my foot fix on the other stretcher at the side of the room, various and sundry family and friends wandering in and out, while a concerned elderly friend of the young men earnestly and repeatedly reminded them that God was trying to let them know that sin did not pay.

I anesthetized the foot wound and cleaned out a large amount of coagulated blood, discovering with dismay the apparently severed end of a tendon. Since she could not move the toe and I do not stitch tendons, it seemed a perfect time to give the brigade orthopedic doc some more experience. Daniel drove her down to them in the mission truck, while I took over the repair of the brother who had been riding behind and did *not* hit the pavement with his face. He "only" needed thirteen sutures for his lacerated hand. Meanwhile, a seventeen-year-old had arrived in labor, vomiting, and Rosmery went to get her settled in while I numbed up the driver's grossly swollen thumb so I could clean what was left after part of his nail and most of the skin on top to the first joint had been deposited somewhere on the road. He had also split open half the underside of his thumb, but that cut was not deep enough to stitch.

By this time, it was 9:00 a.m., two hours after Rosmery was to have gone home to officially start her vacation. She came out of the labor room wrinkling up her nose, saying that the woman smelled like she had an infection and that we had better consult Dr. Maldonado. He needed to come over anyhow to check on the two patients who had been admitted the day before, so we could save him an extra trip by getting all three consultations in one visit. Rosmery left, and I went in to see our new mama-to-be and check her vital signs. I did not smell anything out of the ordinary, but my nose is not noted for its particularly keen discernment of odors, which is sometimes a blessing in this line of work. What did concern me was the fact that my patient's blood pressure was 150/100, definitely not a good thing when one is seventeen and in labor with her first baby. The doctor arrived and disappeared into her room, while I went back to the treatment room and tackled the job of finding and safely disposing of all the used syringes and suture needles in our handy-dandy sharps container: an empty gallon bleach bottle.

Dr. Maldonado emerged frowning, pulled off his gloves, and asked me for a tape measure. Carefully checking the distance between the base of his thumb and a point partway up his middle finger, he shook his head. "There is *no way* that girl is going to be able to deliver that baby here. Her pelvis is *much* too small, she has pre-eclampsia as well, and you must send her to Santa Bárbara for a cesarean section." He asked for a referral paper from our file drawer and wrote busily for several moments, signing his name with a flourish at the bottom of the paper and stamping it with our official *Clínica Luz y Vida* seal.

Breezing into the general ward, he quickly dispatched his exams of the elderly woman and middle-aged man who were waiting to be discharged and wrote the orders for their continued treatment at home. Then, he headed out the gate and up the road in his green pickup, taking with him the pregnant girl's mother-in-law to try to find someone with a vehicle who could take them to Santa Bárbara. It is not that there is no ambulance available in town, but the Red Cross charges 1,100 up front before transporting a patient to Santa Bárbara, 1,300 for the slightly longer ride to San Pedro Sula, and a whopping 4,500 to go clear to Tegucigalpa, four hours away. You can be thankful if you have an ambulance club membership there in the States, right? Just think of all the money saved on a lights-and-siren ride to your local hospital. Remember, though, that we are talking *lempiras* here, not U.S. currency. At the present exchange rate of 18.89 *lempiras* per dollar, you can get to Santa Bárbara for $58.23, still not too bad as typical stateside ambulance rides go. Still, at an average wage of 100 to 150 *lempiras* per day for a manual laborer and 250 to 300 *lempiras* per day for a skilled craftsman, that charge can equal four to eleven days of salary. That is a pretty staggering sum when you can normally buy only one day's worth of food for your hungry children at a time. So if you can find a neighbor with a car who is willing to do ambulance duty for less than the Red Cross, you might save a few precious, hard-earned *lempiras*.

I took out the IV catheters, collected the prescribed medicines, and went over the discharge instructions with the two patients who had been cleared to go home. That was followed by giving a few injections and selling various and sundry pills to the various and sundry people who walked through the door clutching a piece of torn-off notebook paper with the pencil-printed name, often misspelled, of whatever it was they wanted for such-and-such a malady. In the midst of all this, I dashed back to the labor room as frequently as I could to check on and give support to the girl in labor, who had been six-centimeters dilated when Dr. Maldonado wrote her referral. Her membranes had ruptured before she arrived, and her contractions did not seem to be very hard, so I did not do any more exams to check for dilation, as I did not want to increase her chance of an infection.

As average first labors go, had there been transportation immediately available, the likelihood of her getting to Santa Bárbara in good time for a cesarean birth would have been quite good. But it was well over an hour later before her mother-in-law walked back in the front door, saying that she had found a car to take them. I listened to the baby's heart rate one final time, did my first cervical check, and knew immediately that this girl was going nowhere! In fact, five minutes later, she was pushing with each contraction, completely dilated. An hour and twenty-three minutes of contractions, coaching, manual rotation of the baby's head to help it navigate the tight fit through her pelvis, and MUCH encouragement later, a healthy, six-pound boy made his squalling entrance into the world, just the way God designed it to happen. He apparently had not heard the doctor's pronouncement that it *could not* work that way. As is so often the case here in the clinic, I was deeply thankful that God had intervened in what was potentially a life-threatening situation. Had her pelvis truly been too small, both baby and mother could have died. And had mom's blood pressure remained dangerously high, she could have had convulsions. But they did not die, her blood pressure came down, she did not have convulsions, and we rejoiced together as I prayed aloud, thanking God for His goodness.

The baby was born at 12:02 p.m., and it took me the better part of the next hour to help assure that he was nursing well, repair the mama's small tear, wash her up and change her gown, transfer her to the postpartum ward, take frequent vital signs on both of them, and all the while keep a watchful eye on the comings and goings of those still needing to buy various and sundry medicines. Thankfully, we have a clinic secretary who works from 9:00 a.m. to 1:00 p.m., and she covered much of the medicine sales.

I was just getting ready to give the baby his first bath when a frail, elderly woman with pallid, yellow-tinged skin and an *enormously* distended abdomen slowly and painfully shuffled in. I was surprised when our cleaning lady, Suyapa, whose energetic sweeping and mopping rids the clinic of the abundant quantity of mud that is tracked in each day, rushed to help ease her gently onto a bed. "It's my mother," she explained. "She has cirrhosis of her liver, and Dr. Maldonado needs to drain off some more fluid from her stomach."

I do not know what I was expecting, but I can guarantee you that a paracentesis Honduran-style varies significantly from the same procedure in the States. Dr. Maldonado swabbed some iodine onto her skin, stuck an inch-and-a-half-long needle from the end of a syringe into her lower abdomen, fastened it to a length of IV tubing, and dropped the end of the tube into an empty five-liter plastic jug that had not long before held the bright-green, apple-scented disinfectant that we use to clean the clinic. As an unhealthy-looking, dark-red liquid started inching down the tube, he briefly observed its progress, then wrapped a piece of tape about the base of the needle and fastened it to her skin. "Don't let more than two liters drain out," he told me. "If I don't get a chance to return, just pull out the needle, and she can go home when it's done." And that was that. No sterile drapes and gloves, no fancy equipment, no local anesthetic to numb the skin, but the job got done just the same. Half an hour later, the prescribed amount had collected in the jug, my patient's vital signs were stable, and her family saw no need for her to hang around and wait, so back home she went.

Maribel arrived shortly after that so I could go home, and although not every day since that first one has been as full and hectic, I have managed to keep busy enough to keep out of trouble. The brigade's presence in town has actually *increased* our business in one aspect. In my thirty-seven weeks of accumulated time here since I first helped at the clinic in 2001, I had only treated three or four cases of excessive bleeding from tooth extractions. This week alone, more than that have showed up, clenching blood-soaked gauze pads between their gums and wanting me to stop the bleeding occasioned by brigade dentists' having pulled anywhere from two to an entire mouthful of teeth. What was that about not too many patients?

## 54

## Bitten by the Drama Llama

*July 9, 2011 ~ San Luis, Honduras*

I heard the sound of car doors slamming and excited voices chattering moments before our front screen door flew open two mornings ago. Four navy-and-white-clad teenagers carrying the limp form of a fifth teen hustled down the hall toward me, hefting the girl by her arms and legs, her sagging hips nearly dragging the floor. I stepped around the corner of the front desk to meet them and directed them into our two-bed emergency room. They heaved their burden onto the treatment table while the tallest of the young men told me that the girl had passed out at school. "She does this a lot," he explained, as I wrapped a blood pressure cuff around her arm. "When it happens, we bring her here, and they give her a shot." I did not laugh, but I was tempted to as I noted my patient's perfectly normal blood pressure and pulse, her even, nonlabored respirations, and the healthy pink color of her face. "Oh yes, I can give her a shot that will make her all well in about five minutes," I assured the concerned friends and headed for our small pharmacy to prepare the cure.

"Here's another one that's been bitten by the Drama Llama," I told Rachel Gregory, the student nurse from Virginia whose mother served as a missionary nurse in this clinic years ago. Rachel is with me this summer for three-and-a-half weeks of Honduran-style clinical experience. Safely out of sight of the group of young people, we looked at each other and grinned, remembering the eleven-year-old "unconscious" patient from the morning before. Her anxious father had carried her in, cradled in his arms like a floppy, oversized rag doll. "I don't know what's wrong with her, but she's never had anything like this happen before," he stated worriedly. "She was fine when she got up this morning at 6:30, but when it was time for her to go to school, she fell down on the floor and has been this way ever since." While Rachel checked her vital signs, I gently tried to lift one of her eyelids to check her pupil. That was my first clue that something fishy was afloat. She deliberately squeezed her eyelids so tightly shut that it was nearly impossible to pry them open. Her purposeful response, normal pupil size, and the fact that her vital signs could not have been healthier did not merit nearly as much concern as her father was wasting on the situation.

With further questioning, he revealed that his daughter worried a lot about her grades at school and that she had a major exam she was to take today. "I'm sure we can help her feel better very soon," I promised him, drawing into a syringe a one-cc dose of thiamine which Rachel efficiently injected into her thigh. Her flinch at the needle prick further substantiated our suspicions that the youngster had carried off a magnificent acting job with her parent, but the clinical findings were not going to help her avoid taking the test she had dreaded. "That shot will have an effect in about five minutes," I announced confidently, loudly enough that there could be no doubt she heard my words.

Nearly that much time passed, and still she lay on the exam table, eyes closed, unmoving. I looked again at my watch. Time for the vitamin shot to work its magic! "All right, you should be doing fine now, so go ahead and stand up so you can walk out with your daddy," I told her firmly. Immediately, she opened her eyes and slid off the table to her feet, not a trace of unsteadiness in her steps as she preceded her grateful and almost pathetically relieved father to the desk so he could pay the ten-*lempira* cost for the medicine and syringe. Had there been an adequate opportunity to do so, an explanation to him about why the shot had worked so wonderfully and rapidly might have done some good. But in a culture where an injection is firmly believed to cure a wide range of woes, I really do not know how much my attempt at clarification would have benefited either of them. I doubt he would have been convinced that there was actually nothing wrong, or that his little girl had nearly succeeded in pulling one over on him. And I am positive that had I tried to just explain to those tightly closed eyes that she was fine, my words alone would have done absolutely nothing to bring the child out of her swoon.

All of this was on our minds as we readied another one-cc dose of thiamine. Out in the exam room, we could hear the girl's respirations becoming exaggeratedly noisy. As I walked back in with the shot, an older man who had not been there at first motioned me over. "They usually give her oxygen when she gets this bad," he informed me gravely, gesturing toward her heaving chest. "That always helps a lot." I smiled brightly at him. "Oh, but we don't like to give oxygen unless it's really necessary, so I'll check the oxygen level in her blood to see if she needs it," I told him, going to the file drawer behind the desk to get out the box containing a tiny-but-efficient pulse oximeter. I had purchased it a week before coming down, at Miriam's request, in part for just such an occasion as this. The group of students and the teacher huddled around the table, mesmerized, as I clipped it onto the girl's index finger. Each head in turn bent close to the half-inch screen to personally verify the bold blue "99%" which I explained meant that there was nothing whatsoever wrong with her oxygen level. "It's perfect," I assured them. "She doesn't need oxygen at all. In fact, in just a few minutes, she will be ready to go back to school with you." The girl's respirations returned to a normal rate and volume following my announcement, and her classmates helpfully rolled her onto one side so Rachel could give the injection into her hip. "You can go back to class now," I cheerfully assured her when the five minutes were up. Rather sheepishly, she opened her eyes and reached for one of her friend's hands to help her sit up. Score once again for the power of suggestion and a well-entrenched belief in the wondrous properties of anything given via a hypodermic needle!

Please do not think that I am saying that a placebo is all that is needed in every case of someone's seeking our help for *problemas con los nervios* (nerve problems), as such situations are commonly called. At times, Valium is necessary and rightfully prescribed. But a school-aged young person who habitually seeks attention via "fainting spells" does not qualify for such measures, and a fifty-five cent vitamin boost does not drain a parent's pocket nearly so drastically.

There are other occasions when the "Drama Llama" fastens his teeth into a victim and chomps down voraciously, but since it is now after midnight and I am scheduled to work a fifteen-hour double shift tomorrow, I think I will tell you more of his adventures later, letting him chew his cud overnight in peace.

## 55

# When the Death Angel Visits Honduras

*July 16, 2011 ~ San Luis, Honduras*

Working in our San Luis clinic has given me a unique opportunity to experience the opposite extremes of human existence. I have shared in the exuberant thrill of welcoming into the world a new life bursting with vitality and potential. I have also given comfort during the heart-wrenching sorrow that accompanies the departure of a loved one, whether young or old, into eternity. The emotions that accompany both of these events are similar among countries the world over, but the customs connected with each can vary widely.

Take, for instance, a visit by the death angel. In Honduras, as in other Central American countries, burials must take place within twenty-four hours of a person's death, leaving the family no time to carefully plan the arrangements and announce the funeral details several days ahead of time, thereby enabling people to adjust their schedules and attend. Here in the rural areas, a call to the local radio station *this morning* may be the only way to get the word out to family that they need to come to Grandma Rosa's wake *tonight* to pay their last respects, as by this time *tomorrow* she will be in the ground.

Even if the family knows that the departed member was a believer in Jesus, the natural sadness from their loss is compounded by the stress that is an inevitable product of crowding an overwhelming multitude of absolutely essential things to do into a few short hours. There is no such thing as the body being taken to a funeral home where it can be professionally prepared by strangers who are not emotionally involved. If there is any embalming done at all, someone must make a trip to buy a large quantity of formaldehyde and inject it via ten-cc syringes (likely purchased at our clinic) into the corpse's abdomen. Then the body will be lovingly washed and dressed. A beautifully embroidered white dress needs to be purchased for a woman or a plain white shirt for a man. The house must be cleaned and readied for the wake, and food and drinks prepared for the expected guests, who will come and go throughout the entire night. A coffin needs to be chosen and the living room of the home cleared of all furniture except for two wooden sawhorses set up in the center to hold the coffin. Chairs are placed around the perimeter of the room for the guests. If the family is well-known in the community and a large crowd is expected, more chairs may be borrowed to allow for seating the overflow of sympathizers in the yard outside. A large plastic tub needs to be procured, filled with bags of ice, and set on cement blocks under the casket to help keep the corpse's temperature down and slow decay.

The intense whirl of feverish activity largely subsides when everything is prepared, but then follows a night without sleep as friends and relatives gather at the home for the funeral service. Once the singing, priest or preacher's message, and prayers are done, visitors file in and out of the house in a steady stream, pausing to peer through the narrow glass pane in the lid of the simple, wooden coffin before greeting the assembled family. People mill around in the yard, uncomprehending small children dash in and out, laughing and shouting, and an occasional inquisitive dog may meander through the room, snuffling casually at this or that one's shoes.

By daybreak, everyone is exhausted, but there is still the burial to get through. If the family lives within a mile or two of the cemetery, the coffin will probably be carried the entire distance by pallbearers. There may be a dozen or more men and boys who alternate taking turns with each other for this honor, switching places smoothly without pausing in their steady walk. For a longer distance, the coffin is transported in a pickup truck, which creeps along slowly enough for the long line of people streaming behind to keep up, several of whom keep a steadying hand on the cargo sticking out beyond the truck's bed.

It is no wonder that the whole process frays nerves to the snapping point, and our clinic staff can expect to treat at least one or two hysterical patients at some point during or after every funeral. On these occasions, we do use something with stronger stress-relieving potential than the thiamine injection that I told you about in the last chapter. Valium is the only controlled substance we stock, and Dr. Maldonado is well accustomed to receiving phone calls from one of the nurses in the wee hours of the morning, requesting the necessary authorization to give it. It works well, not only because of its own inherent tranquilizing properties, but perhaps equally because people *expect* it to work.

One such occasion occurred a few days back when a woman was carried in, "unconscious" with her grief. We only had one ampule of Valium left at the time, since the order Miriam had placed well before then had not been delivered. We did have some Valium tablets, and I wanted to save the injection for a true emergency; however, if someone is unconscious, she cannot swallow pills, right? So I gave her the stand-by thiamine injection, telling her family that I also had some tablets to help her even more after the shot had taken effect. After sufficient time had passed, I was trying to take the woman's blood pressure again, to see if it was still nice and normal as it had been when she arrived. Because she was still lying totally unresponsive on her stomach, I was having trouble getting the cuff on her arm. Finally, I said to her, "I'm sorry, Ma'am, but I need to take your blood pressure, and I can't get the cuff on. It's been long enough for the shot to work, so can you please turn over and sit up?" And she did! Her BP was still fine, and she was able to swallow the four milligrams of Valium and walk out on her own two feet.

I mentioned about there being a lot of stress, even for families who know that their Christian loved one is enjoying being in heaven with Jesus. For those who have no such assurance, death can be an occasion of profound despair, tolerable only by means of trying to drown one's sorrows in alcohol. I remember years ago in Costa Rica watching a man in drunken woe throw himself into the open grave of his mother and cling to her casket, sobbing wretchedly.

Just last week, Rachel and I walked into the back door of the clinic for the evening shift and heard a slurred male voice moaning loudly, *"Mi querida suegra, oohhh, mi querida suegra!"* (My dear mother-in-law, oh, my dear mother-in-law!) Maribel was coming out of the medication room with two syringes in her hand, and at our inquiring looks, informed us that Suyapa's mother, Angelita, had died early that morning. I was sad to hear the news, but not surprised; I had thought the afternoon before, when helping with her third paracentesis since my arrival, how incredibly frail and weak she appeared. Now she was with Jesus and no longer suffering terribly as she had been.

My first reaction was to wonder how Suyapa was handling things and whether I would have a chance to go to the house to give my sympathy and show support. Obviously, since it happened today, the wake was in progress at this moment, and I would be here at the clinic all night. My next reaction, as I followed Maribel into the general ward, was a kind of amazed shock at the number of people who had managed to pack themselves into the room, and that it sure did not smell like all of them were using deodorant! Mingled with that aroma was the sharply sour scent of the patient's partially digested stomach contents, liberally splattered down the side of the mattress and across a good-sized portion of the floor.

Suyapa's sister was standing by the wall near the foot of the bed, biting her lip and fighting tears as she helplessly watched the thrashing form of her husband. Just a few days ago, after the umpteenth time she had come to buy pain and nausea medication for her mother, I had prayed with her, asking for God's touch on her mother and strength and comfort for the family who were caring for her. I went to the sister now and hugged her, and she clung desperately to me in the midst of a constant flow of people entering and leaving the room. No doubt most of them were family members, but I am sure that others were curious neighbors, in to see the show.

Several pairs of willing hands flopped the man first to one side, then to the other, to receive the needles Maribel wielded. I knew that one of the syringes contained Valium, but was not sure what was in the second. When she told me it was for his stomach pain, I could understand why. I went back out to the nurses' desk with her to get report on the other patients who were in for the night. One was next door in our only private room: a man in his mid-thirty's who had arrived earlier in the afternoon, doubled up with pain from gall stones. At least, now he was no doubt distracted somewhat from his own misery by the carryings-on just a few yards away from his open door. The other patient was a young pregnant girl, admitted for observation of a potential problem. I was to call the ambulance crew to transport her if her situation got worse. Thankfully, she was down the other hall and, amazingly, appeared to have slept through the whole episode.

Sure enough, ten minutes or so later, the grieving son-in-law was carried out, quiet and meek as a rather bedraggled lamb, while Rachel and I were left with the daunting task of cleaning up after the ruckus. The usual afternoon downpour had stopped not long before, so the entire distance from the front door, around the corner, and along the hall, plus the complete floor of the general ward, was a gritty mess of tracked-in mud. Added to that was the large quantity of vomit that the son-in-law had heaved up after his arrival. Suyapa, of course, would not be coming in the morning to do her normal stellar cleaning job. So for the next hour, Rachel and I tackled the situation with rags, brooms, and mop, breathing a sigh of relief when the floor was restored to a presentable condition, bed frame and mattress wiped down, linen changed, and the aroma of the room transformed from sour stomach and sweat to soothing citronella. (The supply store must have been out of our normal green-apple-scented disinfectant that week when the supplies were purchased.)

I did have a chance to go to Angelita's home the next morning after I got off work, and I sat with Suyapa and her family for nearly an hour before the internment. People were still coming and going, though not, I knew, in droves as they had been the night before. At one point, her oldest sister came into the room and up to the coffin, which was sealed closed by a couple of rows of overlapping, clear, two-inch-wide tape, wrapped around the entire seam where the lid met the bed. Laying her head down on the glass pane, she began to sob loudly, asking no one in particular how she was going to make it without her mother. Seven women rushed to cluster around her, led her to a chair, and hovered anxiously over her. One of the women reached for a tiny bottle and began splashing its contents onto her face. Two others massaged her arms. Yet another began vigorously rubbing her chest in circles over her heart. Several of them were talking at once, offering soothing words of comfort. After a few minutes of their combined ministrations, the sister's sobs quieted, and she slumped in her chair, staring straight ahead of her as if in a stupor.

Not long after, a similar scenario was repeated with another grieving woman, complete with a splash in the face of the bottle's contents (flower water, I was told later), vigorous chest rub over the heart, arm massage, and multivoiced words of comfort. I sat quietly and respectfully through it all, not feeling in the least like I had when the school girls were pulling their antics in the clinic. My heart ached with them, and I knew that this was not merely a childish ploy for attention. Our North American culture and inbred reticence do not give us the luxury of spilling our feelings so publicly and with such abandon. Were we to do so, people would be embarrassed and uncomfortable. Here, it is a normal and accepted part of the grieving process, which gives everyone not only a vent for their sorrow, but also the chance to give and receive loving support.

In San Luis, if the deceased person's family does not have much money, his casket will be buried on a spot of land donated by the municipality for the extremely poor. Perhaps a crude, homemade wooden cross will mark the spot. Those who can afford to do so will buy a grave plot in the local cemetery, where a tiered system of vaults provides burial for multiple family members. The first coffin is placed in a cement-lined hole in the ground that is just deep enough to hold it. Three more cement vaults are then built on top, with the ends left open to receive the coffins to come. As each vault is filled, the end is cemented closed. Thus, in the same amount of space that a cemetery in your town would have three people buried, Honduran cemeteries will have twelve.

In Costa Rica, families rent a nonstacked, above-ground burial crypt in which to lay a loved one for his final rest. At least, it normally is a "final" rest—unless the family comes on hard times, such as happened to one of our friends when he was a lad. Even as a grown man, Gilberto is still traumatized by the memory of his dead father's partially decomposed face in the casket that the local cemetery proprietors removed from its crypt when his mother was not able to keep making the rent payments.

Yes, a visit from the death angel in Central America sets in motion a whirl of activity for pagan and Christian alike. It brings either the anguish of an eternity without Christ or the comfort of knowing that a loved one is rejoicing in the joys of heaven. Pray for those who are working to spread the good news of a Savior Who died that men and women and boys and girls in Honduras, as well as around the world, might not perish, but have eternal life.

## 56

## Maternity Math

*July 19, 2011 ~ San Luis, Honduras*

Did you like math when you were in school? Was it your best subject? Even if you did not get all A's, you can probably give me the correct answer to this simple equation. What is the sum of 9 centimeters plus 9 centimeters? If you said 18 centimeters, you were exactly ... WRONG! All right, how about telling me the one time that 10 babies equals 101 babies equals 7,776 babies? You don't know?

Well then, let's try another problem. What do the numbers 40/0, 60/20, 80/30, 90/50, 98/58 and 95/40 have in common with 70/20, 70/20, 90/30, 100/40, 90/50 and 90/60? Come on, that one should be easy to figure out. The obvious shared factor in both of those sets of numbers is the need for lots and lots of fervent prayers and feverish activity.

If you are still scratching your head and wondering where in the world I went to school, let me give you a simple lesson in Maternity Math, from the School of Experience in the *Clínica Luz y Vida*. First, I must confess that I really did not provide you with enough information to calculate the addition equation. Let me clarify things by telling you that there is a HUGE difference between 9 cm + 9 cm + 1, as opposed to 9 cm + 9 cm + 2. Thankfully, it was a 9 + 9+ 2 situation that Rachel and I walked into the other night, and it was precisely because she was here that our math problem was so much easier to solve.

When you enter the back door of the clinic and see one baby-bellied woman pacing the hallway, you think that this shift will probably not be boring. When you round the corner and see another baby-bellied woman leaning over the delivery table, moaning, while her cousin rubs her back, you are fairly sure that not only will it not be boring, you may even keep pretty busy. And when you arrive at the nurses' desk to discover seven people clustered around it while a harried-looking Maribel—usually calm, cool, and collected—rushes into the general ward with a bag of IV fluid in her hand, you are quite certain that you will have absolutely no trouble staying awake all night. *Then* Maribel informs you that both of the pregnant women are in quite active labor, both are nine-centimeters dilated, and the older lady who arrived ten minutes ago is in respiratory distress, on four liters of oxygen, and will need to be transferred if the medicines she has just been given do not help her enough. At that point, you might wonder why in the world you thought it was a good idea to spend five weeks this summer giving the Honduran nurses vacation time!

Believe me, that was the night I was especially grateful for Rachel's presence. She will be starting the last of her four years of BSN nurse's schooling this fall, so has had enough clinical training to be more than just an observer while she has been with me. After four weeks here in our clinic, she will resume her studies in Florida with a wealth of experience more than her fellow classmates. This summer, she has given dozens of shots, successfully started six IV's plus calculated and set the drip rates of many more, assisted with numerous wound dressings, and learned to read mercury thermometers. She has been present for the births of six of the ten babies I have delivered. She has helped make cardboard-and-cloth-strips splints for a grossly malformed broken arm and a broken femur. And the day before yesterday, she even got to put two of the necessary five stitches into the machete wound that we repaired for the fourteen-year-old boy who nicked his foot instead of whatever it was he had been chopping. Although her Spanish is pretty limited, she is good at communicating in the universal language of a reassuring smile, and her soothing touch has helped several laboring women handle their contractions better. As Maribel walked out the door, very happy to go home to her bed, I sent Rachel in to get vital signs on the lady with the breathing troubles, while I turned to the group of people at the desk to see which of them needed tending to first.

To my great relief, they were all accompanying one or another of the three patients and did not require medical attention personally. Since we close and lock the doors at 10:00 p.m., I could explain to them that it was now time to wait outside if they were going to stay around, because we only permit one family member per patient to spend the night inside. The younger of the two women in labor already had her cousin with her, and the other was too shy to allow her mother to stay. Very few of the women who give birth here want anyone with them except the nurse. On rare occasions, I have been able to convince one to have her husband present; most of them do not wish to have even a female relative as a support person.

Fortunately, the medications and oxygen Maribel had given to the fifty-eight-year-old respiratory-distress woman were doing their work, and soon she was no longer sweating, pulling so hard for air, or looking as wide-eyed panicky as she had on our arrival. Although she still wanted to sit up for optimal ease of breathing, her oxygen-saturation level was an acceptable mid-90s range, and she did not require one-on-one care as she had done earlier.

That meant that we could focus most of our attention on the 9 cm + 9 cm + 2 (people) math equation. With *both* Rachel and me available to massage backs, murmur encouraging words, take blood pressures, and monitor fetal heart tones, *both* of the soon-to-be-new-mothers could have individualized nursing attention. At least, it was mostly individualized. Since Rachel cannot evaluate dilation progress or baby descent, I trotted back and forth between the two ladies, checking to see who would need to use the delivery room first. The norm when there are two or more in labor simultaneously is for *one* nurse to juggle her time among however many there are, a feat that is at least made easier by the fact that our labor room has three beds, each about four feet apart, so she only has a few steps to take between patients.

The twenty-two-year-old was having her first baby and had been at the clinic since 7:12 that morning. The thirty-three-year-old had four children already and had arrived at 9:30 p.m., nearly ready to give birth. Both women were completely dilated within minutes of each other, but that is when the neck-and-neck race to the finish line became unequal. Fifth-time mommy clearly had it over on first-time mommy and was happily settled into the post-partum ward with her five-pound, four-ounce daughter long before her room-mate was ready to join her. Rachel, unfortunately, missed seeing that birth, as she was busy coaching "her" lady in the delivery room, while I welcomed "my" lady's baby in the bed in the labor room.

It was definitely nice to have two instead of one to add to the 9 cm + 9 cm math equation that shift, especially with the extra factor of a significantly ill, nonmaternity patient who needed attention as well. We ended up transferring the lady with breathing problems to the city hospital later the same morning, where she died shortly thereafter. I was sorry when I heard the news, but very glad that we had not needed to deal with her death occurring here in addition to the two births.

There had not been two nurses the week before, when I was alone in the clinic to care for the thirty-seven-year-old lady who arrived at 3:20 a.m. and gave birth to her fifth baby three hours and twenty-eight minutes later. She was accompanied by her two daughters, ages twenty and eleven, and her two-year-old grandson, who all waited outside on the porch in the predawn darkness while mom/grandma had their baby brother/uncle inside.

Remember the numbers 40/0, 60/20, 80/30, 90/50, 98/58 and 95/40? What they have in common with 70/20, 70/20, 90/30, 100/40, 90/50 and 90/60 is that they are all blood pressures of that same woman, each set taken over the hour of time immediately following the births of her third and fourth children here in the clinic in 1993 and 1999, when she nearly bled to death.

You do not have to be a medical person to know that a blood pressure of 40/0 is **A VERY BAD THING**. Had I known her history before I delivered her baby, I would have started an IV on her when she arrived, drawn up medication and had it ready to help control postpartum hemorrhaging, and rousted one of the other nurses out of her bed to come be on hand for the birth.

Thankfully, history did not repeat itself, so I did not realize until several days after the woman and her baby had been discharged how scary things *could* have been.

I was filing the chart from this birth with her past medical record, which I had not known where to find that night. I flipped idly through the records of her other two births at our clinic, curious to compare them to the one with which I had just helped. A chill went up my spine when I saw the blood pressure numbers and thought of what could have happened this time. I had asked her when she arrived if she had experienced *any* problems with *any* prior pregnancies, and she positively assured me that there had been *none* whatsoever. Now, someone cannot nearly bleed to death once, let alone twice, and not remember it! However, if she *does* tell the nurse that she has had bleeding problems in a prior pregnancy (or two), she might not be permitted to have her baby here. Obviously, she thought it would be much better to glibly lie and not have to pay for the ambulance to take her to a city hospital.

I told you earlier that the common factors in both of those sets of blood pressure numbers are fervent prayers and feverish activity. Believe me, when I read them, I sent up fervent prayers, thanking God that the feverish activity was not needed this time as it had been with her two previous births. He had intervened and prevented the catastrophe of a woman hurting herself because she wanted to avoid an expensive ambulance transfer. Once again, I was profoundly grateful.

So let's move on to figuring out how 10 babies equals 101 babies equals 7,776 babies. What it means is that at 4:57 on Monday morning, I delivered my tenth baby for this trip, which also happens to be baby number 101 that I have delivered overall, which is the 7,776th baby to be born in the clinic since three American nurses excitedly attended the first birth here on May 2, 1979. Add to that the noteworthy addendum that the baby was her forty-two-year-old mother's thirteenth, and I think it is safe to say that Maternity Math in Honduras adds up to an interesting summer.

# 57

## A Baby Is Worth More Than $5.29

*July 15, 2011 ~ San Luis, Honduras*

We had no warning. The young girl in early labor who arrived shortly after 7:00 on the morning of July 15 had been getting prenatal care, taking vitamins, and looked perfectly healthy. It was her first baby, and she was not exactly sure of her due date, but thought it was sometime this month. I was just getting ready to go home for a good nap, having worked sixteen hours since 3:00 p.m. the afternoon before. In all likelihood, the baby would not be born any time soon, so I should be able to sleep awhile and still experience the joy of welcoming another new life into the world. I set my alarm for 2:30 p.m., but asked Miriam to call me if it looked like this little one was going to make his debut before then.

At 12:12 p.m., Rachel tapped on my bedroom door to say that the clinic secretary was trying to tell her something, but she could not understand what. Rather bleary eyed, I stumbled across the hall and peered sleepily out the open window in Rachel's room. *"Hermana Ana, dice Miriam que ya está lista la muchacha."* (Sister Hannah, Miriam says the girl is ready.) *"Dígale que ya vamos"* (Tell her we'll be right there), I replied, snapping fully awake and scurrying back to my room to dress in something more appropriate for a delivery than my bathrobe.

We dashed over to the clinic just in time for me to hurriedly pull on a sterile gown and gloves and coach the mother through the last few contractions and pushes needed to propel her son into my hands. His tiny body was perfectly formed ... and perfectly still. He made no sound nor response as I rapidly suctioned his mouth and nose with the bulb syringe and briskly dried his limp, blue figure. Quickly clamping and cutting the umbilical cord, I passed him into Miriam's capable hands, briefly examined the mother and directed Rachel to watch for signs of placental detachment, then joined Miriam at the warmer.

Barely a minute had passed since his birth. By now he should have been flailing tiny arms and legs and sucking in great lungfuls of air as he announced his arrival with lusty wails. Anxiously I checked for a pulse. 1...2...3...4...5...6 ...7...8...9...10 beats in 6 seconds. Way too slow! Jerking open a drawer in the side of the warmer, I snatched out an infant Ambu bag. Rachel ran to pull the big oxygen tank closer to the warmer. Fingers fumbling with nervous haste, we connected the tubing, and I started bag-breathing for the baby while Miriam began chest compressions.

Four minutes passed, an eternity when a life is hanging in the balance. The baby's stomach muscles convulsed as he took a couple of faltering gasps. His heart rate crept up to 110 beats a minute. We sent collective fervent thanks heavenward as he started to breathe on his own and the ghastly blue color of his body gradually changed to pink. Still limp (his Apgar scores were one at one minute and three at five minutes), he was definitely not out of the woods yet. I traded the Ambu bag for an infant face mask and slipped the elastic ties around his head, willing those little lungs to keep sucking in the oxygen they so urgently needed. His chest heaved, intercostal rib muscles straining and nostrils flaring with each painful, labored breath, as the peculiar grunting sound of a newborn in respiratory distress filled the room. Arms and legs lay unmoving as his little body poured every ounce of available energy into the struggle to fill his underdeveloped lungs. Time ticked slowly by as we tensely watched his effort, willing him to live.

Suddenly, the room was quiet. Deathly quiet. The grunting respirations that could be heard throughout the whole clinic ceased, and a dusky blue color once again infused the baby's skin. Grabbing a stethoscope, I frantically listened to his silent chest. No heartbeat! Fingers flying, we stripped off the oxygen mask and replaced it with the Ambu bag. Rachel began compressing his sternum in a steady rhythm as I squeezed in oxygen, praying desperately the while.

Miraculously, his heart started back to life, and he resumed breathing on his own. Now what to do? It was obvious that, contrary to what his mother had thought, this baby was not full term. I did a rapid evaluation of his neuromuscular and physical maturity and totaled up the points for each category, not too surprised to discover that his gestational age was more like thirty-five weeks. We simply did not have the resources here to provide the respiratory support that he needed. Miriam talked to the girl, laying out the options. She was unmarried, a bit on the simple side mentally, and really did not comprehend the gravity of the situation. But when she finally understood that her baby would surely die if he did not get more advanced care, she agreed to let us call the ambulance.

By this time, it was after 4:00 p.m., and my next scheduled shift started that evening at 10:00 p.m. If I went with the baby, we would probably get back to the clinic shortly before time to start work, which would mean functioning on six hours of sleep in a forty-two hour stretch. But there was no other nurse available to go. When the Toyota Land Cruiser ambulance arrived, we switched oxygen tubing from the big tank to the smaller portable one in its wheeled carrier, and the Red Cross volunteer gave Rachel a quick lesson in adjusting the valve to control the rate. The problem with these tanks is that they are so old, and have been battered around so much on multiple rough ambulance journeys over the mountain, that they do not hold their setting. It is virtually impossible to get a steady, accurate flow, as every few minutes the rate must be turned up, so that it does not run down to nothing.

I carefully lifted the grunting baby from the warmer, wrapped him in a blanket, and carried him outside to the waiting ambulance. As always, the diesel fumes generated by its running engine left a choking pall in the air, and I ducked quickly into the back of the vehicle to escape the smell. Scooting along the bench to one side, I settled the baby on my lap, and the oxygen tank was maneuvered into place beside us. Rachel climbed in next, taking her place on the bench beside me. The girl's father was just stepping up into the ambulance when his grandson jerked in my arms, thick, blood-tinged mucus bubbling out his mouth and nose. In the space of a few seconds, his breathing once again stopped, and he turned the all-too-familiar sickening shade of blue.

"Let me out, quickly!" I exclaimed, scrambling for the open ambulance door. I ran back into the clinic and down the hall toward the delivery room, with the volunteer dashing along a few steps behind, carrying the oxygen tank. Placing the baby once again in the warmer, I suctioned away the mucus that was choking off his airway and anxiously listened for a heartbeat that was not there. Praying desperately, we started the by-now-too-familiar CPR routine: compress ... compress ... compress ... breath; compress ... compress ... compress ... breath. Several minutes passed. "He's not going to make it this time," I muttered to Rachel. But once more, unbelievably, that diminutive muscle throbbed to life and, chameleonlike, his color reverted from blue back to pink.

We trooped back outside and settled ourselves once more on the bench inside the Land Cruiser: me with the baby in my lap at the far end next to the cab window; Rachel next, gripping the handle of the oxygen tank holder; and the dazed, silent grandfather, totally unprepared for all that was transpiring, last. The driver and his assistant directed the new mother onto the narrow, padded stretcher a mere two feet across from us on the opposite wall and helped her lie down before slamming the doors closed and climbing into the cab.

As we jounced and bounced over the dirt road out of the clinic yard, I braced my legs against the toolbox carrying the ambulance's few first aid supplies. It was totally impossible to completely shield the baby from the jarring ride, but by bracing my elbows tightly to my sides and cradling his tiny body aloft in my extended forearms, I could somewhat protect him from the jolting that he would have gotten if he had been lying in my lap. The oxygen tank rattled and banged against the confines of its holder, and Rachel struggled to keep it upright and in place. The assistant momentarily slid open the window from the cab and pointed to the windows behind our heads. "You'd better open them so it doesn't get too hot back there," he directed. "Otherwise, you're going to get carsick."

The sounds of the baby's labored breathing, so loud in the relative quiet of the clinic, could just be heard over the roar of the motor. I kept an anxious eye on the rise and fall of his chest and the color of his face as we lurched around the sharp curves of the rocky mountain road and forded a couple of shallow streams. So far so good. My arms were beginning to ache with the strain of their effort to keep him from jostling, and we were less than twenty minutes into what was normally a two-hour-and-fifteen-minute journey. I caught a glimpse out the window of some people standing at the side of the road and wondered briefly if they were curious about what the ambulance was carrying this time.

Suddenly, my discomfort was forgotten as the grunting rhythm of the baby's respirations was abruptly interrupted. I saw with horror another large blob of bloody phlegm oozing out his mouth and nose, choking off his struggling breaths. Snatching for the bulb syringe in my lap, I turned him onto his side and frenziedly suctioned at the thick, slimy mess, swooshing the contents of the bulb repeatedly onto the blanket wrapped loosely around him. "Come on, Baby!" I pleaded aloud. "Breathe. PLEASE BREATHE!" No response. I pounded desperately on the cab window. "STOP! STOP!" The driver braked to a halt, and he and the assistant jumped out and sprinted around to fling open the back doors. Inquisitive villagers crowded around, peering in to mutely observe as I balanced the little blue body on my knees and pumped on his tiny chest. Rachel hastily turned up the oxygen level on the tank meter. "Dear God, please help us!" I prayed out loud. Against all odds, the little fellow's heart pitched into gear yet another time, and the grunting sound of his breathing filled our ears like lovely music. What an incredible fighter he was!

I will spare you *all* of the details of the next hour and some minutes of that nightmarish ride. Suffice it to say that it seemed like forever before we finally reached the end of the rough dirt road and picked up speed to over eighty miles per hour on the paved section. Siren wailing, flashing lights blazing, the driver skillfully whipped around cars that stubbornly refused to pull over out of our way. I had thought the bouncing and jostling of the rocky stretch was bad, but as we rocked back and forth precariously on our narrow bench with the increased pace, I did not know which part of the trip was more miserable. At one point, Rachel was thrown on top of me, and I slammed into the front wall, barely bracing myself in time to avoid dropping my precious burden. For the last part of our hair-raising journey, Rachel held the baby, the grandfather corralled the oxygen tank, and I unfastened three buttons at my uniform waist, then hunched over miserably, belching loudly and repeatedly as the chicken soup that I had hurriedly bolted down while we were waiting for the ambulance to arrive doggedly tried to escape my stomach.

Incredibly, we had one more nerve-wracking, pounding-on-the-window-to-stop, bulb-syringe-sucking, adrenaline-pumping, chest-compressing CPR session with the baby before finally pulling up to the hospital emergency room doors. I gratefully stepped out onto solid ground and hurried through the double doors, the attendant once more trailing a few steps behind with the tank. Glancing down at the baby in my arms, I could not believe my eyes. He had stopped breathing and turned blue *again.* For the fifth time! Hospital personnel waved our racing feet down first one hallway, then another, and around a corner into the delivery room. I deposited the baby into their infant warmer, quickly firing off a summary of the events of the past few hours to the doctor who bag breathed for him as my fingers kept up their by-now-familiar CPR rhythm.

I stood to the side, watching and praying as hospital personnel clustered around the warmer, working with the baby. It took a couple of tries, but he was finally successfully intubated and his burden of breathing eased by the tube into his trachea. One doctor inflated his lungs every few seconds by squeezing the bag fastened to the tube, while the other turned to me. "Do you think your ambulance can take him on to San Pedro Sula?" he asked. "We don't have a ventilator here, so we can't possibly keep him, but since our ambulance was in an accident yesterday, we have no way to transport him." I gulped as I thought about what would be involved in such a trip. We would have to give the baby each breath via his endotracheal tube throughout the entire trip, a monumental challenge for a ride of such length even in the best of circumstances. At that moment, the Red Cross volunteer poked his head around the door and motioned to me. "Our job is done," he said. "The driver is going to leave without us if we don't hurry." "But they want us to take the baby on to another hospital," I protested. "Do you think we can do that?" We trooped through the hallways to where the driver was impatiently waiting near the front doors, and the doctor posed the question to him. "It's absolutely out of the question!" he exclaimed, waving his arms vehemently. "I have just enough gas to get us back to San Luis, and no money to buy more. These people didn't have anything to pay for *this* trip, let alone going on to San Pedro Sula."

"What if we give you money for gas?" queried the doctor. He went in search of someone to authorize such an arrangement, while the driver continued his protestations to everyone within hearing distance. "It's going to take us hours, with it being a Friday night. Traffic will be all tied up, and we won't get back to San Luis until 3:00 in the morning." I stared at Rachel in dismay as he continued his blustering tirade. "This doctor is trying to get them to give us 700 *lempiras,* but that's still not enough. They can't expect the ambulance to run on fumes!"

A bystander spoke up. "How much more do you need?" he inquired. "It's going to take at least another 100 *lempiras,*" replied the driver. Immediately the man reached for his hip pocket, pulling out his wallet and extracting a 100-*lempira* bill. "Here, take this," he said. "A baby is worth more than 100 *lempiras.*" I was astounded and moved at this display of generosity from a total stranger, especially in the context of wrenching poverty that characterizes so much of the country. One hundred *lempiras,* or $5.29, is the equivalent of a fast-food meal for you. In Honduras, it is a whole day's wages. The spluttering ambulance driver fell silent as he quietly reached for the money and left to search for the doctor.

I would love to report that we successfully made the trip to San Pedro Sula and that the baby received the intensive care he needed until his lungs matured sufficiently to allow a healthy discharge from the hospital. Instead, an ambulance from another location arrived while we were still waiting for the money promised by the doctor, and our little charge was given to its crew while the San Luis ambulance headed for home. I lay wearily on the cot in the back, numbly aware of the eerie, pulsing flashes of red from the rotating light on our roof that pierced the darkness and reflected off the roadside bushes, advertising our mission and silently pleading safe passage along the dark, bandit-prone road. We pulled safely into the clinic yard with fifty minutes to spare before the start of our next shift.

Three days later, I called the ambulance back to the clinic to transport an elderly woman with a broken hip and a thirty-three-year-old woman with a cerebral hemorrhage. It was then that I learned the outcome of all of our efforts with the baby. He had, indeed, survived his trip to San Pedro Sula, only to die two days afterwards, unable to sustain his herculean struggle to breathe.

Was it worth it? I think of the words of James R. Milstead, MD, medical director for Grace on Wings, the only charity air ambulance in the United States. In his book *Answering the Call*, which tells the stories of patients helped by his ministry, he says, "Sometimes we can question the usefulness of our efforts if we focus only on results others deem worthy or successful. But we can be comforted in knowing God does not expect us to heal every person we serve. He does, however, expect us to show up and use all of the gifts and talents he has bestowed upon us to help those in need. The results are in God's domain, but the work is ours. It is his way of grace."

What if it had been your child, or your grandchild, or your brother or nephew? Would you agree that the value of a human life cannot be measured in terms of dollars and cents or expended energy? Each person born into this world is precious in God's sight, so much so that He sacrificed His own beloved Son to provide eternal life to every one of them. Worth more than $5.29? Absolutely, undeniably, without a doubt, immeasurably so.

(Quotation from James R. Milstead, M.D., *Answering the Call* [Maitland, FL: Xulon Press, 2013], 139. Used by permission of the author.)

CHAPTER

# 58

## A $2,700 Christmas Gift

*October 22, 2012 ~ Lewisburg, Pennsylvania*

I was in Wal-Mart on the first day of October, browsing the aisles for a bargain while I waited for the pictures of our newest grandson, born the day before, to be developed by the store's one-hour photo lab. I could hardly believe my eyes as I turned a corner beside what only a week or so before had been displays of lawn and garden supplies. Instead of neat rows of bird feeders, potting soil, fertilizer, and flower bulbs, the shelves were loaded with brightly colored Christmas tree ornaments, glittering tinsel, boxes of cards with snow scenes, and other such holiday decor. "This is a bit ridiculous," I thought to myself, wheeling my shopping cart on by without even being tempted to pause and look over the enticing array. "The first day of October is WAY too early to be shopping for Christmas."

I still was not thinking of Christmas a few days later when I scooted my chair away from the computer at the nurses' station in the Evangelical Community Hospital Emergency Department where I work part time. I had just charted the vital signs of one of my patients and was hurrying into a room to check on another. I did not notice the two men going with a cart from room to room, gathering something from each one. I did not notice them, but God did, and He knew that I needed to be aware of what was happening.

I love the verse that tells of our heavenly Father caring so much for His creation that He keeps track of the number of hairs on your head (no small feat if you are getting more bald each month). He also knows how many sparrows are left to flit around your back yard, even after the neighbor's marauding cat devours the one that fell from the safety of the nest during last night's high-wind storm. That is the same God who sees the tremendous blessing that *Clínica Luz y Vida* is to the town of San Luis, Honduras. He is quite aware of the many that go there for medical care from one of the dedicated Christian nurses on staff and leave with spiritual help as well. And He knows down to the penny the cost of each box of medical supplies that Miriam, the head nurse, orders each month. Often, the payments which the patients make fail to cover expenses, but no one with a true need is turned away.

That is the God Who saw what the men were doing and made sure that one of them stopped a few feet from my desk with his hands full of IV catheters at the precise time that I was hurrying by. I glanced at what he was stuffing into

.. suddenly realized what was going on. Nearly two months earlier, the ᵤany that manufactures the plastic-tube-over-a-needle device that we use o start the numerous IV's given in our department had sent us a revision of their product to test. It is the same basic IV catheter, but with an added safety feature. The administration had decided to go with the upgrade, and on this day, the men with the cart were collecting all of the older-style IV catheters, which are still much better than the kind the clinic is able to get in Honduras, and replacing them with the newer version.

"I wonder what they are going to do with the ones they are getting rid of?" I thought. The man whom I asked was not sure, but supposed they would be donated to some veterinary hospital. "I can give you a better idea," I assured him, telling him of EFM's clinic. "Why don't you call Dave Humphrey, the storeroom manager?" he suggested. "Maybe he can help you out." I dialed the storeroom extension and marveled at God's perfect timing. It did not just happen that the half hour of time it took for the men to switch the two types of IV catheters occurred during one of the two weekly shifts that I work at the hospital. God was orchestrating events, just as He has done throughout history, just as He did when "in the fullness of time" He gave His Son, the world's first Christmas gift.

Not only did Dave give me all of the IV catheters, he let me go through boxes of other supplies in a back corner of the vast central supply room. They were all still in date, but had been replaced with something else. "Take whatever you want," he invited. "I'll be glad for them to be put to good use." Talk about a shopping spree! I happily sorted through the containers, pulling out packets of sutures, boxes of lancets, and cases of sterile gloves, thinking of how delighted Miriam would be when I arrived at the clinic with my treasures shortly after Christmas. Dave waved a cheerful good-bye as I headed for the service elevator with my cart piled high. THIS kind of Christmas shopping was just my style: no crowded aisles, no long lines or harried clerks, and no mammoth bill at the register. I decided that Christmas shopping in October was not such a bad idea after all.

I was even more excited when I got home and spread out my haul to sort and pack it. I called Dave back. "Can you tell me what your cost per IV catheter is?" I queried. "*We* pay $1.80 apiece," he told me, "but if *you* bought them retail, they would cost you three times that." I grabbed a pencil and did some rapid figuring on the back of an envelope lying on the table. Wow! At just *his* cost, the 1,221 IV catheters lying on my living room floor were worth $2,197.80. Add to that the other miscellaneous supplies, and the total of this Christmas gift to the clinic came to over $2,700.00. Thank you, Evangelical Community Hospital and Dave Humphrey, and thank You, God.

## 59

## Bellyaches, Births, and Bugs
### *January 14, 2013 ~ San Luis, Honduras*

Greetings from the highlands of Honduras, where the January days are still hot and humid, but the nights are tolerably cooler. I am writing at the nurses' station where there is more light and, therefore, fewer mosquitoes.

12:03 a.m. – Just sent home the pitifully emaciated ninety-four-year-old man who arrived as I typed the word "mosquitoes" above. He was carried in like a child in his great-nephew's arms, whimpering and writhing in agony from something that had affected his stomach. Three injections later, he lay quietly and comfortably on the bed, while the four family members who had accompanied him chattered away to me in great detail about him and his siblings, who have all inherited a gene of longevity and general good health. I could not get either of the two fluorescent lights in the general ward to turn on when the patient arrived, which is not unusual. In fact, we do not ever turn off the delivery room lights any more, since we might never get them back on. The man's daughter used the tiny but adequate light on her cell phone to provide enough illumination for me to give the shots. He was so skinny, I was afraid I might hit bone even using just a one-inch needle in his hips.

12:40 a.m. – Sold a ten-cc syringe and an 18-gauge needle to a young man whose aunt died this evening. He needs to take them to someone in the neighborhood so they can inject her body with formaldehyde after removing her abdominal organs. That way, she will be preserved enough to keep from decomposing too badly in the intervening hours between now and her burial tomorrow. His family has been hard hit in the past two days, since this is his second aunt to die in that time. Both of them were relatively young: this one was only forty, and the other was in her early sixties.

1:18 a.m. – Charted on the nursing record of the new baby in bed four of our maternity ward that she just had her first bowel movement. When I changed her, I had to use one of our smaller cleaning rags as a diaper, since a regular cloth diaper would come up to her neck. We are out of diaper pins for the moment, so her diaper is taped on. She was born yesterday morning at 9:24 a.m., and as soon as she slid into my hands, I knew she would not break the scales. Just the same, I *was* surprised that she weighed merely three pounds, thirteen ounces, especially if she is truly only eight days earlier than the due date her mother told us. She is the smallest baby I have ever delivered, but seems to be doing fine. Her ankle is probably not as big around as my thumb, but all of her miniature fingers and toes are perfectly formed, and tiny as she is, she was nursing well within a few minutes of her birth. As I helped her to get her first meal, I marveled again at God's wisdom in creating every human being with the instinct and ability to know what to do to survive, even small as she is. Since she does not have enough body fat to fry an egg, she had some difficulty in maintaining her temperature at a good level for the first couple of hours after leaving the nice cozy world where she had lived for the past nine months. Her mommy has kept her well wrapped and snuggled close all day, and she is pink and healthy looking, with a good set of lungs.

Hers is the second birth I have attended in the first five days of this three-week trip. I am trusting that I will not pick up any nasty bugs that would prevent me from working the seventy-five hours per week for which I am scheduled. There are plenty of the nasty-bug types around to pick up, if one is not careful. My fourteen-month-old pediatric patient on Friday and Saturday certainly could have shared some of hers, had I not been diligent in washing my hands each time I gave her care. Her parents had taken her to the doctor's office Friday afternoon, as she had been vomiting and having diarrhea for a week. He wanted to admit her at that point for IV rehydration and medications, but her family is poor, and the prospect of a big hospital bill was too frightening. They elected to take her home and try the IM injections and oral rehydration fluids which he reluctantly prescribed instead. In the wee hours of the morning, they finally realized that she was so badly dehydrated that she would soon die if they did not get more help for her. Only one bus a day chugs down from their remote mountain home to San Luis where our clinic is located, but they somehow managed to find a way to get here and rang the clinic doorbell at 2:00 Saturday morning. She could barely open her eyes, and when Esperanza started her IV, she offered scarcely any resistance, only cried weakly,

When I began my shift five hours later, she was still weak and listless, and the whole room stank badly with the rank odor of parasite-induced diarrhea. She was wearing the several-times-vomited-on dress in which she had arrived. Most of the time, our patients prefer to wear their own clothes rather than change into a hospital gown. Her stool-soaked diaper desperately needed changing, but her mother seemed oblivious to the situation. Then, her father showed me the half ounce of rehydration fluid left in the bottle they had been trying to give her before she came and asked if she should have any more. One look at her bottle, and it was instantly obvious why the little tyke would have diarrhea. I assured him that the fluids she was getting through her IV were helping her get better and took the bottle from him, telling him that she did not need it now, and I would be glad to go wash it so it would be ready for her later on. I soaked it for several hours in bleach water, and it still took some further vigorous scrubbing with both a cloth and a brush for me to get it clean.

I would have dearly loved to have a tub of warm bath water to soak and scrub the little girl in (without the bleach of course, although that might have not been all bad), but she was too sick to tolerate that at the moment, and no such thing was available anyhow. By midmorning, her mother agreed to let me change her clothes, and I figured that at least a sponge bath could do no harm. The IV was doing its job, and she was looking perkier and able to sit up. It took some time to gently tease the crusts of dried vomit from her hair, but the end result was worth the effort. We both felt better when the bath was done, though she may have just been relieved to have it over. With the help of Mr. Stuffed Cat, donated by friends in the States, I was even able to coax out the only smile she offered me the whole two days she was here.

I gave her parents the be-sure-to-boil-her-drinking-water speech before they left, but with five other children at home to care for, it is not likely that such a thing will happen. If I were cooking for eight people over an open fire and had to wash all of their clothes in a cement sink with a scrub board, possibly carrying all the water for such tasks from the nearest stream, I might think it took too much effort to boil my drinking water as well. Those who survive infancy here build up a resistance to many of the bacteria that would lay anyone of us flat in misery if we ate and drank the same things they do. I keep a bottle of purified water on my bathroom sink and do not even rinse my mouth with what comes from the tap when I brush my teeth. And I definitely do not open my mouth to sing in the shower.

That little one is among the many for whom the clinic exists, providing Christ's love along with quality care. As the popular children song says, "Red and yellow, black and white, they are precious in His sight. Jesus loves the little children of the world."

## 60

## Hurry Up With That Shot; The Hearse Is Waiting

*January 21, 2013 ~ San Luis, Honduras*

The fifty-something gentleman pushed himself up vigorously from his prone position on the treatment table, shaking his head in disgust. "You don't know how to give an injection!" he told me emphatically, adjusting his belt and tucking his shirt back into the pants he had lowered enough to receive the 1.2 million units of Penicillin G Benzathine which I had just attempted to shoot deep into his upper hip. I could not say as I blamed him for being unhappy. The cause of his frustration was a nastily thick, chalky suspension that is famous for its tendency to block even a large-bore needle. I hate giving it for that reason, and every now and then over the years, I have needed to pull the loaded syringe out of the "target," substitute a new needle, and continue with the injection in a new spot. Unfortunately, that is what happened with this man, only this time my failure was even greater than it has been on other occasions: both the first AND second tries were unsuccessful. In spite of my best technique, the penicillin absolutely refused to leave the barrel of the syringe. As I headed back to our medication room for a third needle, my patient decided he had endured enough torture at the hands of this inept foreign nurse.

"I've been coming here every two weeks to get these injections and NEVER had any of the other nurses stick me more than once!" he stridently advised not only me but everyone else in the front part of the clinic, waving his arms for emphasis as he strode down the hall toward the door. "She's NO GOOD!" Our secretary Marleni, working on filing patient records at the nurses' desk, glanced over at me from the corner of her eye, and offered a cautious, sympathetic smile. "I'm sorry, Sir," I told his retreating back. "You're welcome to come back tonight at ten o'clock when Rosmery will be here, and she can give you the shot."

He spun around and walked back towards me. "I can't wait *that* long," he objected. "I have to go home, and I don't live close. I need it right now." By this time I had substituted another twenty-gauge needle for the second blocked one, but I did not think he would take it too kindly if I offered to try just *one* more time. "Elizabeth is here today, Sir," Marleni soothingly interjected into the man's continued disgruntled mutterings. "She knows how to give injections. Perhaps she can help you." Elizabeth is one of the teachers in the Bible institute just up the hill behind the clinic. Most importantly for the situation, she is a Honduran, not a *gringa* from the States. Elizabeth came out from the office where she was working on ledgers, took my proffered syringe, and disappeared into the treatment room with the man. While I turned to the next person waiting at the front desk to be helped, I thought ruefully of the numerous times that someone has told me, "You have a very soft hand; I didn't even feel that," after one of the hundreds of injections I have given.

Any temptation to coddle my bruised ego was abruptly squelched by a flurry of commotion at the door and the entrance of two men awkwardly carrying the inert body of a young woman by her shoulders and legs. They were accompanied by several other women, babbling excitedly as they all hurried in my direction. "Here's another one who needs the injection," one of them informed me as the men hoisted the girl onto the treatment table. "She's the sister of the one we brought to you earlier."

Several hours before, a similar scenario had been enacted, the only difference being that the first young lady had been tossing and moaning while I checked her vital signs and administered ten milligrams of Valium, whereas this one lay motionless. I had learned that she was distressed because her mother was to be buried today, the same woman for whom the young man had come two nights earlier wanting a large syringe and needle to inject formaldehyde. Now it was thirty-six hours later, an unusually long time for the body to still be above ground.

After the first girl's shot, the family had hurried her out the door without paying for her treatment. I was not sure how much to charge, since the price had not been written on the box of Valium ampules that is kept in a locked drawer instead of on the shelves with our other medications. The family had assured me that someone would be by later to pay the bill, but I decided to call one of the other nurses and find out the cost before administering this one. One of the clinic's major problems has been the accumulation over the years of thousands of dollars of unpaid accounts. Sending out reminders has done no good, so recently it was decided to try a creative means of recouping some of this money by announcing on the radio the names of those who are delinquent. Talk about an effective means of bill collection! When the whole community hears that so-and-so has a delinquent bill at the clinic, it behooves a person to get down there and pay it to save face with his neighbors.

I was on my third attempt to get someone on the phone who could answer my question about the Valium price. Meanwhile, several more people had come in the door and were hovering over my patient, anxiously watching her unmoving form. I had already checked her and knew that she was clinically fine, just exhibiting one of the variations of dramatic behavior that is accepted as normal and almost expected in such situations. Our cleaning lady, Suyapa, leaned in close to my ear while I waited for the ringing phone to be answered and softly urged me to go ahead and administer the shot, as the crowd was waiting for the girl. At that moment, Rosmery answered and was able to provide the price I was seeking, so I went to prepare the injection, noticing with surprise the large number of family who had by now gathered. Among them was the gentleman who had been so indignant about my inability to successfully deliver his penicillin dose. As I approached the limp figure lying face up on the table, this man was one of the four people who hurried to turn her so the medicine could be given in the traditionally accepted spot. Grabbing her legs, he enthusiastically helped to flip her over, saying loudly as he did so, "Go ahead and give it to her."

"How very interesting," I thought. "Now that it's someone else, there's no question of my ability." Immediately after the shot was in place, the girl was swung down from the table and maneuvered out the door in the arms of two strong men. I followed the stream of people who poured out into the yard after her. I stopped in shock on the porch. No wonder Suyapa had been so anxious that I get on with the job. The whole funeral procession, with the pickup truck hearse and dozens and dozens of mourners, was stopped just outside our gates, waiting on me. The men sat the girl down beside the gatepost, where she immediately flopped onto the ground. They hauled her upright once more and half-carried her as she stumbled to the truck to ride with the casket instead of following behind on foot with everyone else. I watched as the crowd moved slowly up the hill toward town. I do not think the extra minutes made a great deal of difference in the degree of decomposition of the corpse, since she was already hours past the normal burial time, but I felt bad that I had not realized earlier what was happening so that the mourners could have avoided the lengthy delay.

Shortly after the funeral was over, the second girl was brought back to the clinic for another shot. This time she was agitated, hyperventilating, throwing her head back with great exaggeration, and complaining of numb, tingling hands, arms, and legs. I gave her a vitamin injection, then showed her young, frightened husband how to hold a bag over her face so she would breathe her own carbon dioxide and decrease the cause of the tingling. I knew from many past experiences that she would soon calm down, due in part to a generally held firm conviction that anything given via a syringe is unquestionably curative. And her husband did go ahead and pay for all three of the doses given that day.

Oh yes, I checked with Miriam the following afternoon about her experiences with giving the penicillin injection. To my relief, I discovered that she has also sometimes had to stick someone more than once, even up to three times on occasion, to deliver the thick suspension. I did not ask her if she had ever held up a hearse to give a shot, though. That distinction will probably forever remain the exclusive honor of this *gringa*.

## 61

## Quick! Send a Nurse Now!!
## She Just Had Her Baby in the Toilet!!!
*January 23, 2013 ~ San Luis, Honduras*

At 10 o'clock last evening when my shift ended, I left the clinic and the woman in labor in Esperanza's capable hands and went home to fix myself a snack. Minutes thereafter, a truck raced into the yard, and a man jumped out and ran in the front door. "Can someone please help us? We need a nurse to come to our house right now! My sister-in-law was going to come here to have her baby, but she didn't make it in time!"

Ideally (at least from my standpoint), that is where I would have heard the phone ring when Esperanza called me, and I could have had the adventure that I have been regretting ever since that I missed. But the phone did not work right, and I never heard it ring. And when she looked for the night guard to come over and get me, he was not out in his usual place in the front yard. Knowing that it could be quite late when whoever went with the man to help out returned, she did not want to disturb Miriam, who was scheduled to work at seven o'clock this morning. She ended up phoning an urgent appeal to Rosmery, who is on vacation, but said she would go.

Meanwhile, blissfully unaware of the hubbub just next door, I ate my fried egg and toast and then went over to the home of the Meltons, who had left earlier that evening for San Pedro to attend a wedding. It took me two trips to lug home the stalk of seventy-four bananas someone had dropped off there for me, some bags of baby clothes and diapers donated by a church congregation in North Carolina for the clinic, plus the thirteen pounds of sugar, two hundred sixteen tea bags, and a box of gallon zip lock bags for the tea concentrate I'm making and freezing to help get ready for the medical brigade's visit next month.

By the time I carted everything across their yard, through the gate, down the sidewalk, around my house, and in the front door, fending off the curious investigations of their two large dogs en route, it was 11:00 p.m. Before heading for bed, I decided to go over to the clinic to see how fast the woman in labor was progressing. If you know me well at all, you can imagine my keen disappointment when I learned the details of the home-visit opportunity I had missed.

The poor baby had experienced a rather harsh introduction to life as he abruptly plopped from the warm liquid where he had been peacefully floating, into the frigid water of a toilet bowl. His horror-stricken father scooped him out, yelling for someone to go get help as he stripped off his shirt and enveloped his shivering, startled, squalling son in it. Esperanza grabbed a delivery pack and medications and thrust them into the brother-in-law's hands before he spun out the gate to pick up Rosmery, so she would have what she needed to deliver the placenta, clamp and cut the cord, and give necessary care. What neither she nor anyone else in the house had were diapers or diaper pins, so she "improvised," though she did not elaborate as to how. An hour later, mom and baby were doing fine, and Rosmery was jouncing and jolting over the ruts of an unpaved country road on her way home.

"Dear Lord, You know how much I would have enjoyed having that experience," I prayed as I crawled into bed. "But I trust You to know what is best for me. I *would* appreciate it if I could have at least one or two more deliveries before I leave next week."

Fast-forward about seven hours to the clinic, where Miriam has just attended the most recent of her well-over-a-thousand births and is cleaning the delivery table in preparation for the eminent occurrence of yet another. As she reaches to move the metal gooseneck lamp at the foot of the delivery table, she touches an unseen bare wire in the cord and yells in shock and pain as a powerful jolt of electricity freezes her hand fast to the lamp. Somehow breaking free of the paralyzing force, she nearly passes out from the deep, throbbing ache and tingling in her arm. She manages to dial my number, and this time the phone rings properly. "Would you like to do a delivery?" she queries. "I don't think I will be able to handle it."

I hurriedly brush back my just-washed hair and slip it into an elastic holder, then rush over to see what is needed. The woman who arrived at 8:10 a.m., completely dilated, is lying in the first of the three beds in our labor ward. I would just as soon leave her there where she can be more comfortable while I deliver her baby, and when I am by myself for a birth, I generally do that. But the nurses here prefer using the delivery table next door, and Miriam assures me that it is ready, urging the mother to walk the fourteen steps from her bed to it. At 8:22 a.m., I lift a slick, pink, lustily crying little girl onto her mother's abdomen and towel her dry. "Thank the Lord for another normal, safe arrival," I think. At least, that is my thought for a short couple of minutes, until I hear the steady trickle of blood running down the many-times-washed-and-reused piece of bright-green, heavy plastic that covers the bottom half of the delivery table and directs fluid into a stainless steel bucket on the floor at my feet.

Miriam's arm is still hanging limply, but she manages to lift the baby into the warmer after I hastily clamp and cut the cord, then turn my full attention to removing the placenta, which has only partially detached. At 8:27 a.m., it makes its complete appearance, but the mother's uterus still does not clamp down, and the trickle of blood becomes a stream. For the second time in my life, I am forced to do a bimanual compression of a flaccid uterus, squeezing it tightly from both the inside and out between my hands. How extremely thankful I am for Miriam's extra set of hands which, though still profoundly affected by her recent electrifying experience, are still able to start the IV that I request and draw up the necessary injections to help stop the hemorrhage, all of which I never could have accomplished had I been alone.

An hour later I return home to dry my hair and get breakfast, leaving behind an enthusiastically nursing newborn and mother whose bleeding is now well within the expected normal range. Miriam says she feels like someone violently punched her shoulder, and the burn on her hand from the live current is still tender, but she too is doing better. I marvel, not for the first time, at how God has once more intervened. I can only speculate on the "what if" scenario that might have happened had I been privileged to go out last night for the surprise home birth. I would probably have still been sleeping when Miriam called for help. It is highly unlikely I would have heard in my bedroom the phone's jangle from the living room, since I keep a fan going at night to drown out the outside noises. This was a birth that unquestionably needed the presence of two nurses instead of one, especially with the one not able to use her arm well. "Ok, Lord. You have worked all things together for good, just as You always do. Thanks for having me right where I needed to be, even though that was not where I would have *liked* to have been last night. However, if there is any such chance in the future ... Not that I'm wishing for any more babies to be dunked in the toilet, Lord, but if it's going to happen anyhow, I'll be glad to help out."

## 62

## Going Out With a Bang
*January 31, 2013 ~ San Luis, Honduras*

My time at the San Luis Life and Light Maternity Clinic this month is over. Now that I am back home, it hardly seems like I was away at all, except for the memories, and of course, the fading red marks from the flea bites that are an inevitable part of every such trip and that I am *never* successful at not scratching, in spite of my best intentions. A **BIG** thanks to all of you who were praying for me. I cannot ever remember being more conscious of those prayers and of God's definite touch than I have been this time. During the three weeks that I was there, I worked 228 hours, an average of seventy-six hours a week. I specifically requested that you ask God to give me health and strength so that I could keep up that pace and give as much vacation time as possible to the national nurses. Maribel was able to get the entire three weeks off, during which she got married. Rosmery enjoyed an eight-day break, Esperanza had the opportunity to help her daughter-in-law for five days after her new grandson was born via cesarean section, and Miriam was grateful for an extra weekend to go with her daughter and assist her to settle back into the dorm in San Pedro for her second year of boarding school. Aside from the time I drank the pepper-flavored coffee, I had not a moment of tummy trouble, no sniffles, and very little difficulty in staying awake and alert during the numerous double shifts I worked. I truly give praise to God for so definitely answering the many requests you sent His way on my behalf.

The last few days of my stay were jam-packed to bursting with enough exciting events to give me a grand send off. Marleni, who is our clinic secretary as well as Maribel's sister, had also taken some vacation time while I was there, which meant that she was not available to help with things like selling medications during the sometimes chaotic mornings when there are a lot of people wanting to have fasting lab work done. With Daniel Melton's vision and diligent work to upgrade the current facility's capabilities, our diagnostic services have considerably increased over the past few years. When I first started making these trips in 2001, a glucometer to measure blood sugars was the sole extent of our laboratory equipment. Now, we can also do a basic metabolic panel, as well as check hemoglobin, lipids, uric acid, and H. Pylori. In addition, we have the only ultrasound and EKG machines in a fifty-mile radius, which is a tremendous service to the community, as people used to have to make a trip to

San Pedro to get such tests done.

This progress is wonderful, but it does make simultaneously caring for in-patients, selling meds, monitoring labor progress, tending to a wound, etc., considerably more challenging at times as the extra "balls" of drawing blood and running the tests, or hooking up the EKG electrodes and printing and an-alyzing the cardiac rhythm strips, get added to the juggling act. Especially on Sundays, when the closed Health Center on the opposite end of town means that more patients come our way, the lone nurse on duty is often kept running madly all day. In fact, on my last Sunday, there was so much happening that I did not get a chance to eat the breakfast I had taken to work with me until 4:30 in the afternoon.

It was my next-to-last double shift, memorable not only because of the number and variety of patients, but also because during it I delivered my fifth and sixth babies for this trip. Both mothers were in their teens and giving birth for the first time. I am always especially glad for the opportunity to be able to attend these young women and give lots of emotional support to help make their initial birth experience a good one. Of course, they often require many extra hours of attention, since their labors are typically longer than with sub-sequent pregnancies. When two of them arrive within less than thirty minutes of each other, as they did that morning, plus you add in all the other people throughout the course of the day who come seeking nursing care, you can un-derstand why I had such a late breakfast.

The morning actually started slowly. Sometimes, people come in for lab work as early as 6:00 a.m., but the first client that day was an older, obviously expectant mother who shuffled through the door at 7:45 a.m., a few minutes before either of the teens. She handed me a referral letter to the Santa Bárbara Hospital and queried hopefully, "They told me that I need to take this to the city and have my baby there, since I have varicose veins. Can you please check me and see if maybe I can come here after all?" I escorted her back to the labor room for an exam. One look at the tautly swollen, tortuous veins running up her legs and into the birth canal left me no choice but to regretfully send her on her way. I could only too vividly imagine the potentially serious outcome if she had her wish to give birth here.

When I ushered the disappointed varicose-vein lady back out to the front at 7:54 a.m., sixteen-year-old Nancy Karolina was waiting for me. She had been having contractions during the night and was three-centimeters dilated when she arrived, enough to be admitted. To my delight, when I asked if she would like her husband to be with her for the birth, they were both in agree-ment with the idea. Only at the end of the crazy-full day did I completely realize what a blessing that would turn out to be. I grabbed a gown from our linen shelves in the back room for Nancy and then hurried back to the front to attend the next waiting person.

Eighteen minutes later, while I was checking an elderly gentleman's blood pressure and glucose, Nicol Alejandra slipped bashfully into line at the desk, shy brown eyes mutely hopeful that my exam would give her good news. She lived a fair distance away and had actually spent a good part of the previous day at the clinic, hanging out "just in case" the occasional mild contractions she was having decided to settle into true labor. I had sent her home for the night when it was obvious that nothing was happening. Nicol just turned fourteen this past November. This was her third pregnancy, since she had suffered a miscarriage when she was twelve and another one the next year when she was thirteen. Her boyfriend, his parents, and his twelve brothers and sisters all live on and work Dr. Maldonado's coffee farm, and they have somehow managed to squeeze her into their home as well. When I called to tell the doctor that she was back, but still not in active labor, he wanted me to go ahead and start her on IV Pitocin to crank things into a higher gear. Although her boyfriend did not seem too enthused with the idea of attending the birth, he agreed to stick around as well.

Now, much as I strongly favor the daddy's being present to give comfort and encouragement to his child's mother while their baby is being born, a situation with two young girls in simultaneous labor, each with her baby's father in the common labor room, presents some challenges. But *Clínica Luz y Vida* has not operated successfully since 1979 without learning how to adapt to such dilemmas. Portable folding screens have long since gone out of use in U.S. hospitals with the advent of handy-dandy sliding curtains. Our two such screens are still very adequate to provide a sufficient degree of privacy when they are strategically placed around one of the beds.

Of course, as much as possible, I encourage women in labor to be up and walking about, which made for even more of an interesting day, since I kept jogging (literally!) back and forth to tend to the people at the front desk and in the exam/treatment room, sell meds from the pharmacy, and see to the two pregnant girls walking in the back yard of the clinic. Shortly after 10:00 a.m., Nancy gave up on walking and lay back down, totally understandable since, when I checked her a few minutes later, she was fully dilated. With two girls sharing the labor room, I decided it would not be best to let her stay in bed to give birth, so her husband and mother helped her move next door to the delivery table, while I ran back out front to start a nebulization treatment on an asthmatic woman who had just arrived, telling her to turn off the machine when the vapor stopped, since I was going to be tied up with a delivery. All this time, Nicol was getting IV Pitocin, which meant frequent revisions of the drip rate. Knowing that I could not possibly monitor her IV adequately while delivering Nancy's baby, I dashed out to the back yard one final time to stop the fluids completely, rather than taking a chance on her having contractions that were too strong or too prolonged. There were several people waiting at the front for lab work and to buy medications. None of their needs was so urgent that it could not wait, so as I hurried back into the delivery room, I called down the hall to tell them I would not be available for a while, and that they could either stay or come back later.

Nancy had told me that she was getting prenatal care, and she *thought* her due date was that week. But the baby's heart rate kept dipping alarmingly low as she was pushing, and when I broke her water, the abnormally tiny trickle of amniotic fluid looked like thick green pea soup, both ominous signs of fetal distress. I do not routinely cut episiotomies, but this was definitely a case where one was needed for the baby to arrive soon enough to survive. At 10:38 a.m., a beautiful, six-pound, nine-ounce little girl was born, her green-stained cord, lack of body fat, and deeply wrinkled, peeling skin testifying to the fact that she was well past the average forty-weeks gestation. As I worked to help her adapt to breathing on her own, her enchanted father hung over the warmer, reaching out a tentative finger to her, totally mesmerized by his new daughter. Thankfully, she quickly recovered from the scary final minutes of a too-low heart rate before her birth. *Not* so thankfully, Nancy had a fourth-degree laceration of her birth canal, clear into the rectum. I had never needed to repair a tear of that magnitude, but I knew it would take a L-O-N-G time, a luxury I did not have, since so many other people were waiting for attention. Extremely grateful that the phone was working, I called Dr. Maldonado, who promised to be there shortly. During the hour that he spent stitching, I flitted between giving comfort to Nicol in the back, to giving injections, nebulizer treatments, wound care, and medical advice to the people who kept coming in the front door.

When Nancy was finally ready to be transferred to the postpartum ward, her husband willingly helped settle her in the wheelchair, then stayed in the delivery room to watch over their daughter in the warmer until I could get back to bathe, weigh, and measure her. He was delighted at the chance to help dress his tiny firstborn and proudly carry her to her mother. I was delighted at his unusual (for San Luis) degree of involvement and appreciative of the genuine help he was.

The pace of the day did not slow down. Nicol had a healthy daughter at 6:36 that evening, and she cooperated extremely well with my insistence to not push while I clamped and cut the cord that was tightly wrapped around the baby's neck. In between Nancy and Nicol's deliveries, I also repaired a pretty significant machete cut on a hysterical four-year-old little boy. I had sewn up a few others this trip, but that one was the deepest and (naturally, to go along with everything else that day) took the longest, since I had to get him calmed down enough to elicit his cooperation before I could do anything with the wound. In between and around all of that, I tended to the by-now four inpatients and thirty-one other people who showed up in need of nursing attention in one form or another. Just at the end of the day, I dropped everything to administer the treatment urgently needed by a two-year-old carried in by her grandfather, practically in respiratory arrest, with the worst asthma attack I have ever seen. Shortly after the steroid injection and Salbutamol nebulization had started to work, Esperanza walked in at 9:40 p.m. to relieve me, twenty minutes earlier than she would have needed to be there. I have seldom been happier to see anyone, since moments before, while taking vital signs on the new moms and babies in the postpartum ward, I had discovered that Nicol was bleeding too heavily and needed my total attention. Esperanza capably took over with the little girl, while I did what was needed to stop the hemorrhage, exceedingly thankful that I did not have to choose which of the two emergencies was more desperate.

Daniel and Tiffany and their boys were in San Pedro for part of my last week. When they got back to San Luis late that evening, Daniel came over to the clinic to offer me a big mug of hot mint tea that they had made and to see how things were going. He arrived shortly before 10:00 p.m., just in time to help hold the flailing legs of the two-year-old while Esperanza and I tried to start her IV. After four unsuccessful sticks between the two of us, we let the little tot have a rest for a bit, and I gave Daniel a brief rundown of the day's highlights. He laughed and said, "Nothing like going out with a bang, is there?" I told him I could have contentedly settled for a less-spectacular finale, or at least, having the total events in several day increments! Then I remembered about my disappointment with having missed out on the baby-in-the-toilet experience, and how I had asked God only a couple of days before if He could let me have another delivery or two before I left ... and I concluded that He must have a pretty good sense of humor.

After everything that happened on Sunday, Monday seemed tame in comparison, in spite of needing to do hourly chest percussion and nebulizations on the little asthmatic patient who had been admitted the evening before. It kept me trotting back and forth between the pediatric and labor wards, since I was also various-times-an-hour monitoring Floridalma, a twenty-eight-year-old maternity patient overdue with her second baby, whose labor I was trying to induce. With no IV pumps to automatically deliver the correct number of drops per minute, and with an IV site that was very positional, I had to keep adjusting the rolling valve on the tubing by miniscule increments either up or down, to increase or decrease the flow rate, depending on how she bent her hand. When Esperanza relieved me at 10:30 p.m., the twelve hours of Pitocin were finally having a measurable effect, and mama-to-be was just starting to make progress. As I was getting ready to go over to my house next door, I felt a niggling sense of uneasiness and a growing shadow of dread that something might go wrong. I told Esperanza that I would not turn on the fan in my bedroom as I usually did to drown out the outside noises, so that I could be sure to hear her if she needed help.

I drifted into a restless sleep, uneasily aware of an inexplicable urgency to be ready for trouble. Nevertheless, it was still a rude shock when that premonition proved true. At 4:39 a.m. I jolted awake to the racket of the night guard's forceful tapping on the bars covering the window right above my bed. "Hermana Ana, Esperanza says she needs you RIGHT NOW!" he yelled, practically in my ear.

"Tell her I'm coming!" I hollered back, bolting out of bed and throwing on the uniform I had ready, nervous fingers fumbling to swipe my hair back with a headband. I burst out of my front door, nearly bowling over the large German shepherd watchdog in my frantic dash for the back gate and the open clinic door a dozen steps beyond. Thrusting open the delivery room door, I saw a pale-faced, tight-lipped Esperanza, feverishly working to deliver a partially detached placenta that stubbornly resisted being removed, while a steady stream of blood poured down into the bucket at the foot of the table. "Start another IV and get some Lactated Ringers solution running on her!" she implored. I ran down the hall to the pharmacy, grabbed the plastic container that contains various sizes of IV catheters, alcohol-soaked cotton balls, and tape, and snatched a package of tubing off the shelf. "Please help us, Lord," I silently prayed, hastily snapping a tourniquet on the new mother's arm and swiftly inserting the large-bore needle needed to infuse the fluids as rapidly as possible.

It took three liters of IV solution to get Floridalma's blood pressure back up, following the large volume of blood she lost before the placenta finally delivered at 5:00 a.m. Esperanza told me later that it was the worst hemorrhage she had ever seen. Since she has worked at the clinic for thirty-two years and has delivered well over a thousand babies, you can be assured that it was quite substantial! How thankful we were that God again was watching out for His work and His workers and had an extra pair of hands in the right place at the right time. How glad I am, once more, to have had the great privilege of being a part of what He is doing for the precious people of Honduras through the *Clínica Luz y Vida*. And how great is my respect for and admiration of these dedicated Christian Honduran nurses who face similar hectic shifts and crisis situations day in and day out, all year long, year after year. *They* are the real heroes.

## 63

## Sewing Leads to Sowing—and Reaping
### *August 1, 2013 ~ San Luis, Honduras*

"All right, put the point of your needle a little ways down from where I started the first stitch ... no, not quite that close ... there you go, that's just right. Now, remember when you push it through, to come out on the opposite side at about the same distance from the edge as you are on this side. And be sure to rotate your wrist as you slide the needle out so you follow its curve." I peered intently over my son Jeffrey's shoulder, watching as he carefully followed my step-by-step instructions. The man and woman in the room with us shifted their positions to be able to see better as well, all of us focused on the silver needle pulling its tail of black silk thread through first one side and then the other of the two edges being joined.

"Very good. The next thing is to wrap the long piece of suture around the tip of your needle holder three times ... exactly so. Then, unclamp the handle to open the tip that's through that loop ... grasp the short end of the suture ... and now, pull it through and tighten the knot until the edges are just touching, but not *too* firmly together. Great job! That was perfect!"

The brilliant light above us that was focused on our needlepoint not only provided a shadow-free work area, but also gave some extra warmth to the space around us, something that was not at all necessary given the fact that we were already sweltering in the tropical environment. Apparently, we were not the only ones feeling the heat. The object of the sewing project, an eight-year-old boy who had been in the line of fire of a rock thrown by a neighbor, was also getting overly toasty beneath the blue sterile drape covering his head and shoulders.

He had entered the clinic in tears, blubbering in terror at the prospect of what would be done to the boo-boo on the back of his head. Now, fifteen minutes after the Lidocaine injection had taken effect, he was lying calmly and cooperatively, not making a peep as Jeffrey, an EMT who works stateside as an ambulance attendant, helped to clean and repair the inch-long gash. Unbeknown to either of us, our small patient decided he had sweated under his cover long enough and lifted the edge to peek out and get a breath of fresh air just as his daddy snapped a picture with my camera.

Two stitches later, the task was done, and the sewing lesson ended. Although the result was not the kind of embroidery you could frame and hang on your living room wall for guests to admire, both teacher and pupil felt a glow of satisfaction at the neat row of knots that marched down the side of a thin line that had been a gaping wound just minutes before.

Granted, this was only a small sewing project, not a life or death matter. But once again, as in countless other times since the Light and Life Clinic opened, someone was available to demonstrate the love of Jesus in a very tangible way. To the thousands of people who enter its doors each year, the clinic staff provides not just top-quality medical care twenty-four hours a day. The four Honduran nurses, the secretary, and even the cleaning lady also witness about a loving God who wants to save them and be their very best friend.

There are many who require more extensive sewing, for whom a visit to the clinic is a very serious occasion. Such was the gentleman whose flashing, well-honed machete blade struck his wrist instead of the weeds he had intended to chop. He arrived pale and fading in and out of consciousness, with a bottomed-out blood pressure. His right forearm was tightly tied with a strip of rubber that looked like it had been hastily sliced from an inner tube. Wrapped numerous times below that was a long length of cloth, torn from the sleeve and body of a shirt. The makeshift tourniquet had staunched the spurting blood from the vessels that he had severed, but not before his clothes and the ground around him were liberally saturated with it.

I quickly started an IV and rapidly ran in two liters of fluid while working on repairing and bandaging his wound. In answer to my question shortly after his arrival, he had assured me that he was a child of God, and as his condition stabilized and he became more coherent, he loudly joined me in petitioning his heavenly Father to save his life. As a brother in Christ, he knew the value of prayer and was quite vocal in availing himself of that privilege. It was indeed a relief to praise God together when the whole ordeal was over and he was standing steady on his feet, his arm sporting a clean bandage and splint.

Another kind of prayer meeting took place just a few evenings later when a truck whipped around the gate and into the clinic yard. It jerked to a halt, and a group of four men jumped to the ground, hoisted the miserable, banged-up form of a fifth man haphazardly onto their shoulders, and rushed him inside. One whiff of the man's breath made the reason for his condition pretty obvious. In his inebriated, judgment-impaired state, he had done a colossal job of crashing his motorcycle. In addition to a nasty bump on his head, he had four lacerations that needed stitching and multiple large areas where layers of skin had been scraped off by his violent impact with the pavement.

Daniel Melton was in the clinic when the man arrived, and he stepped into the treatment room to talk with him while Rosmery busied herself with caring for his wounds. "You realize that if that knock on your head had been just a little harder, you wouldn't have made it, don't you?" Daniel questioned. "God was very good to spare your life. He has a reason for allowing you to live." The man started to cry. Then his sister chimed in, "Mama has prayed for you for years, and you know you've broken her heart."

"Would you like to ask Jesus to save you and clean you up?" asked Daniel. Between sobs, the man began praying out loud, fervently calling on God to forgive his sins. Down inside, although rejoicing at the man's apparent change of heart, Daniel wondered how much his alcohol-fumed mind truly comprehended the words that he was saying. Three days later his sister stopped by, bubbling over with the good news that her brother was, indeed, a new man, and rejoicing at the tremendous change she was seeing in him.

A week after the accident, I was working the shift when he came to have his stitches removed. "God was certainly good to you," I told him, carefully snipping a suture and pulling it out. "How did your motorcycle fare?" "Oh, it was completely ruined," he laughed lightheartedly. "But far better to lose *it* and to have my *life* saved for eternity!" As we continued to talk, I was encouraged at his openness to some suggestions that would help him grow spiritually and thrilled to hear his excitement and joy at the difference God was making in his life.

Yes, although the sewing lessons that are given in a clinic are certainly not the kind that a neighborhood ladies' group would enjoy, how rewarding it is to participate in the kind of stitching that enables you to be a channel through which the Great Physician can work to mend shattered lives so greatly in need of a touch from His healing hand.

# 64

## Missionary Nursing: Is It for You?
### *Today - The Town Where You Live*

*"You shall be witnesses to Me in Jerusalem, and in all Judea and Samaria, and to the end of the earth." Acts 1:8*

Here you are, nearly at the end of this book. Congratulations on having arrived, and thank you for sticking with me. Before you go, I have one simple question for you to answer. What does God want **YOU** do for His kingdom? Is He calling you to go into the whitened harvest fields, taking the message of His love and salvation from sin to the millions who still need to hear it? All Christians are to be witnesses for Christ, but for many of you, that will probably not involve moving to a foreign country. You can let your light shine for Jesus right in the neighborhood where you currently live. However, if you feel a tug at your heart to be one of those who dares to go beyond your "Jerusalem," the place that is familiar and comfortable, into "the end of the earth," what might that involve? Could God be asking you to be a foreign missionary? Or even a missionary nurse?

As you think about your answer, I pray that the story of my experiences will help light a fire of determination to follow Him wherever that may lead you and in whatever capacity it may be. I can promise that if God does want you to be a missionary nurse, you will find peace, contentment, and a joy beyond measure in doing His will. The added bonuses are excitement, adventure, variety, and the opportunity to minister to some who would not otherwise have a chance to know the love that He offers them.

Of course, not everyone has the same idea of what it means to be a missionary nurse. I once asked a few high school students for their opinions on that and got an interesting variety of answers. One young person pictured a missionary nurse as someone who took her bag of medical supplies and went from house to house in a village, helping anyone who was sick. Someone else said it was kind of like a nurse and a doctor all rolled up in one, who does everything medical that needs to be done. Another thought of somebody who sews up machete wounds and crazy stuff like that.

One of the teachers in that high school said that a missionary nurse is a nurse who is called by God to practice her skills abroad, not in the States. She prays with people, gives first aid, educates them about the water, and gives them pills for the worms that kids get in their tummies. She assists a doctor with what he is doing, but she might also do surgery herself, as well as give shots, start IV's, and deliver babies.

Wow! It sounds to me as though a missionary nurse is a very busy person, wouldn't you say? It also sounds like she (or he) would probably have some especially interesting stories to tell, if all of those things are really part of the job description. Now that you have read this book, I imagine you can give your own definition. I do not know that I am necessarily typical of *all* missionary nurses, but I think I have given you a pretty accurate picture of some things that *many* foreign missionary nurses experience. Why not review with me for a few minutes and see what you think. If God is calling you to this special work for Him, what might that mean for **you**?

First of all, what about the teacher's idea that a missionary nurse is called by God to practice her skills abroad, not in the States? For simplicity, I will keep using "she" and not "he," since all the missionary nurses I know are female. But men, if God taps your shoulder and whispers in your ear that He wants you to serve Him in that capacity, you can be sure that He is not making a mistake, though you may be in the minority.

So what could be different about being a nurse in another country? For one thing, many times a missionary nurse will need to learn a new language in order to be able to use the expertise she has worked so hard to obtain. So here you are, fresh out of Bible college and nursing school, anxious to put all of your training to work. You arrive in Country X, and instead of grabbing your nursing bag, pulling on your latex gloves, and going door to door with your syringe, ministering to people's souls while you give them shots to heal their bodies, you are stuck in a classroom five days a week, four hours a day, for an entire year, cramming your exhausted brain full of funny sounding words. You may be tempted to think that all of that investment in language study is a waste of time. Why not just get out with the people, immerse yourself in their culture, and pick up what you need as you go?

Let me tell you from experience that unless you learn the language, and learn it well, you will not be effective. What if someone says to you, *"Mi hermano trató de quitarse la vida esta mañana. Tomó una gran cantidad de veneno hace como dos horas, y ahora tiene mucho dolor de la panza, y casi no puede respirar. Se ve muy deprimido, y no puedo traerlo acá desde la casa. ¡Venga y ayúdenos, por favor!"* Unless you know Spanish, you will have no idea what help he is seeking. By the time you get someone to translate and realize that this man is pleading with you to hurry to his house and help his brother, who is barely breathing and looks very sick because he tried to commit suicide by drinking poison, the brother could be dead, and you would not have a chance to help *either* his soul *or* his body. And by the way, that very thing has happened where we were working. The first Sunday after we moved from Costa Rica to Nicaragua, a brother of one of the national pastors drank a bottle of pesticide and killed himself because he was not able to earn enough money to buy food for his children, and he could not stand to hear them crying of hunger. Sadly, I did not hear about the heartbreaking occurrence until after it was much too late to get help for the man. On another occasion at the clinic in Honduras, I cared for a young person who had also tried to end his life in that same fashion, and I was able to help save him. It is sobering to realize that I would not have been of much use at all had I not known how to talk to his family to find out what was going on.

Let us have it as a given, then, that language school is a vital part of missionary nursing. What else is different between stateside and foreign-field nursing? The culture of the country will be unlike what you are used to. That will certainly affect not only your practice of nursing, but also your whole lifestyle. The foods commonly eaten in your country of service may not be typical of those to which you are accustomed. Have you heard how to tell the difference between first-, second-, and third-term missionaries? A fly lands in the first term missionary's bowl of soup, and he jumps up, snatches his bowl off the table, and dumps out all the soup in disgust. A fly alights in the second term missionary's soup; he grimaces, picks out the fly, and then eats the rest. When a fly zooms into the third term missionary's soup, he hollers, "Thank you, Lord, for the extra protein!" and cleans up his bowl, fly and all. Well, we have served nearly ten years in Central America. I guess that means we have not quite arrived at the eat-the-fly-with-gratitude-for-the-extra-protein stage, but we are close!

If your home is so far out in the boonies that you must make a long trip to the closest major city to buy groceries, the street vendors at major intersections will be glad to sell you food and drink if you get hungry en route. Their wares can look pretty tempting, but do be careful not to eat any fresh fruit or vegetables that you are not sure have been properly soaked in bleach or iodine water, as you may end up being a patient in the mission clinic instead of the nurse giving care.

If such an option is available, you may choose to buy your meat at a local market like the one where we shopped every Saturday when we lived in Nicaragua. Some of the ladies who hung their hunks of recently butchered beef on hooks in the open air were fairly vigilant about shooing the flies away, but others did not seem to be too concerned about the contamination with the invisible creepy-crawlies that were deposited with every touchdown made by the pesky insects. Plenty of boiling will destroy the germs, although if you cook beef eyeballs terribly long, they will be too tough to enjoy in the soup in which they are usually served.

You can buy meals at McDonald's in many foreign countries, but you may want something more special, like a freshly caught fish meal such as we enjoyed on a family relaxation day at the ocean. The fish are cooked whole, so it is a bit disconcerting to have your meat staring up at you while you eat it, but you can leave the head and bones on your plate. When I was in Haiti just a few days after the earthquake in January 2010, fresh food was almost nonexistent. We were grateful for the soup flavored with dried fish heads that resident missionary Don Mobley fixed for us. It actually was some of the best food I have ever eaten.

One of my language school instructors thought it great fun to tell us about the man who visited in a home where his hostess served him tamales. Tamales consist of a delicious, spicy dough of corn flour stuffed with meat, rice, and vegetables, wrapped in banana leaves, and boiled in a large kettle of water. The guest polished off his whole plate of food, but when the lady of the house asked if he had enjoyed it, he replied, "Well, Señora, the filling was really good, but the lettuce sure was tough to chew!" If you live in a country where tamales are the Christmas custom, be sure to remove the banana leaf and leave it to the side of your plate. You will not offend your hostess by failing to eat the "lettuce."

I was fortunate to have either a two-burner hot plate or a gas stove on which to do my meal preparation and never had to work with a wood-burning cook stove such as is very common in rural Central American houses. Never once did I hear my husband or sons complain about feeling deprived because they did not have to bring home the fuel to keep those kinds of stoves going. It is a common sight there to see men or boys carrying home on their shoulders a bundle of freshly chopped wood or even a log four to five feet long for the cooking fire that day. In fact, one of the cultural things that makes a missionary nurse's job extra interesting is that the wood is chopped by machetes which are kept well sharpened. Even young boys use them daily. I have had plenty of chances to perfect my skill with a needle through suturing wounds accidentally inflicted by those blades. Many lacerations of that type are not extremely deep, involving skin and muscle only, but there is always a possibility of more extensive damage.

Maybe you grew up working in the family garden every summer and will want to supplement your meals on the mission field with fresh, healthy, home-grown produce. If your yard is fenced or walled in, that may be a great way to save money and add yummy-tasting vitamins to your diet. But if you do not have a means of keeping out wandering animals, your hard effort will probably result in a harvest of nothing but frustration, as our attempt in Nicaragua did. A few years later in Costa Rica, where our yard did have the protection of a cement-block wall, we had the opposite result with our middle son's "garden," consisting of a single chayote plant. Over the course of several months, that one vine spread out to cover more than a twelve-by-sixteen-feet section of the back yard. It also twined and curled its way up the six-feet-high by eight-feet-wide orange metal gate, wrapping itself so thickly that we joked about its being Jack's beanstalk reaching up to the giant's castle in the sky. We reaped an abundant harvest of chayote, much to Benjie's satisfaction.

Adjusting to the size of various foreign-grown critters can be another challenging part of your cultural adaptation. Common, everyday frogs grow to be as large as soft balls and are very plentiful around the mission station in Honduras. Whenever I go over to the clinic at night, I am nervous that I might step on one in the dark. I also get a bit edgy when walking out into the living room or kitchen after dusk without a light, since some impressive-sized tarantulas occasionally lurk in the shadows on the floor near windows or doors where they have managed to squeeze inside.

So far, we have seen that dealing with a different language, eating unusual food, and enduring remarkable critters can make missionary nursing adventuresome. Still, God has called you, so you are ready to go and be the loving hands of Christ. What does "going" involve? First, you will need to get your supplies gathered and packed. That may mean filling a large shipping container, or just coming up with a sufficient number of suitcases and big cardboard boxes to carefully pack and repack as you fill each one to the maximum weight limit without putting in even a pound too much. Then, you have to get to where you will serve. In the U.S.A., you can drive from one state into another without even slowing down at the state line. Not so in a foreign country. Missionary nursing for me entailed many border crossings, with police checkpoints, long lines at ticket counters, passport verifications, and luggage inspections. You may not ever have occasion to be jealous of a cow walking unchallenged under a border gate or need to argue with an official who stubbornly refuses to let you leave his country with your own child, but your border story may be just as noteworthy in its own way.

Do remember to keep your passport current, so you can avoid being denied permission to leave your country of service when you want to take a ministry trip to the land next door. The time I went by public bus from Costa Rica to Nicaragua to hold a women's seminar with sister churches, my passport still had six weeks before it was to expire, but the officials nearly made me get off the bus and stay behind when they checked it at the border, several hours into my journey. Thankfully, some of my generous and caring travel companions, total strangers to me, took up a collection to pay the fine I was charged to be permitted to continue my journey. Keep in mind that it is best to renew your passport at least two months before the expiration date to avoid problems.

Once you make it through customs and settle into your new home, what are some responsibilities that can make your job as a missionary nurse different than that of your nonmedical coworkers? If you have children, you may find that your nursing skills are in demand for your own family. When Benjamin was a toddler, he often had tummy troubles from parasites. My nurse's training gave me the knowledge to know what medications he needed for his frequent bouts with diarrhea. When he fell down our porch steps in Nicaragua and gashed open his scalp, missionary-nurse-mom put in the necessary stitches. When Jeffrey got severe infections two consecutive summers in Honduras, I started his IV's and gave him his medications at home, until he got so sick that he *had* to be treated in the clinic. When the antibiotics that were available in the clinic were not strong enough and we had to take him to a major hospital in the big city, his own private nurse was able to keep the IV's going during the long, bumpy trip in the back seat of the truck that carried him there.

Besides helping your own family, including starting an IV on yourself as I had to do one summer, as a missionary nurse you can be a blessing to your co-workers. Some of my most rewarding memories are of the summers in Honduras when I was privileged to deliver three missionary babies: Daniel and Tiffany Melton's third son, Kenton, and Zach and Sarah Robbert's second daughter, Eleyna, in 2008, as well as the Melton's fourth son, Kaden, in 2013. Sarah had preterm labor at thirty-one weeks, and she needed extensive monitoring throughout the next five weeks, as well as medications to stop her labor on two different occasions. Early on during that difficult time, she had called her obstetrician in San Pedro Sula, wondering if she should move to the mission apartment in the city to wait out the remainder of her pregnancy, so she would be close to the hospital where he practices. Her doctor was afraid that the rough ride down the mountain might precipitate her baby's birth, and when he found out that a missionary nurse, who was also a nurse-midwife, was living right next door, he told her to stay where she was. Sarah was able to remain at home and still get the help she needed, while God protected little Eleyna and kept her from being born too early.

The summer following Kenton and Eleyna's births, I was in Honduras with Stephen and Yvonne DeLong for the birth of their third child, Joanna Brook. We still grieve with them over the loss of their precious baby when Yvonne's uterus ruptured during her labor. But God in His providence saved Yvonne's life, and she did not bleed to death as she may well have done had He not orchestrated events so that a missionary nurse-midwife could be with them to catch the signs of a problem and get her to the hospital in time for the surgery she so urgently needed.

All right. You have gotten to your country, made it through language school, and God has used your training to benefit your own family as well as your co-workers. What about all of those nationals to whom you are called? What will being a missionary nurse mean to them?

If you work in a clinic such as the one established by Evangelistic Faith Missions in Honduras, you will find that your sufficiency definitely is of God and not just from your training when you encounter situations that call for you to be a "doctor and nurse all rolled into one," as one of the high school students said. You will see the heart-wrenching poverty of those who walk a great distance to seek your care. You will experience the tight-knit closeness of extended family support as a crowd of twenty to forty people jostles in to watch you help their injured or sick relative. If your patient needs to be transferred to a facility with more resources, family will help to load him into the ambulance, primitive and crude as it may be. You may get to take a few wild ambulance rides yourself, accompanying someone who needs you to control the bleeding of an extensive injury beyond your ability to repair, or transferring a prematurely born baby who will not live otherwise. And if the baby is just too early to survive in spite of your best efforts, you will cry with the parents as you do your best to comfort them with the bright and certain assurance that the little one that they bury today in the crude cardboard-box casket is forever alive with Jesus, and they can see him again if they trust God to forgive their sins and make Him their Savior.

You may cringe at the dangerous practices that help to keep your services in demand, such as converting a pickup truck into a taxi, packing its bed with more than twenty people. You will probably grit your teeth and grimace as you tug worms the size of your finger out of an infected wound. When the man who gets shot by bandits arrives at the clinic in his bullet-riddled, blood-soaked shirt, you will obligingly dig the bullets out of his shoulder. You will dispense medication from gallon jugs into plastic bags and sell it without a prescription to any adult or child who brings a torn piece of paper with a reasonable request written on it, because prescriptions are not needed in many foreign countries. You will hope no one tries any funny business, because you do not want the gun stored in the clinic broom closet to be put to use!

Maybe you will get to help birth babies in dirt-floored houses like the home of the first foreign baby I delivered in Nicaragua. Or perhaps you will use a headlamp to welcome a new life into the blackness of a night without electricity, as I did in Haiti after the earthquake. You may get called to visit people who live in abject poverty, too ailing and poor to come to you, such as the elderly grandmother that I prayed with several times during the days that I gave her IV fluids in her home in Honduras. Or you can help out good friends like the ones we had in Costa Rica who asked me to start their father's IV so that they could give him loving, personal care at home during his last days on earth.

Yes, missionary nursing is much more than many people realize, but it just might be the thing that God wants *you* to do. You may work side by side with U.S. Marines, taking aid to those who are suffering. Possibly you will even use a flashlight at night as you sew up a wounded mare that has fallen and torn open her head and knees.

You may have the luxury of an autoclave such as is used in the clinic in Honduras to sterilize the instruments that you neatly wrap in packets, or you may kill the germs by using your own pressure cooker, as I did in Nicaragua. Maybe you will have to boil such things over a charcoal fire and spread them on clean towels, such as I did in Haiti when there was no propane for the stove. If you do get to help show God's love to people who are reeling with shock and loss after a disaster that has thrust over 300,000 souls into eternity, you will see and experience things that will break your heart and send you to your knees for strength and wisdom in dealing with the magnitude of the tragedy. Unbelievable suffering combined with unthinkable living conditions made my experience in Haiti much more appalling than I could ever have imagined missionary nursing would be.

We nurses and doctors treated people with horrific wounds and burns. We went to those whose homes had been destroyed and who were living beside the road, too injured to come to us. Missionary nursing done this way definitely gets you out of your comfort zone. Fording streams on a motorcycle while sandwiched between a driver and an interpreter, or wading through a stream on your way to a church-turned-clinic in the mountains, lugging plastic tubs and suitcases with all of the supplies and medicine you anticipate needing for a group of people who have waited hours for you to arrive, is not something for which any amount of schooling can prepare you. And when, no matter how hard you try, your efforts are too late for the baby who dies two hours after you arrive at the makeshift clinic where his mother brought him in hopes that you could help him, you are comforted in your grief with the thought that he is whole and well now in heaven, and there are many whose lives *were* saved because God put you where He could use your missionary nursing skills.

One tiny fellow was too sick and weak to nurse or to take a bottle, so we put a tube through his nose and into his stomach to give him fluids. However, the only thing available to connect to the tube was a suction catheter, and the fluid we were dribbling into his stomach kept leaking out the port in the catheter tip that is supposed to be blocked with your thumb while using the suction machine. We were so busy that we could spare no one to sit there with his thumb over the port. I took the piece of gum I was chewing, stuffed it down into the port opening, cut the finger off a latex glove and stretched it over the gum-plugged port, then tied a piece of a tourniquet around the glove tip to hold it all in place. It worked beautifully with no more leaking, and the baby was able to get the fluids he desperately needed. As a missionary nurse, you sometimes need to be innovative.

I told you about ambulance and motorcycle rides to care for the sick and wounded, as well as about my most exciting ride as a missionary nurse, in the belly of a massive U.S. Air Force C-17 plane. I hope you do not have claustrophobia, since a situation such as that is not exactly conducive to making sure you have your own personal comfort zone of adequate space around you. There were no smartly dressed stewardesses to bring us drinks and a snack, but no one cared. We were just glad to be going home.

And speaking of being home reminds me that missionary nurses can be used of God in unique ways even in the United States. During the Penn View Bible Institute Jungle Camp which is held every other year with the missions students in the deep, dark "jungle" of a friend's woods in central Pennsylvania, I teach emergency childbirth classes, as well as give first aid lessons which are utilized during the night-time search-and-rescue missions in which the young people participate to gain valuable experience in team building.

Maybe the foreign language you learn as a missionary can also be put to good use if God directs you to return to the States for a time and you work in a hospital in your local town, as I am currently doing. My Spanish-speaking ability is often called upon when we get Hispanic patients who have not yet learned English. Such a situation occurred the night a loaded Greyhound bus traveling from New York to Ohio rammed into the back of a semi's flatbed trailer at 1:45 a.m. on Interstate 80 not far from us. My phone rang shortly after 2:00 a.m. "There's been a terrible bus accident on I-80," the ER secretary breathlessly informed me. "We don't know how many of the victims will be brought here, but we know that some of them speak only Spanish. Could you please come in and translate?"

Over the next thirteen hours, I helped calm and comfort an elderly Puerto Rican woman and her married daughter while their injuries were treated. My Spanish knowledge was invaluable as I made various phone calls to locate their husband/father in another area hospital, rode with them to be reunited with him, and reassured frantic loved ones calling from Puerto Rico.

It could be your privilege to mentor not only national nurses, but also missionary-nurses-in-training. Across the years, it has been a joy to have fifteen different young people spend time in the clinic in Honduras with me, learning about what it is like to be a missionary nurse. Your example may inspire another generation to see if God wants *them* to become involved in His kingdom in this way. No matter where it is, if you make yourself available as a channel for His love to shine out to a needy world, your nursing skills will guide people to Him. It is as true now as it has ever been: all people, everywhere, need the Lord. And there is no more fulfilling, exciting, satisfying way to lead them to Him than by giving yourself for service as a **MISSIONARY NURSE!**

# Epilogue
## *October 2014*

---

In January 2014, I went to Honduras to work in the Light and Life Clinic for two weeks as well as to serve on a medical team from the States which held mobile clinics in four rural communities. While there, I learned that this would likely be my last opportunity to give the national nurses vacation time as I have been doing for the past fourteen years.

Another Christian organization is planning to construct a hospital in the town of San Luis, less than a mile from the clinic. Since that hospital will have a full-time doctor on staff and offer more services than our clinic is able to do, it is highly unlikely that patients would continue to patronize the clinic. Therefore, the EFM board has unanimously decided that they will work together with the other group for the good of the community. During the months that the new hospital is under construction, plans are to allow our building and equipment to be used by this organization, and they have agreed to hire any of our nurses who wish to continue to work under the new arrangements.

Since this change is to take place within three months, in all likelihood, I will not be returning to San Luis for any more shifts in the clinic. With a larger pool of national nurses, the hospital will not need outside personnel to fill in as I have done.

When I heard of the proposed clinic closure, I felt acutely disappointed, since I love the ministry that God has allowed me to have there. At the same time, I am excited to think of what other places God may lead me. I am not yet around that bend in the road, but I have full confidence that He will continue to light my path and make clear His further plans for my life.